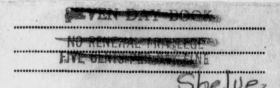

DINOSAURS

E. P. DUTTON & CO., INC., NEW YORK

DINOSAURS

THEIR DISCOVERY AND THEIR WORLD

by Edwin H. Colbert

CONTENTS

ILLUSTRATIONS

FIGURES

DINOSAURS

CHAPTER ONE

SOME NECESSARY PRELIMINARIES

THERE WERE DINOSAURS

One hundred million years ago the continents were inhabited by numerous and varied reptiles which today we call dinosaurs. At that time the dinosaurs had long been residents of the lands; indeed their past history might even then have been measured in terms of millions of years—of some 75 million years, to be more or less precise. And at that time it was to be another 30 million years before they would have disappeared from the face of the earth, before they would have joined the category of completely extinct animals.

These facts are known to us because of *fossil bones* and other indications of dinosaurs that have been found in the rocks of the earth's crust during the past century and a half, and particularly because of intensive studies of these fossils that have been made by curious men all over the world. So much has been learned and so much has been written about dinosaurs that these ancient reptiles have become very familiar to the public, and almost everyone knows, or thinks he knows, what a dinosaur was. Ask someone at random about this and he will probably tell you that dinosaurs were giant animals, now happily extinct, but once very common on the earth. He may not know what kind of animals the dinosaurs were, but he is sure in his mind that they were all gigantic. As likely as not he may add that dinosaurs lived in an ancient world also inhabited by our cave-man ancestors, for this is a common bit of misinformation kept alive by cartoons and comic strips. Since these spectacular animals are now extinct, he will very possibly affirm that here is proof of the fact that these great creatures were failures. Indeed, it is almost axiomatic in modern speech that the word "dinosaur" connotes something that has in a truly monumental fashion failed to survive, whether that something be a real dinosaur or an outmoded type of automobile or a poorly designed appliance that never quite made the grade.

Here indeed is a strange mixture of ideas, some of them right, some of them wrong. As for the facts, the dinosaurs were reptiles and they have been extinct for a long time. They were not all giants, and none of them was ever contemporaneous with primitive man. And even though they are extinct they cannot properly be considered as failures, because they were very successful animals during a span of more than 100 million years—and that is a long time.

What were the dinosaurs? That question will be answered at some length in the pages of this book. The subject of the dinosaurs is a large one, and to many readers an unfamiliar one, so it should be approached with as clear an understanding as possible. Therefore, before entering upon a discussion of the dinosaurs, their anatomical structure, their possible habits, their associations with one another and with other animals living in their world, their environment and various other subjects pertinent to a broad survey of dinosaurian history, some brief introductory excursions will be made into certain subjects that are needed as a background for the consideration of the dinosaurs; such items, for example, as geologic time, the geologic time scale, the nature of sedimentary rocks and fossils, the relationships of animals, and the general characters of reptiles and of dinosaurs. With these subjects in mind the succeeding chapters may be read with a comprehending eye.

GEOLOGIC TIME

About three hundred years ago John Lightfoot, the vice-chancellor of Cambridge University, decided that the exact date of Creation was September 17, 3928 B.C., at nine o'clock in the morning. A few years after Lightfoot had made this deduction, based in part upon his study of the Scriptures, Archbishop Ussher of Ireland concluded that the correct date for the Creation of the earth was October 23, 4004 B.C.

For more than a century thereafter a great many people in western Europe, and in other parts of the world too, literally believed that the earth was something less than six thousand years old. Then as the study of the natural sciences progressed, between the time of Bishop Ussher and the beginning of the nineteenth century, many scholars began to realize that the earth is vastly more than six thousand years of age—that it has been spinning on its axis and making its great annual circuit around the sun for a very long time. Finally, within the past few decades scientists have begun to appreciate, by means of elaborate studies with modern equipment and an increased understanding of the natural world, how very old the earth is.

Our knowledge of the earth's immense age has been gained largely within the realm of the geological sciences, which means that geologists, the men who concentrate on the study of the earth and of its long history, are particularly aware of the importance of geologic time. It is all very well for one—anyone—to say that he believes in the great age of the earth, but unless he has made a study of geologic history it is rather doubtful that he can quite comprehend earth history and geologic time in a realistic way. It takes some firsthand experience—such as going out into the countryside and seeing or climbing up thousands of feet of earth sediments piled into great mountains or cut into deep canyons, or seeing and analyzing hills and valleys as they have been created by the immeasurably slow processes of uplift and of erosion, or seeing and studying the sequence of fossils within the layered mantle of the earth, or recording the way in which radioactive elements in the rocks have broken down and decayed—to impress upon the mind the reality as well as the immensity of geologic time. As a result of such experience geologic time ceases to be an abstract concept—it becomes a lively part of one's thinking.

Stand on the rim of the Grand Canyon, if you will, and look into the vast immensity of that great gorge. The number of days and weeks and years that were needed for the Colorado River to cut down a mile from the canyon rim, and across fifteen miles, from one side of the canyon to the other, and to remove the tremendous tonnage of rock from the entire length of the canyon, depositing it far down the river and in the Gulf of California as sand and mud, almost staggers the imagination. Yet the cutting of the Grand Canyon is geologically a recent event that has occupied only a very small fraction of the totality of geologic time.

Stand on the pediments at the base of the Rocky Mountain front range, or in a valley below the Matterhorn in the Swiss Alps, or on the plains of Argentina facing the high Andes, or at Darjeeling facing the even higher Himalayas, and it would seem as if these great mountains were eternal, as has so often been said by the poets. Yet the uplift of the high, rugged mountain systems of our world took place *after* the dinosaurs had become extinct. In the days of the dinosaurs there were no such mountains, and the land was near sea level. Moreover, the span of earth history before the uplift of the world's greatest mountains and even before the days of the dinosaurs was far greater than that stretch of earth history since the extinction of the dinosaurs and the birth of the mountain chains. The world is indeed an old place.

The cutting of canyons or the uplifting of mountains or the deposition in the seas of immense amounts of sediments that have been denuded from the continents are impressive object lessons as to the vast dimensions of geologic time, but such phenomena do not *measure* time. Our modern concept of geologic time has been reached through the study of radioactive disintegration. For example, uranium in the rocks of the earth's crust decays at a definite rate. As a result of this decay the uranium is ultimately transformed into a certain type of lead. Thus it is possible in certain cases to measure the proportion of uranium in a rock to the proportion of lead derived from that uranium, and, knowing the rate of decay of uranium, to arrive at a figure that will express in reasonably accurate terms the age of the rock.

As a result of cumulative studies made during recent years, it now seems apparent that the earth is at least three billion years old, and perhaps as much as five billion years of age.

THE GEOLOGIC CALENDAR

One of the attributes of man is his keen sense of time. Modern man has divided the day into hours and minutes and seconds, and with these units he measures and regulates the details of his daily activities. The days fall into weeks and months and years. Hours and days, months and years, following in succession, measure out the span of a man's existence.

The span of earth history has been divided by geologists into greater and lesser time units. The largest units of time in earth history are the *eras,* of which there are six. The eras are subdivided for the most part into *periods,* and the periods may be further subdivided into *epochs.*

The six eras of the geologic calendar are, reading down from the youngest to the oldest, the:

Cenozoic
Mesozoic
Paleozoic
Proterozoic
Archeozoic
Azoic.

Of these six eras the three oldest, the Azoic, Archeozoic, and Proterozoic, often collectively known as pre-Cambrian, constitute all but the last half-billion years or so of geologic time. The rocks of pre-Cambrian age contain very few fossils, and those that have been found consist of primitive algae and fungi, and the trails or burrows of worm-like creatures. Animals and plants either were so primitive and soft during pre-Cambrian times that they were rarely preserved as fossils, or the various earth forces to which these rocks have been subjected during the long time of their existence have destroyed any fossils that may have been contained within the rocks. Perhaps the lack of pre-Cambrian fossils is a result of both of these factors.

The Paleozoic, Mesozoic, and Cenozoic eras, constituting approximately the last 500 million years of earth history, contain the fossil record. These eras are divided into several periods, as depicted in Figure 1. Again the arrangement is with the youngest time units at the top, the oldest at the bottom. (This is a standard geologic convention, based upon the fact that young rocks normally are found on top of older rocks.)

THE AGE OF DINOSAURS

The Mesozoic era, embracing from its beginning to its end the Triassic, Jurassic, and Cretaceous periods, and having a duration of about 130 million years, is often called the "Age of Reptiles." But reptiles had become well established on the earth long before the advent of the Triassic period, and they dominated the Permian period, which immediately preceded the advent of Mesozoic history, just as effectively as they did the three Mesozoic periods.

No other reptiles of Mesozoic times, however, command our attention in quite the same way as do the dinosaurs. Perhaps this is in part a result of the liking we, as human beings, have for the large and the grotesque, because there is no disputing the fact that many dinosaurs were very large and, to our eyes, very strange looking. Yet considering the matter objectively and forgetting our own disposition to play favorites, we realize that the dinosaurs must have truly dominated the Mesozoic scene, for they were numerous, they were ubiquitous across all of the large land masses, they were varied, and generally speaking most species of dinosaurs were giants. Furthermore, they were limited to the confines of Mesozoic times (as were some less numerous and less spectacular reptilian groups); they appeared during the Triassic period and suffered complete extinction at the end of the Cretaceous period. The Mesozoic was, above all, the age when dinosaurs were the supreme rulers of the land. It was the Age of Dinosaurs.

ROCKS AND FOSSILS

It is inevitable, I suppose, when introducing a subject as large and complex as dinosaurian history, that words and phrases will appear before they can be properly defined. For this first chapter it would be very nice if, like an invading army, we could move forward on a broad front, simultaneously advancing various ideas along parallel lines. But since words have to follow one after another, we must make the best of things as they are and consider the several introductory phases of this account of the dinosaurs in a linear, serial manner.

Some mention has already been made of rocks and fossils. What are they? Let us first consider rocks.

It should be axiomatic and hardly worth repeating that the earth's crust is made of different kinds of rocks, yet something as obvious as this to a hard-bitten New Englander or to someone who has lived his life in the mountains of Utah or New Mexico may not be so universally apparent a truth to the Iowan, who may spend his life in a region of

---

Figure 1. A chart of that portion of geologic time containing the fossil record

Eras	Dura-tion (Millions of years)	Periods	Life
CENOZOIC	70	QUATERNARY	
		TERTIARY	
MESOZOIC	65	CRETACEOUS	
	45	JURASSIC	
	45	TRIASSIC	
PALEOZOIC	45	PERMIAN	
	80	CARBONIFEROUS (PENNSYLVANIAN AND MISSISSIPPIAN)	
	50	DEVONIAN	
	40	SILURIAN	
	60	ORDOVICIAN	
	100	CAMBRIAN	
		"PRECAMBRIAN"	

deep black soil, with never a rock to break the progress of a plow. But if it is remembered that the soil is essentially disintegrated rock enriched by organic detritus, there is then no difficulty in recognizing the basic truth that rocks are the foundation of the crust of the earth.

There are three primary types of rocks—igneous, metamorphic, and sedimentary. Igneous rocks are those rocks formed by heat, either deep down in the earth, like granites, or at the surface, like lavas. Metamorphic rocks are rocks that have been completely altered from their original condition by heat, or often by a combination of heat and pressure—for example, gneiss from granite or marble from limestone. Sedimentary rocks are, as the name indicates, rocks formed from sediments: limestones from limes, sandstones from sands, and shales from muds. Sedimentary rocks are formed originally by the deposition of sediments in the oceans, in rivers and lakes, or on dry lands; and the agents that cause such deposition may be the waters of the seas, of lakes and of rivers, or winds, glaciers, and other forces. The variety of sedimentary rocks is almost infinite; they may be pure or mixed in composition, coarse or fine, homogeneous or varied. Fossils occur in sedimentary rocks.

And men have been finding fossils in sedimentary rocks for many thousands of years—since prehistoric times, in fact. Fossils have been found associated with the remains of cave men and in the pre-Columbian ruins of the dwellings of southwestern Indians, evidently objects of curiosity or possibly of veneration. They have been found in ancient Greek temples. Many fossils are of such striking appearance that they are bound to attract the attention even of the rude savage. Yet even though fossils have been known to man for a long time, the proper understanding of these objects has come about only within the past two centuries—possibly a little longer.

The word "fossil" is derived from the Latin *fossilis*, derived in turn from the Latin *fodere*, which means "to dig." In early Renaissance times a fossil was anything dug out of the earth, but in 1561, Conrad Gesner, a Swiss scholar, published an account of fossils in which he essentially restricted the term to the remains of ancient life.

According to modern usage fossils are the remains or indications of life that is now extinct. They may take various forms. Quite commonly fossils are the *petrified* hard parts of plants and animals. Shells, bones, and stems commonly have been infiltrated during the ages by mineral-bearing ground waters, so that the interstices of the organic structure are completely filled by mineral matter, a process known as *perminerali-*

zation. Often the organic tissue is partially or completely broken down, molecularly, and *replaced* by minerals. Fossils formed by such permineralization or replacement are usually very hard and brittle. A fossil, however, may be composed of the original shell or bone or wood. Sometimes even the soft parts of the plant or animal are fossilized, either by petrification, by distillation which leaves "carbon copies" of soft tissues, or by the preservation of the original tissue. Fossils need not be the direct evidence of the extinct animals or plants, in the form of preserved shells or bones or stems. They may be molds or imprints in the rocks left by the organism; they may be eggs; they may be footprints made by an animal; or they may even be the preserved structures manufactured by an animal, like nests or tubes or burrows. Sometimes fossils by their nature are very baffling to the student of ancient life.

THE TREE OF LIFE

It is readily apparent that dogs, wolves, and foxes are close cousins— no special training in zoology is necessary to see the quite obvious relationships between these animals. Furthermore, the average observer, without benefit of special knowledge, might guess that dogs (using the word "dogs" here in a very broad sense) and their relatives are related to bears. To the trained zoologist, acquainted with the anatomy of these animals, the relationship between dogs and bears is much more than a mere guess; it is reinforced by hundreds of details into a solid fact. To the paleontologist, who can study the fossil evidence, the relationship between dogs and bears is more than a solid fact; it is an exciting record of growth and development through time. By tracing the fossil evidence back and back, he can clearly see bears becoming more and more dog-like or wolf-like, until at a point in late Miocene times, say about 12 million years ago, he finds animals that are almost perfect intermediates between bears and dogs. They are called "bear-dogs" because they combine so nicely the characters of the dogs and the bears that it is an academic question as to whether they should be classified as dogs or bears. Thus the fossil evidence shows that the bears branched off at a fairly late stage in the history of life from a dog-like or wolf-like stem, to become very large, heavy carnivores, or meat eaters.

This is an illustration of just one small familiar branch of the great tree of animal life. By following hundreds and thousands of branches in this way, from recent living animals through long processions of successively older fossils, it is possible to build up a picture of the tree of animal life growing ever larger and more complex as more and more recent and fossil animals are studied. Thus one can see the bears and the dogs merging with the other meat-eating mammals, the raccoons, weasels, civets, hyenas, and cats, as well as the seals, sea lions, and walruses. In a more comprehensive view, one can see the manner in which all of these carnivores are related to all of the other mammals. One can see the mammals in relation to the other tetrapods, or land-living backboned animals, and all of these in turn to the fishes. Furthermore one can see the affinities of all of these animals, which constitute the great group of vertebrates, or animals with backbones, to all of the other animals—the invertebrates, or animals without backbones. And eventually one can see, on very lowly levels, the probable ultimate relationships of the stem of this tree of animal life with the stem of the tree of plant life. Perhaps a general outline of the great tree of life could be drawn without the evidence of fossils, but there would be many questionable relationships and many, many gaps. The succession of fossils, found in the sedimentary rocks of the earth's crust, add the invaluable fourth dimension of time for a proper understanding of the world.

A very simple diagram of the tree of animal evolution appears on the opposite page.

As can be seen from the diagram, the animals with backbones—the vertebrates—form but one of several large major divisions, or *phyla,* of the animal kingdom. Actually, there are a dozen or so phyla of animals, which for the sake of convenience rather than logic are often thought of as being contained within two moieties, the one phylum of vertebrates, or backboned animals, balanced against the several phyla of invertebrates, or animals without backbones. This is a very unequal division of the animal world, it is true, but among other things it serves to emphasize the importance (at least to us) of the vertebrates. The vertebrates may be arranged on a very simple tree as shown in Figure 2 (and here we bring in the dimension of time to show the dates at which the several groups of backboned animals have arisen).

VERTEBRATES

What are the vertebrates? How can an inclusive definition be made for this phylum of animals, in which are found such disparate members as the fishes and the tetrapods, the latter being the amphibians, reptiles, birds, and mammals? Certainly this array of animals includes a very

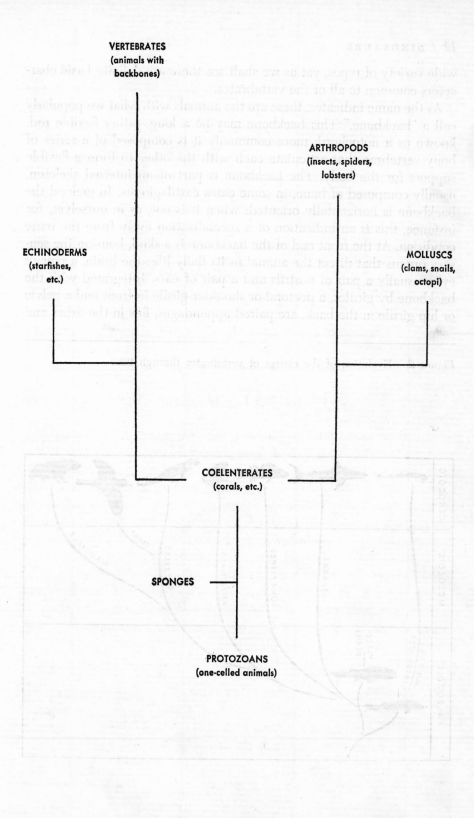

VERTEBRATES
(animals with
backbones)

ARTHROPODS
(insects, spiders,
lobsters)

ECHINODERMS
(starfishes,
etc.)

MOLLUSCS
(clams, snails,
octopi)

COELENTERATES
(corals, etc.)

SPONGES

PROTOZOANS
(one-celled animals)

wide variety of types, yet as we shall see there are definite basic characters common to all of the vertebrates.

As the name indicates, these are the animals with what we popularly call a "backbone." This backbone may be a long, rather flexible rod, known as a notochord; more commonly it is composed of a series of bony vertebrae that articulate each with the other to form a flexible support for the body. The backbone is part of an internal skeleton, usually composed of bone, in some cases cartilaginous. In general the backbone is horizontally oriented; when it is not, as in ourselves, for instance, this is an indication of a specialization away from the basic condition. At the front end of the backbone is a skull, housing the sensory organs that direct the animal in its daily life: the brain, a pair of eyes, usually a pair of nostrils and a pair of ears. Integrated with the backbone by girdles, a pectoral or shoulder girdle in front and a pelvic or hip girdle in the back, are paired appendages, fins in the fishes and

Figure 2. Evolution of the classes of vertebrates through time

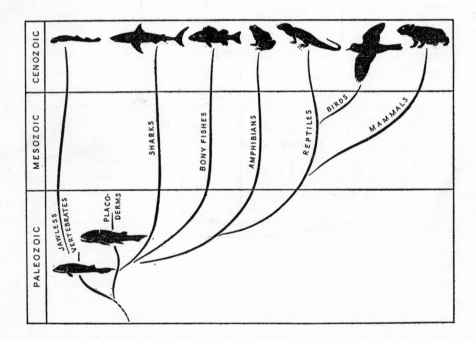

limbs in the tetrapods, for locomotion and balance. In the fishes there are also other fins placed at several locations along the mid-line of the body. The spinal nerve chord, extending the length of the body from the brain, is above the main bodies of the vertebrae; and the circulatory system, the heart, the arteries, and the veins, as well as the digestive system, are below the vertebrae. Breathing is by gills in the fishes and in immature amphibians, and by lungs in mature amphibians and the other tetrapods.

REPTILES

Our particular interest is the dinosaurs, which are reptiles. At last! We are getting past the preliminaries and near the subject of this book.

What are reptiles? Perhaps this word brings to the minds of many people the image of snakes, and certainly snakes are particularly numerous and widely spread among modern reptiles. These vertebrates, usually so harmless to man, and almost always creatures of elegant design and truly surpassing beauty, are commonly thought of as being "cold." And here we have one of the important reptilian characters, for to us they do seem cold. Reptiles, like the amphibians from which they arose, and like the fishes, have no internal means of regulating the body temperature; consequently the temperature of the animal varies more or less according to the manner in which the temperature of its environment varies. If the day is cold the reptile will be sluggish, and if it is very cold the reptile, unless it can burrow underground or protect itself in some other way, may freeze to death. If the day is hot the reptile is active up to a certain point, but if the day is very hot and the reptile is unable to protect itself by going underground or getting into the shade it may die of heat. Reptiles can survive temperatures that may range close to the freezing point of water, but few reptiles can withstand body temperatures that rise much above 100 degrees Fahrenheit. So much for a popular superstition, for it is widely believed that reptiles are fond of the heat and can live happily when the sun is out and the earth is one great oven. That is because reptiles are commonly seen *basking* in the sun to bring their body temperatures up to an optimum level. Be assured, however, that as soon as the body temperature does reach the desired level the reptile leaves off with his basking and goes about his daily business, whatever that may be. Indeed, the tolerances for heat and cold among the reptiles are much less than in the "warm-blooded" birds and mammals, those tetrapods that have an internal heat-regulating mechanism and fairly constant body temperatures.

Furthermore, in the reptiles the heart is not so highly developed as in the "warm-blooded" vertebrates, so that there is a certain mixture within the heart of the "fresh" blood returning from the lungs with the "used" blood coming in from the veins. For this reason reptiles cannot maintain a high level of activity for a long time; they fatigue quickly.

Figure 3. Relationships of the major groups of reptiles

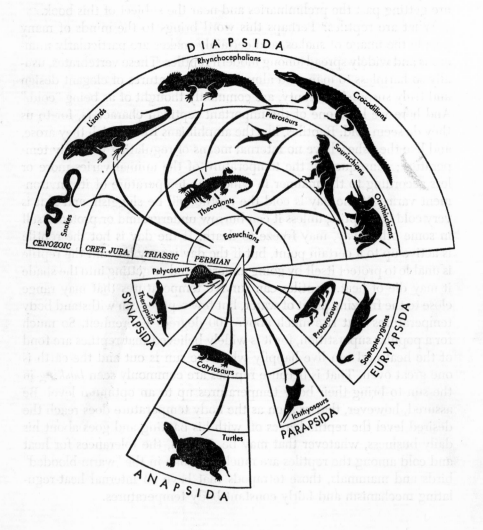

Since reptiles have no internal control of body temperatures, they have no external insulating body coverings:

> "Pigs have bristles,
> Cows have hair,
> Birds have feathers,
> Snakes are bare."

They are covered with a horny or leathery epidermis, which may take the form of scales, as in snakes and lizards, or large, heavy plates, as in crocodiles. One group of reptiles, the turtles, is characterized by a hard shell of bone, covered with horny plates.

Finally, reptiles have a direct method of reproduction. They lay eggs, and from the eggs hatch little reptiles that are miniatures of their parents. Sometimes the eggs are retained within the oviduct of the female, and the young are born alive. In evolving from their amphibian ancestors, the reptiles long ago lost the intermediate stage of metamorphosis, that is, the progression from egg, through tadpole, to adult. This emancipated the reptiles from any dependence upon water for reproduction (a limiting factor in the life history of the amphibian), giving them freedom to roam far and wide across the lands of the earth.

The living reptiles are the lizards and snakes, the turtles, the crocodilians, and the lone tuatara of New Zealand. These are but a forlorn remnant of the many and varied reptiles that lived during Mesozoic times, when the dinosaurs were supreme, as is quite apparent when one looks at a simple family tree of the reptiles.

DINOSAURS

Finally, after this excursion through various subjects with which at least a speaking acquaintance is needed if one is to approach the dinosaurs with any degree of understanding, we do come at last to the dinosaurs themselves. And at this point we shall look very briefly at them, as a sort of introduction to the extended treatment that will make up the rest of the book.

As is evident from the diagram showing the broad evolutionary relationships of the various major divisions or *orders* of reptiles, the dinosaurs do not constitute a single group of reptiles. When they were first studied it was thought that they were all members of a single order, the *Dinosauria*, but the discovery and study of a great deal of fossil material during the past three-quarters of a century have shown quite clearly that the dinosaurs belong to two distinct reptilian orders, as separate from each other as, say, horses are from cattle. The two orders of dinosaurs, called the *Saurischia* and the *Ornithischia*, are closely related, and in turn are closely related to three other reptilian orders, namely, the *Pterosauria*, or flying reptiles, the *Crocodilia*, or crocodiles and alligators, and the *Thecodontia*, or thecodonts, a group of Triassic reptiles from which the dinosaurs, the flying reptiles, and the crocodiles all evolved. These five closely related orders of reptiles can all be lumped together in a big reptilian superorder, known as the Archosauria.

The first archosaurian reptiles, primitive thecodonts of early Triassic age, were bipedal animals, which means that they walked on strong, bird-like hind legs. The front legs were small, the hands being used for grasping rather than for locomotion. The skull was narrow and deep. This basic thecodont heritage for the archosaurian reptiles was carried over to a large degree into the primitive members of the other archosaur orders, so that the earliest dinosaurs also were bipedal reptiles with deep skulls. Any departure from bipedalism in the dinosaurs was a secondary development.

Figure 4. The pelvis, as seen from the right side, in the two orders of dinosaurs. (A) Saurischian pelvis, with a forwardly directed pubis. (B) Ornithischian pelvis, with the pubis parallel to the ischium. Abbreviations: il—ilium; is—ischium; p—pubis

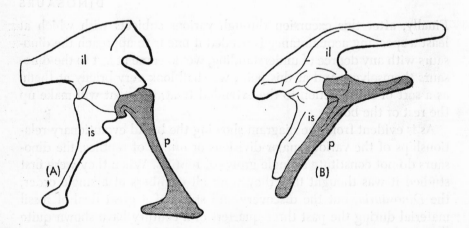

Plate 1.   A fossil in the rock—the leg bone of a large dinosaur in the Cretaceous sediments of the Big Bend National Park, Texas

Plate 2.   Another fossil in the rock—after some of the rock has been removed. This is a portion of the skeleton of *Tyrannosaurus* being excavated from Cretaceous rocks in Montana

Plate 3. Baron Georges Cuvier, the great French anatomist and paleontologist, who examined the bones discovered by Gideon Mantell

Plate 4. Teeth of *Iguanodon* as depicted by Mantell in 1825. These are some of the first illustrations of dinosaur remains

Plate 5. A glimpse into the past. Some Victorian gentlemen and their assistants collecting fossils in the days when Mantell was making his discoveries in southern England

ABOVE. *Plate 6.* Sir Richard Owen, anatomist, first Director of the Natural History division of the British Museum, and a friend of Queen Victoria. He invented the word *Dinosauria*. RIGHT. *Plate 7.* Joseph Leidy, anatomist, zoologist, paleontologist, and the founder of vertebrate paleontology in North America

Plate 8. The full-sized models of *Iguanodon* at Sydenham, in London, as constructed by Waterhouse Hawkins under the direction of Richard Owen. Although inaccurate, they are lively and interesting

Plate 9. The studio of Waterhouse Hawkins in Central Park, New York. On the left is Hawkins's interpretation of *Hadrosaurus;* in the background is his restoration of the skeleton of this dinosaur

Plate 10. Another glimpse into the past. "The Moody Foot Mark Quarry, South Hadley," Massachusetts. An illustration from Hitchcock's monograph on the Connecticut Valley Triassic footprints

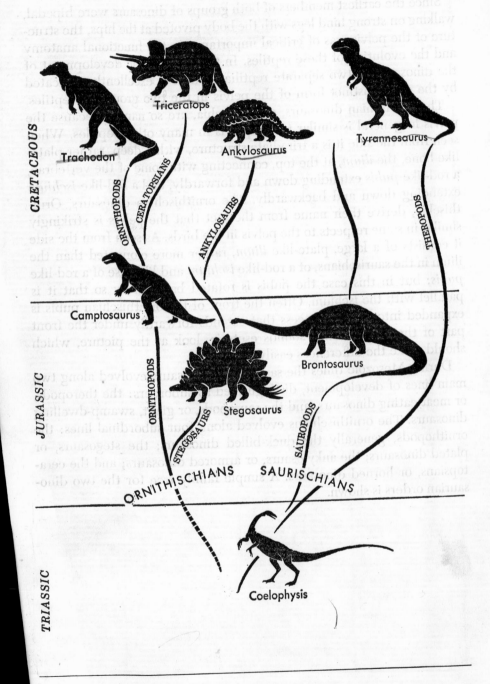

CRETACEOUS

Trachodon

Triceratops

Ankylosaurus

Tyrannosaurus

ORNITHOPODS

CERATOPSIANS

ANKYLOSAURS

THEROPODS

Camptosaurus

JURASSIC

ORNITHOPODS

Stegosaurus

STEGOSAURS

Brontosaurus

SAUROPODS

ORNITHISCHIANS

SAURISCHIANS

TRIASSIC

Coelophysis

Figure 5. Evolution of the dinosaurs

Plate 11. Edward Drinker Cope, paleontologist, ichthyologist, herpetologist, and scientific genius. He described many dinosaurs. He hated Marsh

Plate 12. Othniel Charles Marsh, paleontologist and professor at Yale University. He published some monumental studies of dinosaurs. He hated Cope

Plate 13. A sketch by Arthur Lakes, the English clergyman who was a collector for Marsh, showing Benjamin Mudge, a fellow collector, examining sauropod bones at a quarry near Morrison, Colorado

Since the earliest members of both groups of dinosaurs were bipedal, walking on strong hind legs with the body pivoted at the hips, the structure of the pelvis was of critical importance in the functional anatomy and the evolution of these reptiles. In this respect the development of the dinosaurs as two separate reptilian orders is excellently indicated by the quite distinct form of the pelvis in the two groups of reptiles.

The saurischian dinosaurs, or Saurischia, are so named because the pelvis in general is similar to the pelvis in many other reptiles. When seen from the side it is a triradiate structure, with a deep, rather plate-like bone, the *ilium,* at the top, connecting with some of the vertebrae, a rod-like *pubis* extending down and forwardly, and a rod-like *ischium* extending down and backwardly. The ornithischian dinosaurs, Ornithischia, derive their name from the fact that the pelvis is strikingly similar in some respects to the pelvis in the birds. As seen from the side it consists of a large, plate-like *ilium,* rather more elongated than the ilium in the saurischians, of a rod-like *ischium* and likewise of a rod-like *pubis;* but in this case the pubis is rotated backwardly so that it is parallel with the ischium. Often the front of the ornithischian pubis is expanded into a large process that extends forwardly under the front part of the ilium. If this sounds esoteric, look at the picture, which should make the differences easily apparent.

During Mesozoic times the saurischian dinosaurs evolved along two main lines of development, distinguished as suborders: the theropods, or meat-eating dinosaurs, and the sauropods, or giant, swamp-dwelling dinosaurs. The ornithischians evolved along four subordinal lines: the ornithopods, generally the duck-billed dinosaurs; the stegosaurs, or plated dinosaurs; the ankylosaurs, or armored dinosaurs; and the ceratopsians, or horned dinosaurs. A simple family tree for the two dinosaurian orders is shown.

CHAPTER TWO

DINOSAURS AND VICTORIANS

DINOSAURS ARE DISCOVERED

It does seem strange to think that a mere century and a half ago dinosaurs were quite unknown. So far as man was concerned, at that time there were no dinosaurs—there was not even the concept of a dinosaur. Dinosaurs were still to be discovered, studied, and described.

Without doubt people had seen dinosaur bones in the rock, not only 150 years ago but far back in time, probably back into the days before recorded history when throughout the world men were still primitive savages. But until the early days of the last century even the most knowledgeable men had looked at dinosaur bones with unseeing eyes; they had looked but they had not understood what they had seen. In early historic times, and even through the centuries of medieval history in Europe, people were prone to attribute large fossil bones to giants— a most natural deduction to folks who believed in mythological tales. Indeed, some of the ancient legends of giants may have been based in part on the discoveries of large fossil bones; usually the bones of extinct elephants, but perhaps now and then the bones of other large extinct vertebrates, including dinosaurs.

But by the beginning of the nineteenth century rational explanations for natural phenomena were being sought. No longer were intelligent people satisfied with tales that taxed their credulity; things in nature must be explained in accordance with uniform natural laws. It was the age of reason.

The first dinosaur to be properly described was discovered on a morning in March, 1822, in Sussex, England. Dr. Gideon Mantell, a physician in the city of Lewes, was an unusual man of wide interests, one of that band of devoted amateurs in the Western world who did so much to found the natural sciences during the eighteenth and nineteenth centuries. He was particularly interested in fossils, and for some years had spent his spare hours in the countryside of southern England, searching for the petrified remains of extinct animals. His young wife often accompanied him on many of his excursions into the country, and thus she had gained some experience in looking for fossils in the field.

On this particular day Dr. Mantell drove some miles outside Lewes to attend to one of his patients, and his wife went along for the ride. While he was in the house of his patient, Mrs. Mantell walked up and down to pass the time, and in the course of her walk she saw some rocks that had been piled by the road, to be used for repairs of the surface. As she was looking at the pile of rubble she noticed an object in a rock that looked most unusual, something that had the definite form and the shining surface of a fossil. She picked up the piece of rock containing the specimen, and saw that the object that had attracted her attention was a fossil tooth. Of course, she showed it to her husband.

It was a tooth quite different from any fossil that Dr. Mantell had seen before, and it aroused his curiosity. So, during the ensuing weeks he returned often to the country near where it had been found, and located not only more teeth like it, but also a number of fossil bones as well. All of these fossils were unfamiliar to him.

In those early days of paleontology there was one great authority to whom other students of fossil vertebrates might turn for help, namely Baron Georges Cuvier of Paris. Cuvier was a great leader in the study of animals with backbones, and with good reason he has been called the founder of comparative anatomy and the father of vertebrate paleontology. He was a man of immense erudition and of extraordinary energy, who because of his pre-eminent position as a scientist had lived safely through all of the troubled events that befell France during his long lifetime, from the Revolution, through Napoleonic times, into the days of the Bourbon Restoration. In the 1820's Cuvier was nearing the end of his wonderfully productive life, and he had behind him a vast amount of experience resulting from long years of research on the vertebrates.

Mantell sent his fossils to Cuvier, who identified the teeth as those of an extinct rhinoceros and the bones as belonging to an extinct hippopotamus. In spite of the high authority of Cuvier, Mantell could not accept these identifications because he was certain that the fossils had come from rocks far too ancient to have contained the remains of advanced mammals.

He therefore sought the advice of Dean William Buckland of Oxford University, one of the founders of paleontology in England, a man with whom Mantell had worked. Buckland urged Mantell to do nothing at the time; above all, to publish nothing. Buckland was ready to accept Cuvier's identifications, and this led him to the conclusion that the fossils were remains that had been found in superficial deposits (the *diluvium,* as such deposits were then called) of comparatively late geological age.

But Mantell was not convinced, either by Cuvier or by Buckland, so he decided to make a detailed study of the fossils on his own behalf. At first he made little progress, for he could locate nothing ancient or recent that resembled the fossils in his possession. Then one day in 1825, when Mantell was comparing his fossils with various specimens in the museum of the Royal College of Surgeons in London, he met a naturalist named Samuel Stutchbury, who had just been studying an iguana, a large recent lizard inhabiting Mexico and Central America. Stutchbury immediately saw that Mantell's fossil teeth resembled the teeth of an iguana, but on a much magnified scale. Here was the clue that Mantell needed, and in that same year he published a description of the fossil teeth under the name of *Iguanodon,* which can be translated literally as "iguana tooth" (Plate 4).

When Mantell's description appeared, Cuvier very handsomely acknowledged his own previous error of identification in a statement that may very freely be translated as follows:

"Do we not have here a new animal, an herbivorous reptile? And even as among the modern terrestrial mammals it is within the herbivores that one finds the species of the largest size, so among the reptiles of another time, then the only terrestrial animals, were not the greatest of them nourished on vegetables? Time will confirm or reject this idea.

If teeth adhering to a jaw would be found, the problem might then be resolved."

In the meantime, in 1824, Dean Buckland had described another large reptile, upon the basis of a lower jaw and various parts of the skeleton which had been found at no great distance from Oxford. This was clearly a carnivorous, or meat-eating, reptile, with large blade-like teeth, quite in contrast to the rather leaf-shaped teeth of *Iguanodon*. Buckland gave the name of *Megalosaurus* to the fossil remains.

Megalosaurus was obviously a very large reptile. Cuvier, with whom Buckland had consulted before publishing the description of *Megalosaurus*, advanced the opinion that, judging by the size of the bones, this reptile must have been over forty feet long. Actually, the skeleton of *Megalosaurus* is about half as long as Cuvier had estimated it.

DINOSAURIA

Iguanodon and *Megalosaurus* were thus recognized as large reptiles that had lived upon the land, but what kind of reptiles they may have been was a question as yet unanswered. More fossils were needed.

In 1833 Mantell moved from Lewes to Brighton, because he felt that in the fashionable resort then frequented by royalty he might get adequate support for his work on fossils. (By now he was thoroughly committed to the acquisition and study of fossils, and medicine was to him a necessary money-grubbing profession and little more.) Just before he moved to Brighton he had described a partial reptilian skeleton he had found, and he called it *Hylaeosaurus*.

Two years later a discovery was made near Maidstone, Kent, that at last was to give something of a clue as to the nature of *Iguanodon*. In a quarry a slab of rock was found that contained *Iguanodon* teeth *in association* with various bones of the skeleton. The discovery so prophetically hoped for by Cuvier a decade earlier had finally come to light. *Iguanodon* now began to take form as an animal, rather than as disassociated parts, in the minds of Mantell and other early students of fossils.

By the middle of the 1830's, therefore, three large fossil reptiles had been discovered in the south of England, and named, but beyond that their respective places in the tree of animal life were unknown. These three reptiles, *Iguanodon, Hylaeosaurus,* and *Megalosaurus,* were in truth dinosaurs, but no one realized it. It was to be several years before another Englishman, Richard Owen, would create the concept of dinosaurs.

Richard Owen was the first great comparative anatomist and vertebrate paleontologist of England, a worthy successor of Cuvier. He had a long and distinguished career. In 1842 much of this career was still ahead of him, yet even then, as a comparatively young man, he was Hunterian Professor of Anatomy at the Museum of the Royal College of Surgeons, and his word on the anatomical characters and the relationships of the vertebrates carried a great deal of weight. It was in that year, in one written sentence, that Owen brought the dinosaurs into being, in a report on British fossil reptiles, published by the British Association for the Advancement of Science. Here is what Owen said:

"The combination of such characters, some, as the sacral ones, altogether peculiar among Reptiles, others borrowed, as it were, from groups now distinct from each other, and all manifested by creatures far surpassing in size the largest of existing reptiles, will, it is presumed, be deemed sufficient ground for establishing a distinct tribe or suborder of Saurian Reptiles, for which I would propose the name of *Dinosauria.*"

In a little more than ten years after this, dinosaurs were to be widely known among Englishmen in many walks of life.

OWEN, HAWKINS, AND *IGUANODON*

The first world's fair was the Crystal Palace exposition of 1851, a new kind of fair to celebrate the technology of steam power and the Industrial Revolution that was rapidly making the Western world into something different from what it had been a few decades earlier. In London a great building of iron and glass was erected in Hyde Park, in which many exhibits were displayed and in which concerts and other programs were performed. The Crystal Palace was so popular during the time of the exposition that in 1854 it was removed to a spacious site away from the center of the city, and in the landscaped grounds around the relocated Crystal Palace there were constructed life-sized restorations in concrete of *Iguanodon* and of other animals that had inhabited southern England in the geologic past.

These models were reconstructed by a technician having the unusual name of Waterhouse Hawkins, and they were done under the eagle eye of Professor Owen. The project was carried through with all the scientific exactitude that could be brought to bear upon it at the time.

In those days it was thought that *Iguanodon* was a sort of rhinoceros-like reptile with a horn on its nose, and in this shape it was restored for the Crystal Palace grounds. We now know that *Iguanodon* was a large bipedal dinosaur that walked on strong hind legs, and that the supposed horn placed upon the nose of the beast by Mr. Hawkins is actually a large spike that formed the end of the thumb. But we need not criticize the Crystal Palace models because of our superior modern knowledge; they were laudable and sincere efforts for their time, and they were most effective. A century later they are still standing (Plate 8).

The construction of these restorations was a long and exacting task, and we may well understand the feeling of real accomplishment that came over Hawkins and his assistants as the job neared its end. To

Figure 6. Dinner in the *Iguanodon* model at the Crystal Palace, Sydenham. From the *Illustrated London News,* January 7, 1854

celebrate the completion of the *Iguanodon* model, a party was given at which Professor Owen and other distinguished scientists of the day sat down to what must have been a rather crowded dinner *inside* the model, while the lesser lights banqueted on tables set up around the reconstructed dinosaur. It was a memorable affair.

According to a contemporary report, "Cards of invitation were issued as follows:— 'Mr. D. W. Hawkins solicits the honor of Professor ———'s company at dinner in the *Iguanodon*, on the 31st December, 1853, at 4 o'clock, p.m.' This incredible request was written on the wing of a Pterodactyle, spread before a most graphic etching of the Iguanodon with his socially-loaded stomach, so practically and easily filled as to tempt all, to whom it was possible, to accept the invitation. Mr. Hawkins had one-and-twenty guests around him in the body of the Iguanodon —before the upper part of the back and head was completed. In the chair, most appropriately, sat Professor Owen, occupying part of the head of the gigantic animal; he was supported by the late Professor Forbes; Mr. Prestwich, the eminent geologist; Mr. Gould, the celebrated ornithologist; with other eminently scientific men. This model, it must be remembered, represents the natural size of the animal during life. In building the model the following was consumed as its material:— 600 bricks, 650 two-inch half round drain tiles, 900 plain tiles, 38 casks of cement, 90 casks of broken stone, together with 100 feet of iron hooping, and 20 feet of cube inch bar."

LEIDY, HAWKINS, AND *HADROSAURUS*

During those early decades of the nineteenth century, when Gideon Mantell and William Buckland and Richard Owen were discovering and describing the first dinosaurs to be found in England, the remains of these interesting reptiles were as yet unknown across the Atlantic. More than a decade was to pass after Owen had defined and given substance to the dinosaurs before any dinosaurian fossils were to be recognized in North America, the land that ultimately was to yield the most abundant and the most spectacular dinosaurs to be found in the wide world.

It all began in a very modest way with the discovery of dinosaur teeth near the confluence of the Judith River and the Missouri River in Montana, and of two vertebrae and a toe bone in South Dakota. These fossils were picked up in 1855 by one of the early scientific explorers of our West, Dr. Ferdinand V. Hayden. He took the fossils east with him and gave them to Dr. Joseph Leidy of the Academy of Natural Sciences in Philadelphia, for study and description. Dr. Leidy's account of these fossils was published in the following year.

Dr. Leidy was a remarkable man. Like Mantell in England, Leidy in America was a medical doctor who devoted part of his time to natural history. But Leidy was much less of an amateur than was Mantell; in many respects he was much like the professional scientist of today. In addition to his association with the Academy of Natural Sciences, he was Professor of Anatomy in the Medical School of the University of Pennsylvania, which means that he was thoroughly familiar with the details of human anatomy. Beyond this, Leidy was a man of broad knowledge who spoke with authority on the anatomy of many different vertebrates. Indeed, he ranged so widely in scientific interests that he was also an authority on parasites. Those were the days, a century ago, when a man could become a master in more than one field of science; they were the days of the all-around naturalist, a type that has by now almost completely disappeared. As a pleasant adjunct to his wide-ranging professional competence, Leidy was possessed of a calm and friendly nature that made him well beloved to all who knew him. He was a man of great dignity.

His descriptions in 1856 of the dinosaurian fragments that had been found by Hayden in Montana and South Dakota prepared him for participation in the next discovery of a North American dinosaur, a discovery that was spectacular and significant. This was the recovery in 1858 of a partial dinosaur skeleton in Haddonfield, New Jersey, immediately across the Delaware River from Philadelphia.

In the summer of that year a Mr. W. Parker Foulke of Philadelphia was spending some time in Haddonfield. While there he heard stories of bones that had been found several years before in a marl pit on the farm of his neighbor, Mr. John E. Hopkins. Foulke's interest was immediately aroused by the accounts of the bones, and he tried to locate some of the fossils. In this he was doomed to disappointment—the bones had all disappeared. Nevertheless Mr. Foulke made arrangements with Mr. Hopkins to reopen the pit where the fossils had been discovered, and as a result he unearthed various additional bones—vertebrae, the front and hind limbs, parts of the pelvis, some jaw fragments, and nine teeth. There was no skull, which was most unfortunate. Even so, he had a considerable portion of a skeleton, and all of this material was turned over to Dr. Leidy at the Academy in Philadelphia. Leidy described the bones and teeth very carefully and showed that they belonged to a hadrosaur, or trachodont, one of the so-called duck-billed dinosaurs related to *Iguanodon*. He named the new dinosaur *Hadrosaurus foulkei*.

Hadrosaurus was discovered at a time when most Americans were preoccupied with the great dispute that was growing ever more acrimonious and ever more ominous between the northern and southern states. Within three years after the finding of this first dinosaur skeleton in America, the country was torn by its most fearful trial, and there was little time for fossils. Consequently a lapse of several years occurred during which the bones of the new dinosaur gathered dust on the shelves of a case in the Philadelphia Academy, while outside in the streets columns of blue-uniformed men marched off to war.

After the war was over who should appear in New York but Mr. Waterhouse Hawkins, to begin work on some life-sized reconstructions of ancient animals that were to be displayed in a large iron and glass museum in the newly created Central Park. Mr. Hawkins intended to add a touch of local color by constructing a full-scale model of *Hadrosaurus*, as a companion to the other "antediluvian monsters" he was bringing to life in such a substantial fashion. The work was well under way when the "iconoclastic Central Park Commission," as Mr. Hawkins bitterly designated the men in charge of the Park, forced him to end his labors. The reason for this change of plans was complex, and in part was a result of some unsavory politics of the Tweed era. Poor Hawkins was the innocent victim of all of this, and he had to see his partially constructed models, including *Hadrosaurus*, unceremoniously buried in the park, where presumably they are still interred, awaiting the attention of some future archaeologist.

Waterhouse Hawkins then went to Philadelphia—the year was 1868 —to set up the skeleton of *Hadrosaurus* for the Academy there. This task was carried to its successful conclusion, owing partly to the skill of Mr. Hawkins and partly to the liberal use of plaster in reconstructing missing bones. Certainly an impressive-looking plaster and bone skeleton was erected, but its resemblance to *Hadrosaurus* as we now know that dinosaur was anything but absolute. His effort remained visible for many years, to be seen by several generations of museum visitors. It was only shortly before the Second World War that the Hawkins restoration of the hadrosaur skeleton was finally dismantled.

Even though he had labored long, and had successfully restored the skeleton of *Hadrosaurus*, Waterhouse Hawkins still was not satisfied to rest upon his laurels; he wanted to fulfill his frustrated ambition of making a full-scale restoration of this dinosaur as it had appeared in life. In a report published by the Philadelphia Academy of Natural Sciences in 1874, we read that "the opportunity was afforded by the trustees of the New Jersey College at Princeton, who desired to possess for their museum one of Mr. Hawkins's restorations of an extinct animal of New Jersey. For this purpose they selected *Hadrosaurus* . . ." But alas! it would appear that even in Princeton Mr. Hawkins was unable to bring to reality his plans for a model of *Hadrosaurus;* at least there seems to be no record of his ever having completed this work. Consequently, *Hadrosaurus* for the public remained a name, a collection of bones, and a reconstructed skeleton in Philadelphia.

DINOSAUR TRACKS IN THE CONNECTICUT VALLEY

Although the *Hadrosaurus* specimen unearthed at Haddonfield in 1858 was the first dinosaur *skeleton* to be described from North America, indications of dinosaurs on this continent came to light at a much earlier date—at the beginning of the nineteenth century, as a matter of fact. These were dinosaur footprints, found in the valley of the Connecticut River, but since Mantell and Buckland and Owen were not to describe and define dinosaurs for some years to come, the true nature of the footprints was not then realized.

In 1802 a New England farm boy named Pliny Moody found fossil tracks in sandstones exposed near his home in South Hadley, Massachusetts (Plate 10). These footprints looked as if they had been made by gigantic birds, for which reason they were regarded by some people as the fossil tracks of ground-living birds, perhaps similar to modern ostriches. By other people they were designated as the tracks of "Noah's raven." Within the next two or three decades more and more of these "bird tracks" were found up and down the length of the Connecticut River Valley, in rocks of Triassic age.

The tracks had a particular fascination for one man—the Reverend E. B. Hitchcock, president of Amherst College. He ferreted out stone footprints, wherever they might be, spending years and all the money he could scrape together on the project, and in 1858 published his monumental tome *Ichnology of New England*, a volume brought out by the Commonwealth of Massachusetts. In this work he described the tracks, most of which he considered to have been made by ancient birds, and figured them in beautiful full-page lithographic illustrations. He gave them names. And he established for himself a reputation as a solid man of science.

Professor Hitchcock envisaged a special building at Amherst to house and exhibit the tracks that he had collected through the years. About this time Mr. Samuel Appleton of Boston had willed a large sum to be used for benevolent and scientific purposes, and Hitchcock tapped this fund for ten thousand dollars, a sum sufficient in those days to construct a very adequate and suitable museum building. Thus there came into being the "Appleton Cabinet," the entire lower floor of which was devoted to the display of Triassic footprints.

Even as late as 1863, when a supplement to Hitchcock's *Ichnology of New England* was edited by his son, the tracks were still considered as having been made by ancient birds. But already in 1861 the oldest unmistakable fossil bird had been found, the famous skeleton of *Archaeopteryx*, a fossil many millions of years later in age than the Connecticut Valley tracks. Therefore it soon became apparent that the New England tracks were too ancient to have been made by birds; in short, there were no birds on the earth when these tracks were formed. The Connecticut Valley tracks clearly had been made by small primitive dinosaurs, the bones of which were turning up in sediments contemporaneous with those containing the tracks.

So the tracks took their rightful place as the first evidences of dinosaurs to be *found* but certainly not the first to be *recognized* in North America. It required a considerable advance of knowledge about the ancient life of the earth before the tracks were finally identified correctly. As the nineteenth century drew to a close, man's knowledge about past life of the earth had become established on a solid foundation of facts, the result of many discoveries of fossils. Dinosaurs were no longer known from mere isolated fragments; there were now respectable if not abundant collections of bones in various institutions. The pioneer days of discovery were past.

PROFESSOR MARSH AND PROFESSOR COPE

The history of the discoveries and the early studies of dinosaurs is a continuing story, as any history is bound to be, and its division into stages or phases is an artificial, man-made pigeonholing of events, as are any such divisions of history. Yet these artifices help us to remember things. Let us, therefore, regard the first half-century or so of work on the dinosaurs as the "pioneer" period—a span of time ending with the beginning of the last decade of the nineteenth century. This pioneer period, so defined, was a time of groping, rather haphazard efforts in the field, and of intellectual groping in the laboratory, a period when the depths and limits of our knowledge of dinosaurs were first being realized.

In Europe the first period of early, undirected investigations of the dinosaurs gradually merged into a more modern period of field work and research, based upon a greatly augmented knowledge not only of the dinosaurs but also of their relatives, of all extinct life, and of the past events of earth history. In North America the first phase of work on the dinosaurs was brought to an exciting close by the unrivaled discoveries and researches of two men, and by the ensuing acrimonious dispute between them.

The collecting of dinosaurs in North America during the seventies and eighties was very colorful and romantic, to put it mildly, and studies on the fossils so collected were far removed from the quiet, objective activities that are supposed to encompass scientific research. The reason for all of the excitement is to be found in the conflicting personalities and ambitions of Professor Marsh and Professor Cope.

Othniel Charles Marsh was born during the year 1831 in Lockport, New York. He grew up in a region where there were woodlands to explore and where there were many cliffs and outcrops of rocks containing fossils that would be of interest to a boy having a larger than usual bump of curiosity and an interest in nature. When he was a young lad his mother died, and subsequently he came under the patronage of his uncle, George Peabody, a man of wealth and influence. Marsh attended Yale College, graduating in 1860, after which he studied in Germany for several years. To the great good luck of Marsh, his uncle left him an ample income for life. Thus Marsh became independent, and devoted all his time to fossils. He returned to Yale in 1866 as Professor of Paleontology, and immediately launched upon an active career of research on fossil vertebrates at Yale. He persuaded his uncle to found the Peabody Museum at Yale, which under the direction of Marsh was to become one of the outstanding natural-history museums of North America. He never married. He died in 1899.

Edward Drinker Cope was born in Philadelphia in 1840, the son of a wealthy Quaker philanthropist and the grandson of a shipowner. His mother died when Cope was a very small boy, but he had the good fortune to acquire a loving and understanding stepmother. He also was fortunate in having a very sympathetic father. Cope was amazingly precocious, and at the age of seven was making detailed and sophisticated notes concerning the fine points of the anatomy of an ichthyosaur that was on display at the Academy of Natural Sciences in Philadelphia. At nineteen he was publishing scientific papers. He also went to Europe during the early sixties, and returned to become a Professor at Haverford College. But he did not remain at Haverford for long; he had too independent a personality to be confined within the bounds of any institutional organization. Consequently, for much of his life he was an independent worker, financing his own field work and research with the fortune that had been left to him by his father. In the course of time he became an outstanding world authority in at least three fields—the study of recent fishes, the study of recent amphibians and reptiles, and the study of fossil vertebrates. He published prolifically and stands as one of the great men of American science. During his middle age he invested heavily in mines and virtually lost the fortune that had been his. In the last years of his life (he died in 1897) he served as Professor at the University of Pennsylvania, and this appointment helped him through the last difficult, and in a sense tragic, years. He married his cousin, Annie Pim, and they had one daughter.

Cope and Marsh were able men; both were brilliant (Cope was a true genius), both were inordinately ambitious, both had money, and both were very independent people, accustomed to getting what they wanted. What both wanted was to collect and describe extinct vertebrates of all kinds. They put their wishes into actions, and in so doing they literally discovered a vast new world of dinosaurs.

Cope and Marsh began their scientific careers immediately after the Civil War, during an expansionist period of American history. They became acquainted with each other in the early seventies, and at that time they had some pleasant trips together in eastern North America, searching for early dinosaurs and other fossils. Then they turned their attentions to the great open country west of the Mississippi. They began to collect in the Great Plains and in the Rocky Mountain region, and in a very short time all of western North America was not big enough to accommodate the two of them. Their rivalry and their jealousy of each other grew by leaps and bounds, and exceeded all reasonable limits. Each man became a monomaniac with regard to the other, and their activities assumed almost the nature of open warfare. They spied upon each other, and the collectors they hired likewise spied on each other. They tried to keep secret their fossil localities. Upon at least one occasion their collectors engaged in a free-for-all fight among the lonely ridges of Wyoming. They engaged in vituperative attacks upon each other in the newspapers, and they promulgated all sorts of machinations in scientific societies, in the government surveys on which they both served, and in the universities and museums with which they were connected. Indeed, the story of Cope and Marsh would make a swash-buckling novel.

Yet all of this had its good side: their intense rivalry stimulated them to collect and describe fossils on a grand scale. They sent back tons of bones to New Haven and to Philadelphia, to be cleaned by their technicians, drawn by their artists, and measured by their assistants. In doing so they laid the groundwork for our modern methods and techniques of vertebrate paleontology. Marsh and Cope did not rely upon the chance discovery of fossils. They planned well-integrated campaigns of fossil hunting and collecting. They developed methods for taking large bones out of the ground that are still in use. They maintained laboratories, staffed by assistants. They published their research studies in two veritable blizzards of scientific reports.

Of course, Cope and Marsh ranged far and wide in their search for dinosaurs, but each made certain outstanding discoveries. Cope discovered and described primitive Triassic dinosaurs from New Mexico. He opened a large quarry in the Jurassic Morrison deposits near Canyon City, Colorado, and there excavated some excellent skeletons. One of his specimens, the skeleton of the meat-eating dinosaur *Allosaurus*, was still in boxes, unopened and unstudied, when the American Museum of Natural History purchased the Cope collection. This dinosaur now occupies a prominent place in Brontosaur Hall in New York. Cope also described Cretaceous dinosaurs, especially from along the Judith River in Montana.

The outstanding dinosaurian discovery by Marsh was the great deposit of skeletons in the Morrison sediments along Como Bluff, in eastern Wyoming. From this place Marsh and his collectors excavated a veritable treasure-trove of skeletons, some of which are finely displayed in the Yale Peabody Museum. This is one of the most prolific and famous dinosaur localities in the world, and incidentally one that Cope's men tried to invade when it was being actively worked by Marsh collectors. Marsh also collected Cretaceous dinosaurs, especially from the region near Denver. It was from this locality that he first made known the existence of horned dinosaurs.

The work of Marsh and Cope amazed and overwhelmed paleontologists in Europe and in other parts of the world. (Because the feud between Marsh and Cope reached such intensity, Joseph Leidy retired from the field and turned his attention to other things. Leidy was a gentle man and he could not put up with the fireworks of the Cope-Marsh affair.) In short, these two men expanded the knowledge of the dinosaurs from scattered descriptions, based largely upon parts of skeletons or isolated bones, to a large body of knowledge founded upon an imposing array of skulls and relatively complete skeletons.

As far as dinosaurs are concerned, Marsh was clearly the winner. He collected more and described more than did Cope—perhaps largely because Cope's interests were wider than Marsh's. Cope had a greater variety of fossils to study than did Marsh, and in addition he was at the same time studying and publishing on recent fishes, amphibians, and reptiles. The box score: Marsh described 19 genera of dinosaurs; Cope trailed behind with only 9.

With the passing of Marsh and Cope, shortly before the turn of the century, the pioneer period of work on dinosaurs was truly ended. In this country and abroad, partly as a result of the great work done by these two men, the modern period of dinosaurian field and laboratory studies was inaugurated.

CHAPTER THREE

THE TWENTIETH CENTURY

THE LEGACY OF THE INNOVATORS

Marsh and Cope, by their vigorous efforts and their unparalleled discoveries in the West, pointed the way toward exciting possibilities for future explorations and studies in the field of vertebrate paleontology, not only on this continent but also in other lands. What they did in a quarter of a century gave some clear indication of what might be hoped for and accomplished in the future by paleontologists using their methods (in a sensible way, of course, and without all of the verbal fireworks and unpleasantness that made the Marsh-Cope affair such a disgracefully colorful episode in the history of North American paleontology). The great collections of dinosaurs and of other fossils that they accumulated were concrete, tangible proofs as to the effectiveness of their methods.

These two men showed that the best way to obtain good complete skeletons of ancient backboned animals is to go out and *search* for them, to search at firsthand, hard and diligently, and not to depend upon chance discoveries by local inhabitants of a region or by geologists and other scientific and technical field workers. They showed that good fossil skeletons are best discovered by men trained to the work of looking for such things, men with eyes that see bones in the rocks, and particularly men who can devote their whole time and their undivided attention to the quest for such fossils. They showed that the successful paleontologist, like the successful general, plans his campaign carefully. He knows what he wants to do in the field, and he bends every effort to accomplish his purpose. They showed that it requires care and very special methods to collect fossil vertebrates, and this applies with particular force to the dinosaurs. One doesn't dig up skeletons of ancient animals like potatoes. Marsh and Cope devised methods to get skeletons, large and small, out of the ground without breakage, and with the numerous bones of each skeleton retained in proper relationships to one another. They showed that if one is to go out after big things like dinosaurs, one had better be prepared to throw great amounts of manhours and effort into the job, which means men and time and equipment. They showed that the proper sequel to the collecting of complete skeletons in the field is the long and tedious preparation of these skeletons in the laboratory, so that each specimen becomes a significant fossil, to be studied, interpreted, described, and not infrequently to be exhibited in a museum.

Marsh was especially interested in the development of techniques and advanced methods for the excavation of fossil bones and for their transportation in safety to the laboratory. Some of the details of how collecting methods were improved by Marsh, and especially by certain of his assistants, make an interesting story, a story that is more often than not unknown to modern paleontological workers. Here are a few of the high lights.

According to Marsh, in a conversation he had with Professor Charles Schuchert of Yale in 1892, the early days of fossil collecting in the West might be called the *pick-rake-sack* period. The fossil hunter, having found a bone or a skeleton, would thrust a pick under the fossil and pry it out of the ground. Then he would rake all of the pieces together (there were *always* a lot of pieces when bones were taken out by this rough-and-ready procedure) and stuff them into a sack. Afterward it was up to the poor, harassed technician in the laboratory to try to fit the pieces together and make a little sense out of the fossiliferous jigsaw puzzle that confronted him. It was not a very efficient way to collect scientific specimens. In extenuation it might be said that the pioneer collector often was working under difficulties, including certain mental hazards, for in those days the fossil hunter could never be quite sure as to how he was going to be received by the Indians in his general vicinity. Said Professor Samuel Wendell Williston, "Modern methods were impracticable with rifle in one hand and pick in the other."

Who devised the modern method known as the bandaging technique is a matter of some dispute, but it may have been the aforesaid Williston, one of Marsh's most able assistants, and subsequently one of the very great men of American paleontology. Williston had obtained a degree in medicine before he began his work as a collector for Marsh, and perhaps he was thinking of the methods of setting a broken limb in a cast when he wrote to Marsh in 1877 from the great dinosaur quarry near Canyon City, Colorado: "Will it do to paste strips of strong paper on fractured bones before removing? . . . Those strips are put on with ordinary flour paste and can be removed I think easily." This first crude attempt at "bandaging" fossil bones was reasonably successful, and Williston managed in that year to send back to Yale many bones so treated, instead of the usual sacks full of broken fragments.

At about this time Cope and his collector, Charles Sternberg, working in Montana, tried the expedient of boiling rice into a thick paste in which they dipped burlap strips or flour bags, pasting these pieces of sacking over and around the bones. When the paste hardened, the bones that received this treatment were held reasonably secure.

The use of plaster of Paris instead of paste was initiated also at about this same time, perhaps by Arthur Lakes, another of Marsh's collectors. In 1877 Lakes was excavating dinosaur bones at Morrison, Colorado, and he wrote to Marsh, in part as follows:

"I do not know whether you wish us to use plaster of paris but if it is not an obstacle in your final clearing up of the bones it would be often a great assistance to us in keeping together very fragmentary bones. The rock is so intensely hard, so destitute of good cleavage and seamed in every direction that it is next to impossible to prevent fractures and not infrequently the seam breaking right across the bone has a tendency to break it up into minute fragments. To obviate this I have occasionally laid on a strong coat of plaster of paris on the outside of the bone to preserve it whilst the rest of the rock was being jarred by the hammer."

Still another Marsh collector, David Baldwin, who was working in New Mexico in 1876 and 1877, hit upon the idea of shaping pieces of wood to fit the bone in a rough way; then he tied such shaped pieces securely to the bone with strong hemp cord. Thus was devised a system of "splints" that prevented a bone, crossed by many cracks and fractures, from breaking into small fragments.

By combining these separately devised techniques the modern method of collecting fossil bones was developed, and by about the year 1880 had become firmly established. It is a method that in its essential features is still being used.

Briefly, a modern fossil hunter, when he finds a bone or a series of articulated bones that make a skeleton or part of a skeleton, first exposes the fossil material sufficiently so that he can see the outlines of his specimen. All exposed surfaces of bone are then treated with thin shellac, or with one of the modern organic compounds, such as alvar. Thin tissue paper or Japanese rice paper is then shellacked to the bone, and when this dries it makes a tough protective film over the delicate surface. After this, the fossil is completely encased in burlap strips dipped in plaster of Paris, so that it is wrapped in a "bandage," in much the same way that a broken limb is set in a cast by a physician. Some fossil hunters use flour paste instead of plaster, because it is not so heavy, but it has disadvantages, not the least of which is that mice dearly love to invade a storeroom full of bandaged specimens, to eat the flour paste. Finally, heavy sticks, "splints," are plastered onto the bandaged specimen. After the plaster is hard the specimen can be moved and packed and shipped without suffering any damage. Single bones or even complete skeletons (if they are not too large) can be treated in this way.

INTO THE FIELD FOR DINOSAURS

One of the commonest questions asked the paleontologist is: "How do you find the fossils?" And not infrequently he is asked: "How do you know where to dig? Do you go out and just start making a hole in the ground?" To the uninitiated it does seem mysterious that a paleontologist can go out among the cliffs and badlands with the avowed intention of finding fossils—and find them. It is especially mysterious to the person who has tramped over the very ground that is traversed by the fossil hunter, without ever seeing a trace of what the paleontologist is seeking.

Let us begin at the beginning, and follow the development and practice of a modern expedition for dinosaurs, an expedition that owes much to the early work of Cope and of Marsh and their associates, and especially to the methods and techniques initiated by them.

The search for dinosaurs is a good deal of a gamble, even in this modern age, but it is carried on with as much foresight and as much planning as possible. Nothing is haphazard about it.

In the first place, the modern fossil hunter goes into the field with a definite purpose in mind. He does not sally forth willy-nilly just to look for fossils; rather he goes to definite localities in the hopes of discovering definite kinds of fossils. And what he is looking for is decided in part by his own interests, by the research problems in which he is engaged, and in part by the policies of the institution for which he works. When the search involves dinosaurs, there had better be some very carefully formulated plans and policies, because dinosaurs are expensive fossils to collect.

When Cope and Marsh began their work in western North America, they were entering a land that scientifically was virtually unknown. Consequently some of their early efforts were in the nature of blind groping in the field; they had to establish the age of the rocks they were exploring by the contained fossils, and then, knowing the age of the rocks, they had to search in rocks of certain ages for the fossils they were interested in collecting. It was a sort of round robin of reasoning and practice, a method that must still be applied in those remote areas of the world where little geologic work has been done. But today, thanks to a century or more of work in the field and laboratory, most of the world has been geologically mapped (in many regions, it must be admitted, in a very sketchy and superficial manner) so that the fossil hunter can go to the area in which he is interested with at least some idea as to the nature and the age of the rocks containing buried paleontological treasures.

Obviously the dinosaur hunter will go to regions where Mesozoic rocks are exposed in cliffs and in badlands, there to search for the remains of the great reptiles that once ruled the land. Furthermore, his objectives are apt to be more limited than this, for he is more likely than not looking for Triassic or Jurassic or Cretaceous dinosaurs, and thus he confines his attention to rocks of one particular age. In any locality the rocks of each age have their own peculiar physical expressions; they may form vertical cliffs or rounded badlands or buttes or gullied plains. Whatever the topography, it is the task of the fossil hunter to go over it on foot and in detail, if he is to find the bones he hopes for.

Be it understood that the paleontologist never digs until he has something to dig for. That is why he spends many hours and days in the hot sun, tramping across hills and badlands or skirting the bases of cliffs, with his eye constantly scanning the surface for the telltale fragments of bones. It can be very tedious at times.

A practiced and trained eye is required to see most fossil bones in the field. More often than not the presence of a dinosaur skeleton may be indicated by a few broken fragments of bone scattered on the talus slope at the base of a cliff. To the casual explorer such bones may look like pieces of rock; to the paleontologist they are recognized for what they are—possible leads to an important discovery. The clue is not so much in their shape, because they may be irregular fragments, as in their *texture*. Fossil bones have an organic structure that indicates their real nature—the smooth shine of the bone surface, the spongy appearance of the inner portion of the bone. But then petrified bone may be encrusted with an outer covering of iron oxide or some other mineral, which complicates things for the fossil hunter. It is mainly a case of getting used to what fossil bones in any particular formation may look like, and then trying to find them.

Once the bone fragments have been located, the next step is to try to find the place from which they are weathering, the original source. Fossil bones are of little value unless they are found in place. Perhaps they are weathering out of a vertical cliff face above a talus slope; perhaps they are weathering from the bank of a small gully; perhaps they are weathering out on a flat surface of ground. When the source has been located, it is then necessary for the paleontologist to start a preliminary excavation, to see if the specimen is worth collecting. This takes some time, often several hours, spent in digging around the specimen, to determine its limits and its condition. Frequently—all too frequently in the lexicon of the paleontologist—the specimen is not worth taking, so it is abandoned. But now and then a good specimen or a concentration of good specimens is found.

If it be a dinosaur, this may require a quarrying operation of considerable size. The whole specimen, or the group of specimens, must be uncovered, which may necessitate the removal of tons of rock. So it is that the paleontologist and his assistants become pick-and-shovel men, unless they are so fortunate as to get the use of a bulldozer or dynamite, or other methods of assistance. Alas! It is the common lot of the fossil hunter to find his bones in some inaccessible place, where bulldozers and such mechanical aids to human muscle power cannot be had, and so he reverts to the time-honored method of the pick and the shovel.

Once the mass of rock is removed from above the fossils, the limits of the bones or of the skeletons are explored. This is done with hammers and chisels and awls, and near the bones such tools must be used with great care. As bones are exposed they are protected with shellac or with other hardening preservatives, and further protected with tissue paper or rice paper, as has already been described. Then the bones or the skeletons must be "blocked out" for removal from the ground.

A dinosaur skeleton is more often than not too large to be taken out as a unit. So it is divided into reasonably convenient blocks that can be isolated for removal, and if the skeleton is closely articulated this takes a bit of doing. Each block is outlined and cut around the sides, so that it stands on a pedestal of rock. Its top and sides are bandaged with burlap and plaster, according to the method outlined in a preceding paragraph of this chapter. Then the pedestal of rock is cut away from beneath the block, the block is turned over, and its lower surface is plastered. This is not always as straightforward a process as might be gathered from a simple description, for the business of undercutting and turning over a block can be very wearing and very frustrating, and more than one fossil hunter has seen a block disintegrate within its plaster cast during the process of turning it over. But with skill and good luck the several blocks are finally freed from the mother earth and are ready for packing and for transportation to the museum or to the university to which they are destined. And during the course of the quarrying many photographs and field notes have been made to record the types of fossils uncovered, their physical relationships to one another, their levels within the rocks, and the details of the local geology.

All of this work has taken a summer, or perhaps several successive summers, and yet the work in the field is just the beginning of a long process that makes a dinosaur skeleton something of scientific value and significance (Plates 14–22).

IN THE LABORATORY

The business of going out into wild places to look for dinosaurs has a very romantic aura about it, especially in these days of concrete highways and air-conditioned motels. The days of the Old West are long gone, but the dinosaur hunter of today still feels some kinship with his predecessors who worked with Marsh or with Cope, for in spite of the advances in methods and the many amenities that are enjoyed by the modern paleontologist in the field, there are still cliffs to be climbed and badlands to be explored, out and away from almost all reminders of our modern world. So this part of the paleontologist's life attracts and appeals to many people who get glimpses of it.

Yet the work in the field is only a small fraction of the whole; as has been said it is only the beginning, though a necessary and important beginning, of the task of resurrecting the dinosaurs and bringing them into our lives. It is the gathering of the raw data with which the paleontologist works. Raw data are necessary in every scientific discipline— fossils for the paleontologist, minerals for the mineralogist, beetles for the entomologist, pots and flints for the archaeologist, chemicals in test tubes for the chemist, measurements of energy for the physicist— but such data are not science; they need manipulation and interpretation if they are to be useful.

So it is that the fossils as they come from the field into the laboratory have only potential value. There is still much to be done with them, and the next step after their arrival, and after they have been unpacked, is known as *preparation*. The work of collecting a dinosaur may take weeks or a few months; the work of preparing the fossil bones generally will require months and years of skilled application on the part of trained technicians. This must be done before the scientist, the professional paleontologist, can truly begin his studies of the specimens.

First the plaster bandages must be soaked and removed from the blocks. When this is done, the careful work of freeing the bones from the enclosing rock begins in earnest. It is not easy. Fossil bones are commonly hard, but they are usually as brittle as glass, and a false blow with a hammer can shatter a priceless specimen. Moreover, these fossils are all too often enclosed in a difficult matrix, a hard, refractory sandstone that clings to the bone surface, or an enclosing encrustation of

Figure 7. The work behind the fossils. First the field campaign is carefully planned. Fossils are excavated from the rock in the field, and completely prepared in the laboratory. The interpretation of the fossils is the purpose of research. After the fossils have been studied, they are described, discussed, and pictured in scientific publications. Those suitable for display are placed in the exhibition hall and the remainder (usually the bulk of the collection) are stored for future reference and study and for exchange with other museums

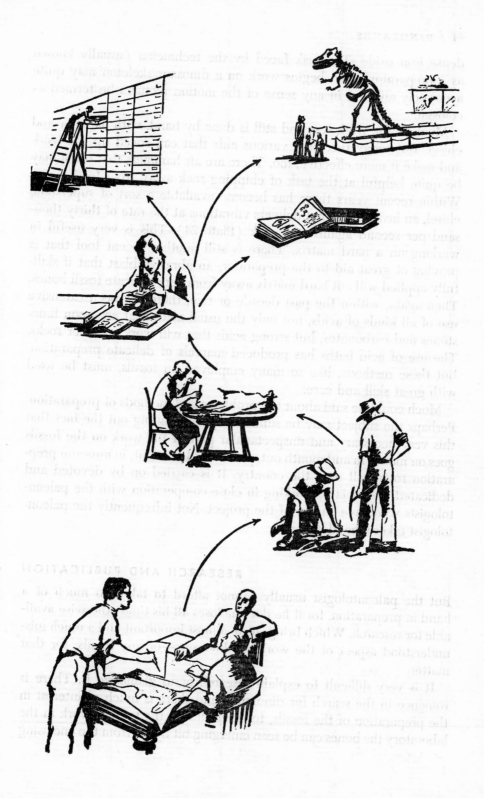

dense iron oxide. The task faced by the technician (usually known as a preparator) who begins work on a dinosaur skeleton may quite accurately and not in any sense of the motion pictures be termed as colossal.

Much of the work was and still is done by hand, with hammer and chisel. But today there are various aids that can speed up the work and make it more effective, too. There are air hammers that often may be quite helpful at the task of chipping rock away from fossil bone. Within recent years there has become available a sort of supersonic chisel, an instrument that delivers vibrations at the rate of thirty thousand per second against the rock (Plate 24). This is very useful in working on a hard matrix. There is still another recent tool that is proving of great aid to the preparator, an abrasive blast that if skillfully applied will cut hard matrix away from very delicate fossil bones. Then again, within the past decade or two, there has been extensive use of all kinds of acids, not only the usual acids that act upon limestones and carbonates, but strong acids that will work on other rocks. The use of acid baths has produced marvels of delicate preparation, but these methods, like so many employed on fossils, must be used with great skill and care.

Much could be said about the problems and methods of preparation. Perhaps the subject may be summed up by pointing out the fact that this very necessary and unspectacular part of the work on the fossils goes on month in and month out, year in and year out, in museum preparation rooms all over the country. It is carried on by devoted and dedicated technicians, working in close co-operation with the paleontologists who have charge of the project. Not infrequently the paleontologist takes a hand, too.

RESEARCH AND PUBLICATION

But the paleontologist usually cannot afford to take too much of a hand in preparation, for if he does he loses all his time otherwise available for research. Which brings us to a most important and a much misunderstood aspect of the work on dinosaurs—or any fossils, for that matter.

It is very difficult to explain research or to glamorize it. There is romance in the search for dinosaurs, and there is much of interest in the preparation of the fossils, for even during the tedious work in the laboratory the bones can be seen emerging bit by bit from the enclosing stone, but research on fossils is not at all impressive to watch. Yet this is the end toward which all the work in the field and in the laboratory is oriented. It is the process of study and interpretation that gives meaning to the fossil bones.

It is the careful comparison of fossil bones with other fossil bones, either directly bone with bone, or less directly by matching the fossil against descriptions and figures of other fossils in publications. It is the comparison of the fossil bones with the bones of recent animals to which the extinct forms may be related. It is the making of measurements. It is the use of these measurements in statistical studies. It is the difficult task of trying to see crushed, distorted skulls and bones as if they were perfect. It is the baffling exercise of trying to make sense out of something that is quite different from or even unlike anything known to us.

It is the unsure attempt to decipher the meaning of puzzling structures. It is the reading of the soft parts of animals from their hard parts. It is the gathering together of all the information that can be had concerning the fossils and their contemporaries, to see what bearing such information has on the past relationships of the continents, on climates of former ages, on the evolution of life, and on many other subjects. It is the delving into thousands of byways in all directions. It would seem as if there are no ends to the paths of investigation that are open to the scientist.

Yet research as such is useless unless it is made available to the world at large—the world of science and the everyday world beyond the borders of scientific discipline. That is why the paleontologist, like every other scientist, must write in detail about his investigations, this writing to be published in scientific papers and monographs. So it is that the field work, the laboratory preparation, and the research lead finally to publication, and it is through publication that the fossils attain their true value.

A collection of fossils that has not been studied and described in a publication has a value in being, but only that. Fossils that have been described and discussed in scientific publications are useful to all men throughout the world and for all time to come, as long as there are printed pages in the world. It is the publication of the results of research that gives the paleontologist and the institution for which he works real authority. Men pass on, the fortunes of institutions wax and wane, the specimens may even disappear, but the printed page lives through the ages.

Consequently our knowledge of dinosaurs rests basically on the fossils that have been dug out of the ground, but beyond that upon the studies and interpretations of these fossils as they have been presented in publications in many lands and in many languages.

IN THE MUSEUM HALL

Many dinosaurs have been collected and prepared and studied and published on. A small proportion of the choicest ones have been placed in museum halls, where they can be seen by visitors. This does not mean that the paleontologist and his colleagues try to distort the picture as it is presented to the public; it is not a situation like that of putting the nicest strawberries on the top of the box. The selection of the strawberries with the biggest ones on top is a direct attempt to deceive the purchaser, who knows that the box is full of strawberries, but who, unless he is experienced and cynical, can only suppose that the ones underneath are like those on top. The paleontologist, because he is a specialist, works from all types of fossils, some good and some bad. He can interpret the incomplete fossils, but it is difficult for him to try to explain them to the public in a way that will make them meaningful. That is why only the choice, most typical and most significant specimens are chosen for display. If such a choice were not made, the museum hall would become a hopeless clutter—which it often was a half-century ago.

It used to be that the halls of natural-history museums essentially were rooms for the open storage of all sorts of specimens, good and bad. This is one reason why the word "museum" came in many minds to be synonymous with "musty" or "dull." The weary visitor was confronted with row upon row of shelves, seemingly extending for miles, on which specimens were arranged in ranks and files, each accompanied by a small label to identify it. One may still occasionally encounter such a museum.

But museums have evolved and changed, as have most of our present-day institutions, so that now the aim of most museums is to present a significant story in the exhibition hall and to present it in an attractive fashion. There is no more reason for a museum to display a large proportion of its specimens than there is for a department store to clutter up its show windows with a large array of wares. A few things well displayed are much more effective than a host of objects that confuse the eye and tire the mind.

Therefore the modern museum is like an iceberg—a large part of it is not generally visible. Most of the specimens, once they have been prepared and studied, go into the storeroom for future study and exchange, and only certain selected things are placed in the hall for public display. This is as it should be. With recent natural-history specimens there is much repetition and duplication in the collections; one good lynx on display is typical of dozens or even hundreds that may be in the collections, these numerous specimens of inestimable value for scientific studies but of little use in the exhibit hall. As for fossils, and especially fossil skeletons, there is less close duplication, because the various specimens differ as to completeness or as to their method of preservation; yet it is still valid to pick one or two of the best and most complete specimens from a series for the exhibition hall, because these specimens represent what all of the fossils *would* be like were it not for the accidents of fossilization.

The art of mounting dinosaurs and other fossil skeletons has shown much progress during the past century, as may be imagined. A dinosaur skeleton, especially a large one, is not easy to set up in its articulated form. An iron or steel framework has to be constructed to hold the brittle, heavy bones in their proper positions, which requires some very special kind of craftsmanship in iron. Strong rods and bars must be heated and bent into all sorts of queer shapes. Clamps must be designed to hold the bones. In the early days of museum practice it was common to make the iron framework of a skeleton quite elaborate and very visible. Those were the days of "open plumbing" mounts for dinosaurs. Today every effort is made to keep the ironwork as unobtrusive and as honest as possible. And what is "honest" ironwork? It is ironwork that admits its presence as proper support for the skeleton; neither is it overelaborate nor is there resort to undue subterfuge in an effort to conceal completely its presence and its proper function.

The setting up of a large dinosaur skeleton may take many months of effort by several trained technicians. But once the skeleton is mounted and in place, it does make a prime exhibit, a treasure of which the museum may be justly proud.

Of course, the display of dinosaurs does not have to depend entirely upon skeletons. Skulls, feet, and other portions of the skeleton, fossilized skin, eggs, and footprints, all attractively set up in exhibit cases, add much to the value of the hall. In addition, restorations of the animals as they appeared in life, in the form of small paintings or large murals or scaled models, are of immense aid in helping to visualize a world far removed from the one in which we live. In short, a modern exhibit hall of dinosaurs is much more than a mere display of impressive fossils: it is an integrated unfolding of the story of dinosaurian evolution, an essay on how and where the dinosaurs lived, an exposition of what the world was like during the time when these great reptiles ruled the continents, an effort to tell what brought about the rise and the fall of the dinosaurs, and why they are no longer with us.

Such an exhibit hall can only come into being under the guidance of men who have expert knowledge of the subject. Briefly, such a hall is an outgrowth of the *research* that has been done on the dinosaurs, research that has behind it the necessary field work and laboratory preparation to give the paleontologist the materials he needs in order to carry out studies of past life on the earth.

MEN AND MUSEUMS

From what has been said one may readily understand that the search for dinosaurs, the preparation of these fossils in the workroom, the proper study of the bones, and the display of selected specimens according to the principles of good modern museum practice, necessitate an ambitious, well-supported and long-range program on the part of the museum that undertakes to carry on this aspect of natural history. That is why only a few of the larger museums in metropolitan centers, or a very few university museums, have attempted to collect, prepare, study, and display dinosaurs. A list of the places where dinosaurs may be seen in the United States and Canada will be presented at the back of this book, but at this place there will be a brief discussion of some of the modern work carried on in field and laboratory by institutions interested in dinosaurs.

We have already seen how Marsh and Cope made the pioneer efforts in work on dinosaurs in North America. Marsh's collection was made for Yale University, as a result of which the Peabody Museum of that institution, where for many years Professor Richard Swann Lull devoted much of his time to work on dinosaurs, has been one of the important centers for research on these extinct reptiles. Cope's material went to the American Museum of Natural History about the turn of the century and of course added materially to the collections of fossils at that institution. A full program of dinosaurian research was, however, instituted at the New York Museum by Professor Henry Fairfield Osborn some years before Cope's death, and as a result of Osborn's leadership

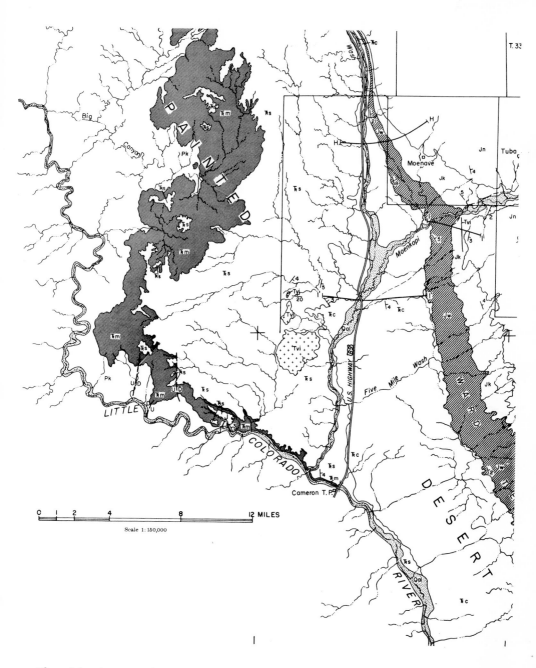

Plate 14. A section from a modern geologic map. A fossil hunter using this map would look in the white areas marked *Tr c and J k* for dinosaurs

Plate 15. In the Triassic badlands that form the lower part of this section of Mesozoic rocks at Ghost Ranch, New Mexico, were found many skeletons of primitive dinosaurs. Plate 16. The first discovery of dinosaur bones in the Triassic Chinle formation, at Ghost Ranch, New Mexico. What this led to is shown in following plates. Plate 17. Digging away the "overburden" to expose the almost horizontal rock layer, extending into the hillside, that contains dinosaur bones. Plate 18. The edge of the rock layer containing dinosaur skeletons has been exposed. Strips of burlap dipped in plaster of Paris are being applied to form a jacket over the fossils

Plate 19. The bone layer is divided into suitable blocks, each of which has been covered with a plaster jacket. A block is here being undercut. Plate 20. The block, having been cut free from the earth, is being turned over in order that its lower surface can be encased in a burlap and plaster jacket. Plate 21. It's one thing to dig a large block of fossils out of the ground; it's something else again to get it to a road. Plate 22. And now some blocks tied to a sled are being towed to a spot where they can be loaded on a heavy truck

Plate 23. Here the bones are being cleaned in the laboratory. After the fossils are prepared they will be studied and described in a publication. They thus become significant specimens

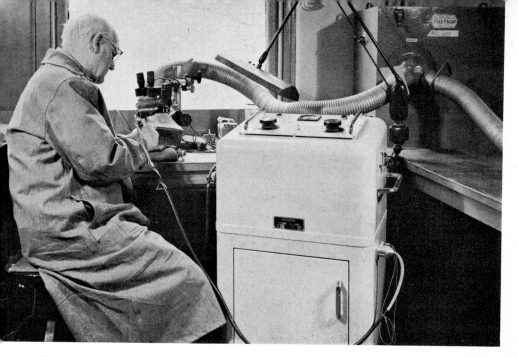

Plate 24. Today there are various technological aids available to the preparator, such as this electronic chisel

Plate 25. This picture shows a brontosaur skeleton being mounted at The American Museum of Natural History, near the turn of the century

Plate 26. The ancestors of the dinosaurs were small pseudosuchian reptiles that probably looked very much like the Triassic genus *Ornithosuchus*, shown here. By Neave Parker

Plate 27. A restoration based upon complete skeletons from Ghost Ranch, New Mexico, of the Triassic theropod *Coelophysis*. By Lois Darling

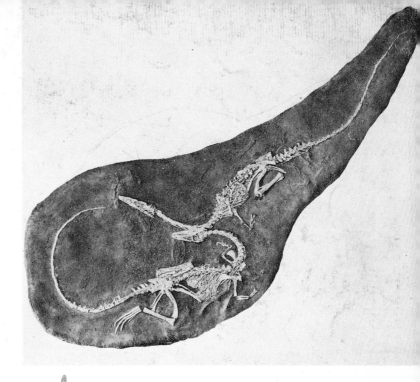

Plate 28. Two skeletons of the Triassic dinosaur *Coelophysis*, exposed as they were found at Ghost Ranch, without any of the bones having been moved. The skeletons are about eight feet long

Plate 29. *Plateosaurus*, a prosauropod dinosaur from the Triassic beds of southern Germany. The skeleton is about twenty feet in length

Plate 30.   Restoration of *Plateosaurus.* By Robert Kane

and the long-continued efforts by a distinguished group of paleontologists, particularly Barnum Brown and Walter Granger, the American Museum has become a mecca for work on dinosaurs, not only for North America but probably also for the world. In no other institution is there so large a collection of dinosaurs, nor has there been so extended a program of work on these reptiles. It is natural, of course, that the American Museum collection is dominated by the dinosaurs of North America, but there is also a good representation here of dinosaurs from Asia, and a few from other parts of the world.

The United States National Museum, being the official governmental museum, and having the resources of government surveys available, has also enjoyed a long and distinguished place among the institutional leaders in dinosaur research, especially under the leadership of the late C. W. Gilmore. Many fine monographs and papers have issued from the National Museum, setting forth knowledge of the dinosaurs.

Early in the present century Andrew Carnegie became interested in museums and particularly in dinosaurs. As will be told in a following chapter, one of the paleontologists of the Carnegie Museum in Pittsburgh made a great discovery of dinosaurs near Split Mountain, Utah, and opened a quarry that for years was worked by the Carnegie Museum field parties. This is the quarry that subsequently was made into Dinosaur National Monument. An incredible tonnage of dinosaur bones was taken back to Pittsburgh, and the Carnegie Museum took its place in the forefront of those institutions devoted to work on the dinosaurs. W. J. Holland, for many years the director of that museum, J. B. Hatcher, Earl Douglass, and O. A. Peterson played prominent roles in the Carnegie Museum dinosaur program.

Two Canadian institutions have been outstanding for their work on dinosaurs, the National Museum in Ottawa and the Royal Ontario Museum in Toronto. The programs of both of these museums are based upon field work done in the rich Cretaceous dinosaur deposits of Alberta. As a result of long years of exploration in western Canada, of active preparation in the laboratory and of vigorous research by a number of paleontologists, the museums in Ottawa and in Toronto have added significantly to our knowledge of dinosaurs, and have been able to present excellent displays of these reptiles for public view. The work at the National Museum was carried on for many years by Lawrence Lambe and by Charles M. Sternberg, at the Ontario Museum by W. A. Parks, Levi Sternberg, and L. M. Russell.

In past years many fine dinosaurs, including some excellent skeletons, have been collected in the Cretaceous beds of southern Argentina, and these are to be seen in the museum at the University of La Plata, about thirty miles from Buenos Aires. At the present time significant discoveries of dinosaurs are being made in the state of São Paulo, Brazil, and are being studied by Llewellyn Price, paleontologist to the Brazilian Government.

As might be expected, the British Museum in London was an early leader among the institutions that devoted important efforts to the dinosaurs. One might say that the British Museum had a head start, because a century and a half ago it was one of the few great museums in Europe. Things naturally gravitated to the British Museum. Moreover it was the headquarters during many years for Sir Richard Owen, the great English anatomist. And after Owen there were H. G. Seeley, Richard Lydekker, C. W. Andrews, and Sir Arthur Smith Woodward, while today interest in dinosaurs at the British Museum owes much to the stimulating influence of Dr. W. E. Swinton. There are dinosaurs from many parts of the world in the collections of this great institution.

Two museums in Germany have been especially active in the field of dinosaurian research, the Museum für Naturkünde in Berlin and the museum of the University of Tübingen. The museum in Berlin is famous for the great collections of dinosaurs made in East Africa, largely prior to the First World War. Here are fine skeletons of late Jurassic dinosaurs, comparable to the Morrison dinosaurs of North America, that have been studied in detail by Werner Janensch. At Tübingen are Triassic dinosaurs from Germany, and many other fossil reptiles, the result of a long lifetime of work by Professor Friedrich von Huene and his associates. Von Huene is one of the great and prolific modern students of the dinosaurs.

Some other universities and museums in Europe have given particular attention to the dinosaurs, and of these mention should be made of the Royal Museum in Brussels, Belgium, which was, so to speak, catapulted into a program of field work and research by the discovery of a superb series of large dinosaur skeletons in a Belgian coal mine. Some details of this discovery will be set forth in a later chapter; suffice it to say here that in 1877 the Belgian Government found itself the owner of a large collection of the dinosaur *Iguanodon*, and this led the Belgian paleontologist Louis Dollo into research on these giant reptiles. The score or more of *Iguanodon* skeletons studied and described by Dollo today make an imposing display in the Brussels museum.

In France, Charles Deperet, Jean Piveteau, Albert F. de Lapparent, and René Lavocat have been prominent among modern scholars doing research on dinosaurs, most of their work being under the auspices of the famous Museum of Natural History in Paris. In recent years French paleontologists have devoted their attention in detail to dinosaurs found in North Africa, with outstanding results.

At the University of Uppsala, Sweden, Professor Carl Wiman made many important contributions to our knowledge of the dinosaurs, especially those from the Cretaceous beds of China, collected by Scandinavian paleontologists during the third decade of the present century.

A program of intensive and large-scale field work, preparation, and research on dinosaurs, particularly the dinosaurs of Central Asia, was instituted by Russian paleontologists after the Second World War, and has been carried on vigorously ever since that time. As a result many fine dinosaurs have been collected and described, and some of them have been placed on display in Moscow. This work has been done under the supervision of one of the great paleontologists of the present time, J. A. Orlov, of Ivan Efremov, A. K. Rozhdestvensky, and E. Maleev. Dinosaurs from Central Asia also are to be seen in the museum of Ulan Bator, the capital city of Outer Mongolia.

Chinese scientists, too, have been very actively engaged during the past two decades in the excavation, preparation, and study of dinosaurs, this work being directed by Dr. C. C. Young of Peiping. Many new, important dinosaurs from eastern Asia have thus become known to us recently as a result of this program of basic research.

From this brief and perhaps incomplete survey it will be seen that what we know about dinosaurs is the result of much work by many men, supported by many institutions, the world over. It is an impressive body of knowledge that has thus been amassed, and modern work in various parts of the world is constantly bringing to light new knowledge about the dinosaurs we know, and new dinosaurs hitherto unsuspected. There is still much to be learned about the great reptiles that for one hundred million years were the rulers of the earth.

CHAPTER FOUR

ADVENT OF THE DINOSAURS

DINOSAUR ANCESTORS

The dinosaurs lived a long time ago, and we frequently think of them as being immeasurably ancient. It has been 70 million years or more since the last dinosaurs disappeared from the face of the earth, and it was perhaps 100 million years before that, that the first dinosaurs arose, a date of incredible antiquity to anyone who is not accustomed to dealing with geologic time. Yet back beyond the days of the first dinosaurs were millions of years of reptilian evolution, and the Triassic period, when dinosaurs first wandered across the lands, is less than half of the distance through time to the date when the backboned animals made their appearance in the geologic record.

Thus the first dinosaurs, so ancient that they lived millions of years before the uplift of the Rocky Mountains, were nevertheless the heirs of a long evolutionary history, and consequently were well-constructed and rather advanced reptiles. They were the direct descendants of reptiles that were specialized far beyond any stage in reptilian evolution that can be considered as primitive. These ancestors of the dinosaurs were the thecodonts that arose during the early phases of Mesozoic history when the Triassic period was still young. To understand the basic structures and adaptations of the dinosaurs it is necessary to become acquainted with their forebears, the thecodonts.

It was mentioned, when introducing the dinosaurs in the first chapter, that their thecodont ancestors were bipedal reptiles that walked on strong, bird-like hind limbs, that they had small forelimbs, and that they had deep, narrow skulls. This is but the beginning of a definition for the thecodonts; much more needs to and will be said about them. But before we consider the thecodonts let us give a little attention to the subject of bones, since what is to be written here, and what is to follow on many pages of this book, will concern fossil bones.

The Prophet Ezekiel spoke of being set down "in the midst of the valley; and it was full of bones . . . and lo, they were very dry." Certainly there is a widely spread and stereotyped belief that because bones are very dry the study of ancient bones must also be very dry and difficult. How can any perceptive person believe this?

Bones are truly fascinating things, marvels of structure and form, and aesthetically pleasing in shape and texture. Georgia O'Keeffe, one of the great artists of America, has in many of her paintings emphasized the beauty of the curving lines, of the ridges, and of the textured surfaces of a cow's skull, or of a leg bone or of the pelvic girdle of a horse. Everything about a bone has a meaning: it is a structure shaped for strength or for a particular function; its surface reveals the attachments of muscles or perhaps the course of blood vessels; and its total aspect shows how it fits and interacts with other bones, all of which combine to constitute the skeletal frame of a living, moving animal. There is nothing static about a bone, for it is an integral element of a dynamic, mobile animal, the complexity of which makes our vaunted mechanical vehicles seem simple and crudely limited. Truly the study and interpretation of bones is anything but dry.

The astute paleontologist sees in his fossils more than petrified bones. In his mind's eye he can clothe the bones with muscles and the other soft parts of living animals, and he can cover the ancient animals with skin or scales or hair and picture them as they once appeared in their native environment. He can see in the forms of the bones how the animals they represent are related to other animals, or how these animals may be more primitive than some of their cousins and more advanced than others. By studying many bones from different strata in the earth's crust, he can see the unfolding of an evolutionary story. He can see the steady progress of animal life through time. It is almost as if he can see animals changing under his eyes, changing in form and proportions, changing in their adaptations to a changing world.

One might think that he is akin to Ezekiel, who said; "So I prophesied . . . and the bones came together, bone to its bone. And I beheld, and, lo, there were sinews upon them, and flesh came up, and skin covered them above. . . . and the breath came into them, and they lived."

Yet even though we clothe the bones in flesh, these bones are still the primary objects with which we must deal. They are the undisputed remains of animals that lived great ages ago, and it is about bones that we must speak. May our words never be dry.

Figure 8. A single bone of a dinosaur. Perhaps this excellent line drawing of the ilium of a sauropod dinosaur will give some impression of the beauty of bone form. About one-tenth natural size

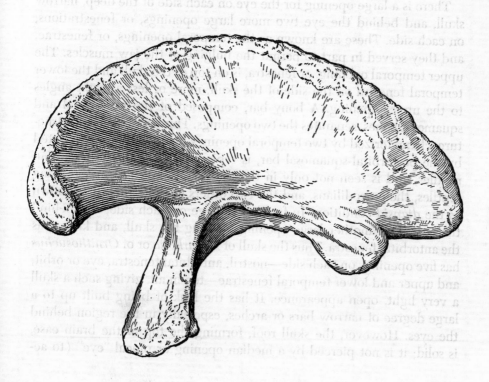

To return to the thecodonts, suppose we look at the skeleton of a primitive member of this reptilian order, the remains of an animal that lived during the Triassic period, an animal that typified in its essential characters the ancestor of all of the archosaurian reptiles. Good skeletons are not common but some have been described, such as *Euparkeria* from the Lower Triassic beds of South Africa, *Ornithosuchus* from the Upper Triassic beds of Scotland, and *Hesperosuchus* from sediments of the same age in Arizona.

The lightness, one might say the fragility, of the skeleton of one of these primitive thecodonts is at once striking and apparent. The bones are delicately formed, and many of them, such as the long bones of the legs, are hollow, as are the same bones in birds. (Parenthetically, it might be pointed out here that birds are descended from thecodont ancestors and in many respects have retained reptilian characters. It is not overly fanciful to say that birds are "glorified reptiles.")

In such thecodonts the hind limbs are elongated and the forelimbs are relatively small. The body is pivoted at the hip joint, and the weight of the body in front of this pivotal joint was in life effectively counterbalanced by a long tail.

There is a large opening for the eye on each side of the deep, narrow skull, and behind the eye two more large openings, or fenestrations, on each side. These are known as the temporal openings, or fenestrae, and they served in part to permit the bulging of the jaw muscles. The upper temporal opening, or fenestra, is on top of the skull and the lower temporal fenestra on the side of the skull, more or less at right angles to the upper opening. A bony bar, composed of the postorbital and squamosal bones, separates the two openings. This particular skull structure, characterized by two temporal openings behind the eye, separated by the postorbital-squamosal bar, is typical of all of the archosaurian reptiles, and is seen not only in the thecodonts but also in the flying reptiles, the crocodilians, and the two orders of dinosaurs. It is known as the *diapsid* condition. In front of the eye on each side, and behind the nostril, is another large opening piercing the skull, and known as the antorbital fenestra. Thus the skull of *Euparkeria* or of *Ornithosuchus* has five openings on each side—nostril, antorbital fenestra, eye or orbit, and upper and lower temporal fenestrae—ten in all, giving such a skull a very light, open appearance. It has the look of being built up to a large degree of narrow bars or arches, especially in the region behind the eyes. However, the skull roof, forming the top of the brain case, is solid; it is not pierced by a median opening or pineal "eye" (to accommodate a light sensitive organ), as is typical in the earlier and more primitive reptiles. The jaw, like the skull, is lightly built, and it also is laterally pierced by a large opening. There was obviously a strong evolutionary trend among these early thecodonts to reduce as much as possible the amount of bone in the skull and the jaw, thereby cutting down the weight of these structures. The teeth in the thecodonts are confined to the margins of the jaws, both above and below, and there are no teeth on the palate, as is the case in many of the primitive reptiles.

The bones of the pelvis are strongly constructed and firmly attached to the vertebral column, as is necessary in a bipedal animal. (In this respect we can appreciate some of the structural problems that beset the primitive thecodonts. We too are bipedal animals, and some of our sacroiliac troubles are sharp reminders of the penalties of getting up off of all fours.) The ilium, or upper pelvic bone, may be somewhat elongated, especially by a growth of its forward portion, to give a long surface of attachment for the sacrum, that series of vertebrae forming the connection between the "backbone" and the pelvis. The two lower bones of the pelvis on each side, the pubis and the ischium, instead of being plate-like as they are in primitive reptiles, tend to be rather elongated and downturned, partly as a response to the changes in muscle attachments and muscle directions that took place during the evolutionary shift of these reptiles from a four-footed to a bipedal posture. Along with this, the hind legs are pulled in close to the body, to give them a fore-and-aft swing, quite different from the rather sprawling pose of the limbs in more primitive reptiles.

In accordance with this development, the femur, or upper leg bone, is characterized by its rounded head being set off at something of an angle to the shaft of the bone. This allows the head of the femur to fit into a socket on the side of the pelvis (which socket by the bye is an open hole), while at the same time the shaft of the femur is carried close to the body. The lower part of the leg is elongated, making the entire hind limb very long to effect the pendulum-like swing so necessary to a bipedal running animal. Compare in your mind's eye the gait of this early thecodont with the gait of a swift-running ground bird, like the road runner of our southwestern states, and you can get a picture of early archosaurian locomotion.

Comparisons of this ancient reptile with modern birds are apt and valid, for it is close to the ancestry of the birds as well as that of the dinosaurs. Therefore one should not be surprised to find that the hind feet are very bird-like. The three middle toes are the functional digits, and they terminate in sharp claws. The foot is long, and the ankle joint may be simplified and strengthened. There very likely was little rotation in the ankle; almost all movement probably was in a strictly fore-and-aft direction, which is advantageous for a long-legged running animal.

The forelimbs were not used at all for locomotion in this primitive thecodont, hence they are small. The fore feet or hands are literally hands and in life served for grasping food and other objects. In the

Figure 9. The skeleton of the pseudosuchian *Hesperosuchus*, showing the "basic patents" (bipedal pose, small forelimbs used for grasping, bird-like hindlimbs, long counterbalancing tail, open skull with long jaws and sharp teeth) that were inherited by the first dinosaurs. The enlarged skull of *Euparkeria*, another pseudosuchian, shows in more detail the skull characters of these reptiles. Skeleton about one-sixth natural size, skull about one-third natural size.

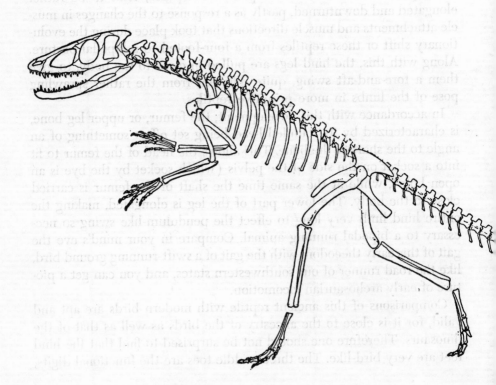

shoulder girdle the scapula, or shoulder blade, is the dominant bone and is very long. Most of the other bones of the shoulder girdle, so prominent in the more primitive reptiles, are either greatly reduced or completely suppressed.

The vertebrae are well articulated and make a strong but flexible support. Double-headed ribs are attached to them, from the skull back to the pelvis. And above the backbone is a double row of bony armor plates.

What did *Ornithosuchus,* to which the foregoing description largely applies, look like, when alive? It must have been a very quick-moving, alert little animal (as shown in Plate 26), capable of darting rapidly across the ground in search of the small reptiles or insects that it fed upon, for it was undoubtedly carnivorous, as indicated by its sharp teeth. It had a sort of articulated armor on the back, and very probably a leathery skin over all of the body. As for its color—who can say? Perhaps it was brightly colored, as are many of our modern lizards; perhaps it was relatively dull, as are modern crocodiles. That is a question about which we can only speculate.

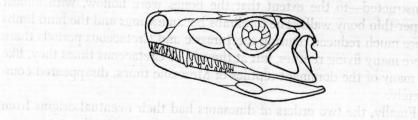

This description of the bony skeleton of a primitive thecodont affords a general picture of the structural ancestor for all of the archosaurians, which evolved along their several different lines. For example, the more advanced thecodonts developed by becoming increasingly larger, until some of them, the phytosaurs particularly, grew to almost giant stature. They abandoned the bipedal pose and became elongated quadrupedal, or four-footed, reptiles that inhabited the shores of streams and lakes. Throughout their evolutionary development the various thecodonts retained the armor plates that were so characteristic of the primitive types, and some of them grew into very heavily armored animals, veritable Triassic tanks.

The crocodilians followed a line of development that paralleled in a most remarkable way the evolution of the phytosaurs. This is a prime example of *parallelism* in evolution; of animals arising from an eventual common ancestor to evolve along closely similar but separate lines. The crocodiles, in a word, occupied the same "niche" in the natural world from Jurassic days to the present time that was occupied by the phytosaurs during the Triassic period. The general form and habits of crocodilians are well enough known to need no further elaboration at this place.

The flying reptiles diverged most sharply from the other archosaurians. They remained small for the most part, and became very lightly constructed—to the extent that the bones were hollow, with almost paper-thin bony walls. The forelimbs became wings and the hind limbs were much reduced. During the Jurassic and Cretaceous periods there were many flying reptiles, but at the end of Cretaceous times they, like so many of the dominant reptiles of Mesozoic times, disappeared completely.

Finally, the two orders of dinosaurs had their eventual origins from ancestral thecodonts similar to the one described in the foregoing paragraphs. The saurischian dinosaurs arose quite directly from the primitive thecodont type, making their first appearance during the latter part of Triassic history. The origins of the ornithischian dinosaurs are more obscure. No ornithischians are definitely known in rocks older than the Lower Jurassic, and at the present time the problem of ornithischian origins is unsolved—a situation that may hold far into the future.

Let us now turn to some of the earliest dinosaurs that lived during late Triassic times.

COELOPHYSIS, AN EARLY COELUROSAURIAN DINOSAUR

A few years ago, by one of those rare instances of luck that make fossil hunting such a fascinating and occasionally such a rewarding activity, a large series of primitive dinosaur skeletons was found in northern New Mexico by a party of fossil hunters from the American Museum of Natural History. These skeletons were discovered among red and yellow cliffs of unsurpassable magnificence and beauty at Ghost Ranch, to the north and west of the very picturesque village of Abiquiu, New Mexico. They were found in the greatest profusion, piled one on top of another, with heads and tails and feet and legs often inextricably mixed in a jackstraw puzzle of bones. Some of the skeletons are absolutely complete, down to the tiniest bones, and must rate as among the most perfect dinosaur skeletons ever discovered. They represent a range of ages, from very small animals to those obviously fully adult. All of this rich material, coming from a single quarry that was perhaps thirty feet square, certainly indicates the remains of animals belonging to a single species that may have been overwhelmed by some local catastrophe and buried together. Or perhaps the deposit indicates a concentration of carcasses that were washed together by a stream. But the complete articulation of so many skeletons and the lack of scattered bones that would be expected in a deposit accumulated by stream action suggests some unusual mode of death and burial for these little dinosaurs. Perhaps we shall never be able to solve the riddle of the dinosaur burial at Ghost Ranch, but at least we can be thankful for this lucky concentration of such complete skeletons. They give us excellent information on an early dinosaur, the name of which is *Coelophysis*.

Coelophysis, like its thecodont ancestor, was a lightly constructed reptile that walked and ran on strong, bird-like hind limbs. It must have been a very agile and a very active animal, ranging across the dry land in search of its prey, with ever an alert eye looking for food and watching for enemies, with ever its nervous mechanism keyed up to set this dinosaur off at an instant on a rapid swinging run away from danger. *Coelophysis* was not large nor was it impressive, as were many of its cousins of later geologic times, but it was admirably adapted to the world in which it lived.

Coelophysis was about eight or ten feet in length when full grown, which sounds as if it were an animal of some size, yet this reptile was so light and attenuated that in life it probably weighed no more than forty or fifty pounds. The bones are very delicate; all of the long bones are hollow, and many of the flat bones, such as those of the skull, are very thin. This dinosaur has a long neck and a very long tail, the one extending forward from a rather narrow body and the other back from the hip region, to give *Coelophysis* a racy appearance. The legs are long and slender.

The skull in *Coelophysis* is elongated, and pointed in front, a sort of wedge directed forward from the sinuous neck. It is characteristically archosaurian, with large openings, or fenestrations, in front of and behind the eye. The jaws are very long and are set with many thin, bladelike teeth, an apparatus that makes an excellent trap for seizing small animals, for holding them securely, and perhaps for slicing them into bite-sized pieces. There are fine, sawtooth edges or serrations on the teeth, quite evidently an adaptation for slicing flesh. (Manufacturers have discovered in recent years that if steak knives are edged with somewhat similar serrations the cutting of meat at the banquet table is much facilitated.)

Figure 10. The skeleton of *Coelophysis,* a coelurosaurian dinosaur of the late Triassic age. About one-tenth natural size

The pelvis of *Coelophysis* is fully saurischian—much advanced in its specializations beyond the thecodont pelvis. For instance, the ilium is a long, expanded blade to afford a large surface for the attachments of sacral vertebrae, to make a very strong joint between the hips and the vertebral column. And to ensure the strength of this attachment, there are five vertebrae so joined. In the primitive reptiles two vertebrae are attached to the ilium, and such a juncture of vertebrae and pelvis is sufficient for a sprawling animal that spends much of its time on its belly. But in *Coelophysis*, permanently up on its hind legs, a two-verte-brae attachment was not enough, so that three additional vertebrae

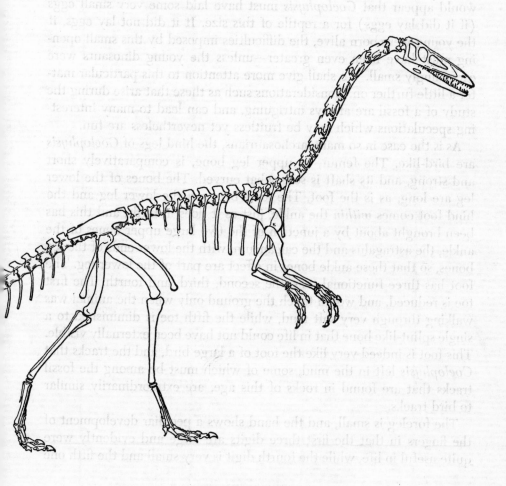

also have been added to the sacrum, to make a long, strong joint. These sacral vertebrae are, moreover, fused to each other, making a single, solid bony element that joins on each side with the pelvis.

The two other bones of the pelvis on each side, the pubis in front and the ischium behind, are greatly elongated, a development that had only begun in some of the thecodonts. The pubis is actually longer than the femur, or upper leg bone, and the two pubes, right and left, join each other in a long, plate-like junction, known as a symphysis. The two ischia are likewise joined, but for a shorter distance. At their upper ends, where they connect with the ilia, they diverge from each other, making a sort of triangular-shaped opening between them for the cloaca, the common exit for the digestive and reproductive systems in reptiles. This opening in the back of the pelvis is surprisingly small, and it would appear that *Coelophysis* must have laid some very small eggs (if it did lay eggs) for a reptile of this size. If it did not lay eggs, if the young were born alive, the difficulties imposed by this small opening must have been even greater—unless the young dinosaurs were exceedingly small. We shall give more attention to this particular matter a little further on. Considerations such as these that arise during the study of a fossil are always intriguing, and can lead to many interesting speculations which may be fruitless yet nevertheless are fun.

As is the case in so many archosaurians, the hind legs of *Coelophysis* are bird-like. The femur, or upper leg bone, is comparatively short and strong, and its shaft is somewhat curved. The bones of the lower leg are long, as is the foot. The joint between the lower leg and the hind foot comes *within* the ankle, just as it does in birds, and this has been brought about by a junction of the two large upper bones of the ankle, the astragalus and the calcaneum, with the lower ends of the leg bones, so that these ankle bones in effect are part of the lower leg. The foot has three functional toes, the second, third, and fourth. The first toe is reduced, and would touch the ground only when the animal was walking through very soft mud, while the fifth toe is diminished to a single splint-like bone that in life could not have been externally visible. This foot is indeed very like the foot of a large bird, and the tracks that *Coelophysis* left in the mud, some of which must be among the fossil tracks that are found in rocks of this age, are extraordinarily similar to bird tracks.

The foreleg is small, and the hand shows a peculiar development of the fingers in that the first three digits are large and evidently were quite useful in life, while the fourth digit is very small and the fifth one missing. This dinosaur had a grasping hand, useful for helping the animal to catch and hold its prey, but it was a three-fingered hand. We shall see this pattern of hand development continuing in many of the later, gigantic meat-eating dinosaurs. The three functional fingers are provided with sharp claws.

There are no traces of any bony armor in *Coelophysis*; this little dinosaur probably had a pliable, leathery skin.

Among the many skeletons of *Coelophysis* found at Ghost Ranch are two exceedingly fine ones, each in complete articulation, with the bones in place as they were when the animal died (Plate 28). And within the body cavity of each of these skeletons are the remains of small *Coelophysis* skeletons. Here we are faced with a paleontological puzzler: Are these the skeletons of unborn young (assuming in this case that *Coelophysis* gave birth to its young rather than laying eggs, as do various modern lizards and snakes), or are they the skeletons of young animals that were captured and devoured by their cannibalistic elders, in the same way that young crocodilians are frequently caught and eaten by adult members of the same species?

If these are unborn young they seem very large. Nevertheless serious consideration must be given to this possibility. For example, the modern night lizard, *Xantusia*, of the southwestern deserts, gives live birth to two young lizards that are perfectly huge in comparison with the mother. The little lizards, when born, are fully half the length of the female, and one wonders how she manages to stow away two such ample embryos during the last few days before their birth. If *Xantusia* can manage this, there is no reason why something rather similar might not have taken place in *Coelophysis*. But one real difficulty is the small size of the posterior opening in the pelvis, mentioned above. The vision of an embryo *Coelophysis* of the size indicated by the bones within the body cavities of the two adults negotiating a birth passage as small as that shown in the same adult skeletons creates an image that seems to have an aspect of the unreal about it. The whole thing just doesn't seem possible. Another difficulty is that the small bones within the body cavities of the adults are well formed ones, and not the cartilaginous, embryonic bones that one might expect if these were true embryos.

Perhaps, therefore, they are the remains of cannibalistic feasts. If this is so, the bones are remarkably uninjured. There are some uncrushed leg bones that one might expect to have been chewed or fractured, but in this connection it is instructive to consider how a Komodo lizard, the giant among modern lizards and a reptile that may attain a length of ten feet or more, feeds upon a chicken. The fowl is swallowed with one or two or three great gulps—swallowed whole—feathers, feet, and all. And evidently there is little injury to the skeleton during this rapid ingestion of the bird: the whole thing takes place too fast for that. With this in mind it is reasonable to think, therefore, that the small fossil skeletons may in fact represent young dinosaurs that were eaten by their elder relatives.

Perhaps this gives us one small bit of insight into the life of these ancient reptiles. That they were active, rapidly moving animals is apparent from the light construction of the entire skeleton. That they were carnivorous is apparent from the long jaws and the sharp, blade-like teeth. That they may have been compellingly voracious is possibly indicated by these small skeletons within the large ones.

However that may be, it does seem evident that *Coelophysis* in North America, and its relatives in other parts of the world, were important constituents among the animal assemblages, the *faunas*, of late Triassic times. They were among the aggressive hunters of those distant days, although they were of necessity the hunters of small game. And although the days of complete dinosaurian dominance were still in the future, *Coelophysis* none the less had within its structure the potentialities that were to lead to the spectacular developments so obvious among some of the giant dinosaurs of Jurassic and Cretaceous times. The "basic patents" are there in *Coelophysis*.

The *coelurosaurs*, of which *Coelophysis* is one of the most completely known examples, are structurally the most primitive of the dinosaurs, even though, as we have seen from the description of *Coelophysis*, they are highly specialized reptiles. In this connection it must be remembered that the words "primitive" and "specialized" are relative terms, and must be used in context with the subject that is being discussed. *Coelophysis* is a highly specialized reptile, as are all of the coelurosaurs, but it is nevertheless a primitive dinosaur, because all of the dinosaurs are in many respects at the very pinnacle of reptilian evolution, and are highly specialized. To say that the coelurosaurs are primitive is something like saying that the first jet airplanes are crude affairs; in both cases one must keep in mind the levels of comparisons that are being used.

Even though the coelurosaurs were in effect the ancestors of the giant theropod and sauropod dinosaurs that became so numerous and widely spread during Jurassic and Cretaceous times, it must not be supposed that the small coelurosaurs were eventually supplanted by their giant relatives. The emphasis among coelurosaurs on lightness in weight, agility of movement, and adaptations for the pursuit of small animals enabled these little dinosaurs to continue through the Mesozoic era, to the very end of the Cretaceous period. There was a place in the Mesozoic world for small dinosaurs, just as today there is a place for small jungle cats that live side by side with their tiger cousins.

The coelurosaurs continued as small reptiles because certain of their characters, for example, the lightly constructed skeleton and the fragile bones, barred them from growing into giants. The trend toward large size was established among other Triassic dinosaurs that are close relatives of the coelurosaurs. These are the early carnosaurs.

THE FIRST CARNOSAURS

There is a general appearance of robustness about the skeleton in the carnosaurs that sets these dinosaurs apart at an early stage from the coelurosaurs. This can be seen in any late Triassic carnosaur, in *Teratosaurus,* for example, the bones of which have been found in southern Germany.

Teratosaurus, although not particularly large by later dinosaurian standards, was a reptile of some size, for the skeleton may be as much as twenty feet in length. In life it must have weighed many hundreds of pounds, perhaps as much as a half or three-quarters of a ton, which means for one thing that it did not have the hollow bones that are so typical of the coelurosaurs. Large animals need strong bones, and in *Teratosaurus,* as in the other carnosaurs, the vertebrae are strong and the leg bones are solidly constructed. As far as proportions go, the skeleton of this dinosaur is distinguished from the skeleton of its more primitive relatives by a relatively large skull, a neck that is only of moderate length as contrasted with the very long, sinuous coelurosaur neck, and legs that are not so long proportionately as they are in the small, rapidly running dinosaurs. The tail is long—a counterbalance for the heavy body.

The pelvis, of characteristic saurischian form, is also heavy, as contrasted with the coelurosaurian pelvis, and the reason for this is obvious. When *Teratosaurus* was a living organism, the pelvis was subjected to very great strains and pressures because it transmitted the entire weight of this dinosaur to the strong hind limbs, and through them to the ground. The hind feet of *Teratosaurus* are heavy, as might be expected in an animal of considerable weight. The three middle toes are the functional ones, as in the more primitive theropods, but the foot is not quite so bird-like as is the case in the coelurosaurs. It is a rather broad foot, with the three toes spreading widely to give good support. The first toe, though short, is a relatively robust digit that was carried more or less parallel to the other large toes. (As we shall see, the thumb in the later carnosaurs became turned backwardly, to form a sort of prop at the back of the foot.) The fifth toe is much reduced.

The stout forelimbs of this dinosaur are about two-thirds the length of the hind limbs. The fingers of the hand are reduced so that in *Teratosaurus,* as in the more primitive coelurosaurs, the hand is made up of three functional fingers, all armed with large, curved claws. The thumb, though not the longest of the three fingers, is by far the heaviest, and has a very large, hook-like claw. Here we see a hand adapted to grasping the prey, or possibly, to some extent, for slashing.

But the major part of predation, that is, of catching and killing other animals, was concentrated in the skull. That is one reason why the skull is proportionately so large, because a large skull furnishes the animal with large jaws, and in this dinosaur the size and strength of the jaws were of prime importance to its manner of life. These jaws are furnished with blade-like teeth—cruel weapons of offense.

Now, a large skull like this cannot be carried efficiently on a long, flexible neck, even though the skull is lightly built, and even though it is pierced by various large openings to reduce the weight and to eliminate any bone surfaces that are not absolutely essential. Consequently the neck is comparatively short, to reduce the length and increase the efficiency of the lever that is carrying the skull.

Does this give an adequate picture of *Teratosaurus*—a Triassic carnosaur that had set the pattern of adaptations so typical of the large meat-eating dinosaurs of later ages? It is to be hoped so. Think of this dino-

---

Figure 11. Evolutionary trends in the skulls of Triassic dinosaurs. In the small coelurosaurs (middle), the skull is low. In the large carnosaurs (above), the skull is deep and the teeth are enlarged as dagger-like weapons. In the large prosauropods (below) the skull is relatively small and the teeth are spatulate. The black triangles show the proportions of height to length in each skull

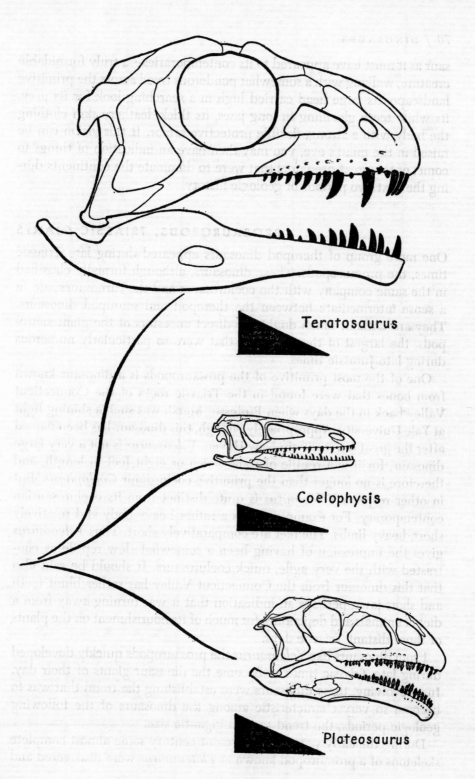

Teratosaurus

Coelophysis

Plateosaurus

saur as it must have appeared to its contemporaries—a truly formidable creature, walking with a somewhat ponderous tread across the primitive landscape, its large head carried high in a searching look for its prey, its white teeth gleaming in long jaws, its thick, leathery skin clothing the body with a strong, flexible protective armor. If this vision can be raised in the mind's eye, you may then have an indication of things to come, of the great predators that were to dominate the continents during the next two periods of geologic history.

PROSAUROPODS, TRIASSIC GIANTS

One more group of theropod dinosaurs appeared during late Triassic times, the prosauropods. These dinosaurs, although formally classified in the same company with the coelurosaurs and the carnosaurs, are in a sense intermediate between the theropod and sauropod dinosaurs. They are without much doubt the direct ancestors of the giant sauropods, the largest of the dinosaurs that were so particularly numerous during late Jurassic times.

One of the most primitive of the prosauropods is a dinosaur known from bones that were found in the Triassic rocks of the Connecticut Valley back in the days when Professor Marsh was such a shining light at Yale University. Appropriately enough, this dinosaur has been named after the great university in New Haven. *Yaleosaurus* is not a very large dinosaur, for it is a reptile of some seven or eight feet in length, and therefore is no longer than the primitive coelurosaur *Coelophysis*. But in other respects *Yaleosaurus* is quite distinct from its coelurosaurian contemporary. For example, it has a rather heavy body and relatively short, heavy limbs. The feet are comparatively short. Thus *Yaleosaurus* gives the impression of having been a somewhat slow reptile as contrasted with the very agile, quick coelurosaurs. It should be said also that this dinosaur from the Connecticut Valley has rather blunt teeth and short jaws, perhaps an indication that it was turning away from a diet of animals and depending for much of its nourishment on the plants of those distant Triassic days.

From dinosaurs like *Yaleosaurus* the prosauropods quickly developed during late Triassic times to become the dinosaur giants of their day. In so evolving, these dinosaurs were establishing the trend that was to become so very characteristic among the dinosaurs of the following geologic periods, the trend toward gigantic size.

During the early years of the present century some almost complete skeletons of a prosauropod known as *Plateosaurus* were discovered and excavated by Professor Friedrich von Huene of the University of Tübingen, in southern Germany. It was a great find, for it provided the materials for a detailed knowledge of *Plateosaurus* and, in a larger sense, for this entire branch of dinosaurian evolution. Then a closely related type, *Plateosauravus*, was found in South Africa. And finally, during the years of the Second World War, still another closely related genus, *Lufengosaurus*, was taken from the Triassic beds of Yunnan in western China. All of these prosauropods are essentially of one stamp, and they indicate that in late Triassic times the ancestors of the giant swamp-dwelling dinosaurs were wandering widely across the Old World continents.

The salient features of *Plateosaurus* (and of its closely related cousins in other parts of the world) are these. This reptile (Plate 29) is of considerable size, being twenty feet or more in length. It has broadly arched ribs that enclose a capacious thorax and abdomen. This indicates that it probably ate bulky food. It has stout hind limbs, with broad hind feet, in which there are four strong, forwardly pointing toes. These limbs are clearly for the support of the heavy body; an animal of the proportions of *Plateosaurus* could hardly have the long, slender limbs that are seen in the small Triassic meat-eating carnivorous theropods. The forelimbs, though much smaller than the hind limbs, are none the less stout, with broad, spreading hands, and this would seem to indicate that while *Plateosaurus* may have walked habitually on its hind limbs it nevertheless could come down on all fours—something that could not be accomplished by the Triassic meat-eating dinosaurs. This is a departure from the primitive bipedalism of the dinosaurs, a secondary return to quadrupedalism, a specialization in the dinosaurs that goes back to the *primitive* method of locomotion among land-living vertebrates. *Plateosaurus* has a long and rather heavy neck, at the end of which is a comparatively small skull. This again is a trend that foreshadows the condition that was to be so characteristic of the great swamp-dwelling dinosaurs of Jurassic and Cretaceous times. And in the jaws are blunt, spatulate or leaf-shaped teeth, clearly showing that this dinosaur had abandoned, probably completely, a diet of meat, and was living entirely upon soft vegetation. Finally, *Plateosaurus* has a long, heavy tail.

A SUMMING UP

This brings us to the end of our consideration of the first dinosaurs, the dinosaurs that lived during late Triassic times. It has been shown in the foregoing discussion and description that these dinosaurs, arising from

Triassic thecodont ancestors, followed essentially three lines of evolutionary radiation. They were all theropods, but as such they were coelurosaurs, carnosaurs, and prosauropods. The coelurosaurs were small, lightly built, primitive types, probably preserving in their structure many of the ancestral dinosaurian traits, many of the basic patents from which dinosaurian evolution was to be shaped. The carnosaurs were enlarged derivatives from the coelurosaurs, the logical development of large meat-eating dinosaurs from small meat-eating dinosaurs. They showed a trend toward giantism as an adaptation to the pursuit and capture of giant prey. The prosauropods were another branch from a coelurosaurian stem in which there appeared modifications of the basic theropod plan. Here was a dinosaur grown to considerable size with consequent adaptations in the skeleton for supporting weight, and specializations in the skull and teeth for feeding upon a diet of plants.

This tripartite development among the late Triassic dinosaurs is significant, for while it did not in itself lead to any very great variety among the early Mesozoic dinosaurs, it foreshadowed the evolutionary trends that were to take place during middle and late Mesozoic times. By the end of the Triassic period the dinosaurs were among the dominant reptiles of their time, although they were not completely dominant on the land, as they were to become in the Jurassic and Cretaceous periods. None the less they were reptiles with great potentialities for development through the long procession of years that was to make Jurassic and Cretaceous history.

CHAPTER FIVE

THE THREEFOLD DEVELOPMENT OF THEROPOD DINOSAURS

As the events of Jurassic history unfolded, following the end of the Triassic period, there was a decided increase in the variety and perhaps in the numbers of dinosaurs that lived on the Mesozoic continents. These reptiles began to develop beyond the basic patterns that had been set by the ancestral dinosaurian types, to become adjusted in their structure and adaptations to various environments throughout the world, and thereby to become established as the dominant animals on land—a role they were to enjoy for many millions of years.

That these reptiles were dominant in Jurassic and Cretaceous times as they had not been during the Triassic period is clearly shown by the fossil record. In brief, the Jurassic and Cretaceous periods were truly the Age of Dinosaurs, when dinosaurs were numerous and of many different kinds, and reigned supreme, with very little competition from other animals.

For example, in late Triassic times there were many dinosaurs on the earth—of that there can be no doubt—but they were not greatly varied for different modes of life. There were the small meat eaters that preyed upon other small reptiles and perhaps on other forms of animal life, dinosaurs such as *Coelophysis,* described in the last chapter. There were the moderately large predators that fed upon other large reptiles, such as *Teratosaurus,* which has also been described. And there were the rather heavy prosauropods, like *Plateosaurus* (already introduced), that may have fed to some extent upon plants. Along with such dinosaurs there lived the giant crocodile-like phytosaurs, truly the archpredators of Triassic times, the large armored thecodont reptiles, and various active mammal-like reptiles, some of which were the ancestors of the warm-blooded mammals. So it was that the Triassic dinosaurs shared the land with other numerous, well-adjusted, and frequently aggressive reptiles. To use a modern simile, there was a good deal of shoving and elbowing among the Triassic dinosaurs and other large inhabitants of the land.

But with the close of the Triassic period the large phytosaurs and the various inoffensive but space-consuming armored thecodonts became extinct. The mammal-like reptiles also disappeared, some of them by straight extinction, others by transformation into the first mammals. This gave room for the dinosaurs to expand, so that early in Jurassic times there were not only the meat-eating dinosaurs that had carried through from Triassic days, but in addition large plant-eating dinosaurs, specifically the early giant swamp-dwelling sauropods and the first of the plated dinosaurs. These dinosaurs were augmented during successive stages in Mesozoic history by a great variety of duck-billed dinosaurs and their relatives, by armored dinosaurs, and by an almost bewildering array of horned dinosaurs. The only other reptiles that evolved as large land-living types during Jurassic and Cretaceous times were the crocodilians, fearsome enough, it is true, but for the most part no match for the giant predatory dinosaurs that had by this time spread widely across the lands.

Even though the dinosaurs branched out along diverging lines of evolution during the middle and late stages of Mesozoic history, the predatory types—in formal terms the theropods—that had been so successful in the closing phases of the Triassic period continued through the rest of the Age of Dinosaurs, some with very little change, others with some modifications ("improvements" if you will) but with no great changes in the basic design, and still others with extreme specializations that fitted them to very particular modes of life. There is always a place for predators in the animal world; the theropods had become established as successful predators at the beginning of their history, and thus they lived on through successive geologic ages.

The evolution of the later theropod dinosaurs may be viewed in simple terms as proceeding along three lines. One of these lines was composed of the small, comparatively primitive coelurosaurs, in which the structural plan of the ancestral theropod dinosaurs was retained through Mesozoic times without much change. They might be called the "foxes" among dinosaurs. A second line of coelurosaurs that branched from the central coelurosaurian stem during the Cretaceous period is known as the ornithomimids, the so-called "ostrich dinosaurs." These large, lightly constructed coelurosaurians can with good reason be called the "ostriches" among dinosaurs, because in late Cretaceous times they must in a general way have lived the kind of a life that large ground birds do today. Finally, the third line of theropod evolution, continuing from the Triassic to the end of the Cretaceous period, consisted of the great aggressive predators known as the carnosaurs, the largest of all land-living carnivorous animals. These might be called the "tigers" among the dinosaurs.

THE PERSISTENTLY PRIMITIVE COELUROSAURS

At the turn of the century the American Museum of Natural History was engaged in a large quarrying operation at Como Bluff, Wyoming, where the skeletons of various gigantic dinosaurs of late Jurassic age were being taken out of the ground. Among the skeletons that came to light during the course of these operations was one, notable for its very small size, quite in contrast to the huge fossil remains that so characterized this particular quarry. This little skeleton (Plate 31) was of a small coelurosaur, and was named *Ornitholestes* by Professor Osborn, who described it.

Ornitholestes preserves the essential features of the primitive Triassic coelurosaurs, thereby illustrating very nicely how a structural ancestor may persist through the ages. It might be said that *Ornitholestes*, a contemporary of giant carnosaurs such as *Allosaurus* and *Ceratosaurus*, indicates what the ancestor of these great predators was like.

To describe *Ornitholestes* in detail would be to repeat much that has already been said in the description of *Coelophysis* in the preceding chapter; consequently we may consider this dinosaur very briefly. It is about six feet in length and lightly built, with many hollow bones. The hind limbs are long and slender; the joint between leg and foot is below the two upper bones of the ankle; the feet are bird-like, having three functional toes ending in sharp claws, and a short inner toe (the first) that did not reach the ground. The body is pivoted at the pelvis, which is typically saurischian, with an elongated ilium, a long pubis extending down in front, and an almost equally long ischium extending down in back. The forelimbs are considerably shorter than the hind limbs, with the first three fingers preserved as rather long, grasping digits, armed with large sharp claws. (It was because of this structure of the hand that *Ornitholestes* was given its name, which means "bird catcher," by Osborn. He envisioned this dinosaur as leaping up and catching primitive birds with its hands, and it was restored in such an attitude by the great portrayer of prehistoric animals, Charles Knight. Very probably *Ornitholestes* was not spry enough for this; it more likely pursued small reptiles, such as lizards, and other small ground-living animals.) The outer two fingers are lost. The vertebrae are lightly constructed but strong, and the tail is long, serving in part as a counterbalance to the body. The neck, though sinuous and flexible, is not so long as in the Triassic coelurosaur *Coelophysis*. The skull is comparatively small and lightly built, as might be expected. It has a large opening for the eye, and the usual openings in front of and behind the eye, these latter for the accommodation of the jaw muscles. The jaws are set with sharp teeth, about fifteen on either side in the skull and a dozen or so on either side in the lower jaw.

Ornitholestes typifies the small primitive coelurosaurs that continued into later Mesozoic times, of which there were many in various parts of the world. To describe or even to list all of them would be a tedious affair, and would not add greatly to what already has been said. They were all much of one pattern. A few may be mentioned.

Perhaps the best known of the European coelurosaurs is *Compsognathus* (Plate 35), noteworthy for being one of the smallest, if not the smallest, of all dinosaurs. This little dinosaur is no larger than a big fowl. An entire skeleton is beautifully preserved in a fine-grained lithographic limestone, a sediment of late Jurassic age, in southern Germany. This skeleton of *Compsognathus* is also of interest because within the body cavity is a partial skeleton of what seems to be another small dinosaur, which confronts us with the same problem that we encountered in our consideration of the Triassic coelurosaur *Coelophysis*. Do we see here an unborn embryo within the body of *Compsognathus*, or rather is this the remnant of an exceedingly small dinosaur or some other reptile that had been devoured by *Compsognathus?*

Velociraptor is another small and lightly built coelurosaur found in the late Cretaceous deposits of Mongolia. Similar small carnivorous theropods have been found in other parts of Asia, in India, in Africa, Australia, and in South America.

THE OSTRICH DINOSAURS

The so-called "ostrich dinosaurs," the ornithomimids, are coelurosaurs that grew to considerable size during the Cretaceous period. As has already been said, these dinosaurs, at the present time known only from North America and Asia, are so named with good reason, because in size and probably in habits as well they show developments similar to what we see in modern ostriches. The most completely known of these dinosaurs is *Ornithomimus*, of which a number of skeletons have been found in the late Cretaceous Belly River beds, along the Red Deer River in Alberta (Plate 33).

Ornithomimus (the name means "bird imitator") is a coelurosaur grown large and retaining most of the coelurosaur characters. The bones are hollow; the hind limbs are long and nicely adapted for fast running; the body is pivoted at the hips; and the forelimbs are short, with three-fingered grasping hands. But there are some differences.

For instance, the neck is proportionately much longer than in the other carnivorous dinosaurs. It looks like the long, sinuous neck of a modern ostrich or rhea or cassowary or emu. And on the end of this flexible neck is a small skull, very lightly constructed, in which all of the teeth have disappeared, so that the jaws are beak-like, quite like the beak of a bird.

One significant fact about *Ornithomimus* is that it has forelimbs proportionately longer than the forelimbs in its more primitive coelurosaurian relatives. This can only mean that the forelimbs, the "arms" in this dinosaur, were secondarily elongated, but not for locomotion. Rather the long arms, and particularly the long three-fingered hands, look as if they were adapted for pulling and clutching and tearing.

One can think of *Ornithomimus* as running across the uplands of the Cretaceous continents, pulling fruits from trees, snapping up little lizards or insects with its bird-like beak, digging into the ground for delicacies of various kinds, not the least of which might have been the

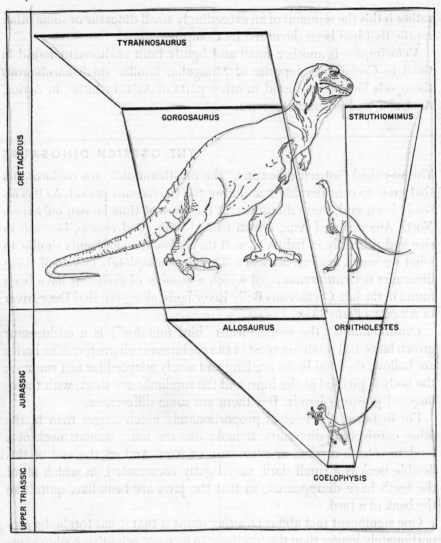

Figure 12. Evolution of the theropod dinosaurs along two lines of adaptation. The ancestral coelurosaurs gave rise on the one hand to a long line of coelurosaurian evolution in which size increase was only moderate, and on the other to the carnosaurs, which became giants. Heavy horizontal lines indicate the lengths of the various genera listed in this chart, all drawn to the same scale

eggs of other dinosaurs. Perhaps it is no mere coincidence that in Mongolia the skeleton of an ornithomimid which has been named *Oviraptor* (egg stealer) was found intermingled with a nest of eggs of one of the horned dinosaurs. It may be that we have here a glimpse into past animal relationships.

GIANT HUNTERS

There is something to be said for being big. The giant suffers certain disadvantages, but he also enjoys certain advantages that cannot be denied. For one thing, the giant has less to fear from other animals than do his smaller contemporaries. He is to a large degree immune from attack, so that his life is less subjected to alarms and excursions than is the lot of smaller animals. Growth to gigantic size can be and often has been very successful in the evolutionary sense.

The carnosaurs became giants, and as giants they prospered during Jurassic and Cretaceous times. They were the archpredators of the Mesozoic world, and indeed were the largest meat-eating animals ever to live upon the land. They had their beginnings during late Triassic times (as we have seen) as large reptiles, but these early carnosaurs, large though they might have been, were nevertheless modestly proportioned animals as compared with their later Mesozoic descendants. The Jurassic and Cretaceous carnosaurs were truly awesome reptiles.

The evolution of the carnosaurs from their Triassic ancestors was essentially a single-track line of development, a progression toward ever-increasing size. As time wore on, the carnosaurs became larger and still larger, until at the very end of the Cretaceous period they reached the culmination of their evolutionary development in size, and in the specializations that accompanied size. Then they became extinct.

These were giant dinosaurs that preyed upon other giant dinosaurs. While the agile coelurosaurs evolved as the seekers of small game, depending upon rapid movements for the success of their hunting, and for escape from their enemies as well, the carnosaurs grew into mighty hunters, relying upon their great strength and ferocity for their success in life.

One of the characteristic carnosaurs of Jurassic times is *Allosaurus*, known from skeletons found in the Upper Jurassic sediments of North America. This dinosaur lived along with brontosaurs and other giants, and there is good reason to think that the big vegetarians were the main source of food for *Allosaurus* and his kin. In fact, there is a series of brontosaur vertebrae in the American Museum of Natural History showing on them numerous tooth marks that coincide very well with the size and the spacing of the teeth in *Allosaurus*. One might suppose that an allosaur tore at the muscles originally attached to these vertebrae, and in the process left marks of his teeth on the bones. It looks that way.

The skeleton of *Allosaurus* (Plate 36) is about thirty feet in length; this dinosaur weighed several tons when it was alive. In a general way this skeleton is an enlargement of the skeleton of the ancestral theropods—a skeleton in which the body is pivoted at the hips, the hind limbs are strong and bird-like in general structure, the forelimbs are short and obviously adapted for grasping objects, the tail is long to serve in part as a counterbalance to the weight of the body, and the skull is large, having long jaws furnished with sharp, cutting teeth.

In detail it is not quite so simple as this. The business of growing into a giant involves more than a mere increase in size. For example, the slender, hollow leg bones of a coelurosaur are hardly the structures, even if magnified many times, for supporting the great weight of a giant dinosaur, so the bones in *Allosaurus* and in other carnosaurs have lost their hollow structure and have become solid, while at the same time they are proportionately heavy, an adaptation to the great stresses to which they were subjected. The hip region, being the focal point for the immense weight of this dinosaur, is greatly strengthened. In the ankle one bone, the astragalus, has an ascending bony process that is pressed closely against the front surface of the leg bone, the tibia, to strengthen the union between these bones. This development is typical of all the giant theropod dinosaurs. The vertebrae are heavily constructed and strongly articulated, to make a very strong column, a sort of flexible beam, if such a word picture makes sense, for supporting the weight of the body.

An interesting feature of *Allosaurus* is the very large size of the skull and lower jaws. As the carnosaurs, characterized by *Allosaurus,* grew into giants from their Triassic ancestors, the growth of the skull was at a faster rate than the growth of the body. Consequently the skull is huge. This growth of the skull to great size had the effect of equipping *Allosaurus* and other such carnosaurs with very long jaws in which there were large blade-like teeth. The utility of such long jaws and large teeth to a predator feeding upon gigantic victims is obvious.

The large skull of *Allosaurus* would have been an impossible structure to carry about without some provision for lightening its weight. So

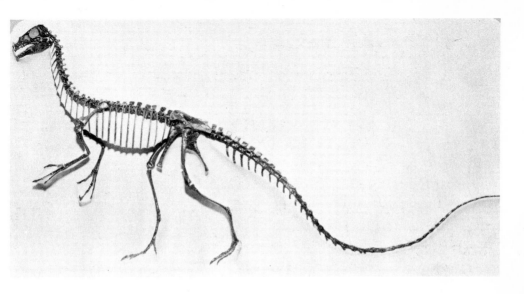

Plate 31. Ornitholestes, a small theropod dinosaur from the Jurassic Morrison beds of western North America. The skeleton is about six feet long

Plate 32. Ornitholestes shown catching the Jurassic bird *Archaeopteryx.* This excellent drawing demonstrates the light build and the agile movements of the coelurosaurian dinosaurs. By Charles R. Knight

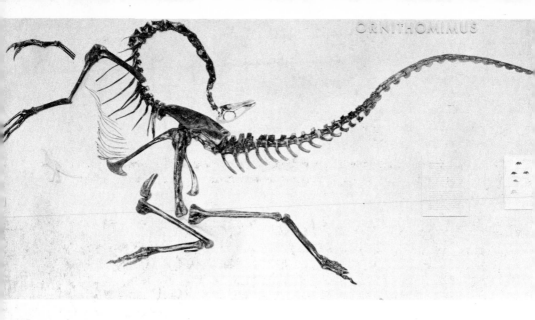

Plate 33. The North American Cretaceous dinosaur *Ornithomimus* as it was found. After death, drying of ligaments pulled the neck back in a sharp flexure. The skeleton is about fourteen feet long

Plate 34. *Ornithomimus* was an active dinosaur that probably haunted the upland jungles in search of a wide variety of animal and vegetable food. By Erwin S. Christman

Plate 35. One of the smallest known dinosaurs, *Compsognathus*, from the Jurassic beds of central Europe. The skeleton is about the size of a small chicken skeleton

Plate 36. The Jurassic theropod *Allosaurus*, mounted as if feeding upon a brontosaur skeleton. This allosaur skeleton from the Morrison beds of Colorado is about thirty feet long

Plate 37. A beautifully designed predator in action. The body of *Allosaurus* was nicely suspended and balanced at the hips. The jaws and the front feet worked together. By Charles R. Knight

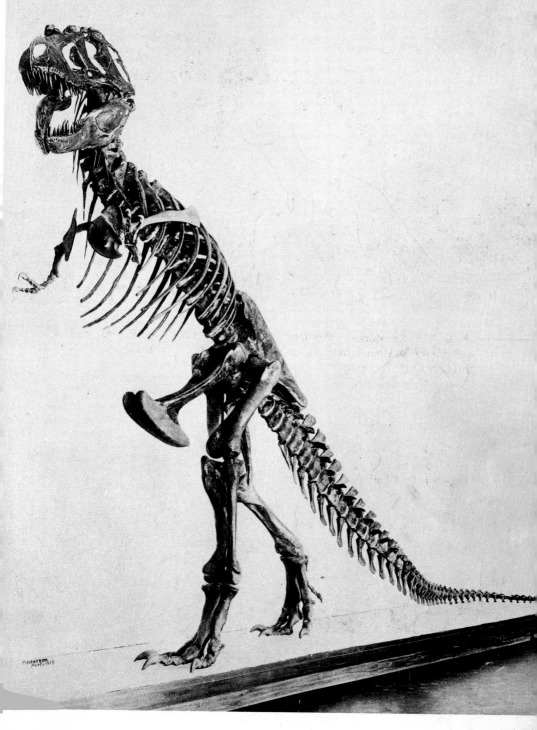

Plate 38. *Tyrannosaurus*, the greatest of all land-living predators. The skeleton, from the Cretaceous beds of Montana, is about fifty feet long, and stands about eighteen feet high

Plate 39. A restoration of *Tyrannosaurus*. By Charles R. Knight

Plate 40. The Jurassic carnivorous dinosaur *Megalosaurus*, of Europe. This theropod was about twenty feet in length. By Neave Parker

Plate 41. Six famous paleontologists and collectors at the Bone Cabin Quarry in 1899. Seated: Walter Granger, Henry Fairfield Osborn, William D. Matthew. Standing behind them: Richard Swann Lull, Albert Thomson, Peter Kaisen

Plate 42. How to be comfortable while looking at dinosaurs in the field. The museum at Dinosaur National Monument, Utah, built over an exposure of Morrison sediments containing many bones

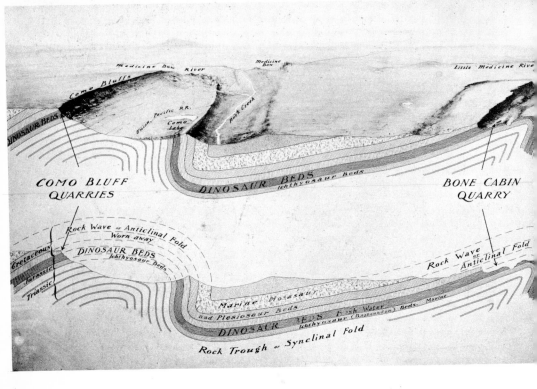

Plate 43. The geologic section at Como Bluffs, Wyoming. Earth movements cause folds; erosion wears away the rocks. Thus cliffs and valleys are formed. In some of the cliffs there may be bones

Plate 44. A diagram showing how the bones were found at the Bone Cabin Quarry. More often than not scattered parts of skeletons are found, as seen here

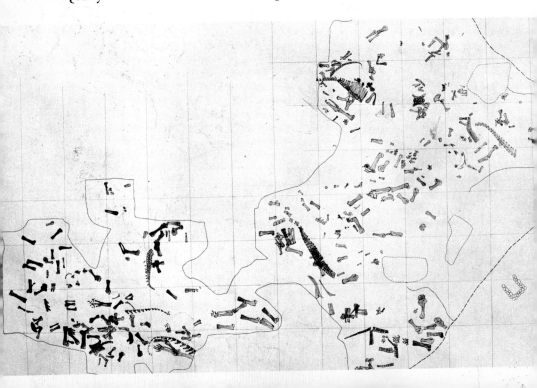

ABOVE. *Plate 45. Cetiosaurus,* a gigantic sauropod dinosaur, sixty feet in length, that lived in southern England during late Jurassic times. By Neave Parker. RIGHT. *Plate 46.* The greatest of all sauropods, *Brachiosaurus,* from the Upper Jurassic Tendaguru beds of Africa. This skeleton, seventy feet long and forty feet high, is in the Berlin Museum

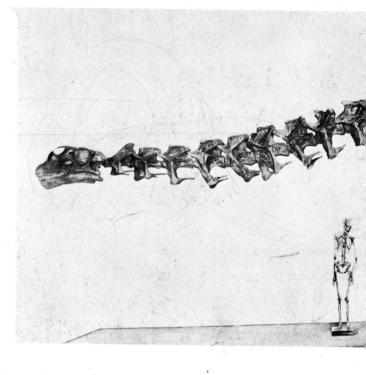

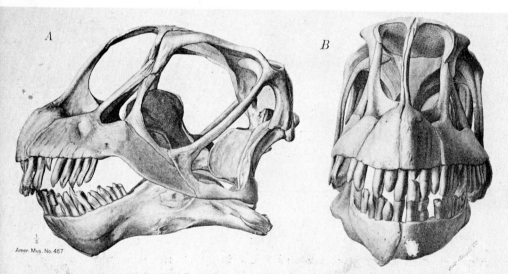

A

B

1/6

Amer. Mus. No. 467

Plate 47. *Brontosaurus* (more properly *Apatosaurus*) from the Upper Jurassic Bone Cabin Quarry at Como Bluffs, Wyoming. The skeleton is about seventy feet long

Plate 48. The skull of *Camarasaurus* is a lightly built and remarkably open structure. The jaws and teeth are those of an inoffensive plant-eater

Plate 49. Brontosaurs in their native habitat. By Charles R. Knight

Plate 50. The attenuated, elongated sauropod *Diplodocus*, from the Upper Jurassic Morrison beds of western North America, was about eighty feet in length. By Charles R. Knight

LEFT. *Plate 51.* *Hypsilophodon,* a primitive ornithischian dinosaur about five feet in length, lived in southern England during early Cretaceous times. It may have been a tree climber. By Neave Parker. BELOW. *Plate 52.* *Camptosaurus,* living in North America during late Jurassic times, was a generalized type of ornithischian dinosaur, probably similar in form to the ancestor of all ornithischians. By John C. Germann

Plate 53. The living *Iguanodon*. Compare this superb restoration with the interpretation of a century ago shown in Plate 8. By Neave Parker

Plate 54. One of the *Iguanodon* skeletons found in a coal mine at Bernissart, Belgium, in sediments of early Cretaceous age. The skeleton is about thirty feet long

Plate 55. The skull of *Pachycephalosaurus*, an ornithopod of late Cretaceous age, from Montana. The domed skull roof is formed of solid bone

Plate 56. *Pachycephalosaurus* and a late Cretaceous mammal. By Margaret M. Colbert

it is that the skull in this carnosaur and in other similar giant predators is a structure of bony arches and bars, with unusually large openings or vacuities between them. The temporal openings behind the eye are enlarged, giving room for the play of muscles, and there are two openings on each side of the skull in front of the eyes. One gets an impression of extraordinary lightness and strength combined, when looking at the skull of *Allosaurus*. Yet in spite of its strong construction, the skull had a certain degree of mobility within itself. The quadrate bone, the skull element with which the lower jaw articulated, is loosely attached to its adjacent skull bones, and the bones of the skull roof are so joined that some movement was possible between them. It would seem that such adaptations allowed some springiness in the skull when *Allosaurus* bolted great chunks of flesh—a parallel to what is seen in a much more refined development among many modern lizards and snakes. The brain case in this dinosaur is of relatively small size.

Even though the skull of *Allosaurus* is lightened by fenestration,—it is still a massive bit of mechanism to be carried at the front end of the vertebral column. A skull such as this could hardly have been supported on the end of a long, flexible neck of the type so characteristic of the coelurosaurs. Consequently the neck in *Allosaurus,* and in all of the large carnosaurs for that matter, is relatively short and very strong. An analogy to this is seen in the huge skull and the very short neck of the modern elephants.

In *Allosaurus* and related carnosaurs the functions of attacking foes and of feeding upon victims were seemingly shared by the great jaws and by the relatively small but powerful and mobile forelimbs. In these carnosaurs the first three fingers of the hand are large, and terminate in very large, sharp claws, of which the first claw, the one on the thumb, the largest. Evidently *Allosaurus* launched an attack with jaws and claws together, biting and ripping, clawing and tearing. It was a formidable and terrible animal.

From this description we can perhaps get a picture of the adaptations *Allosaurus* for the specialized kind of life that it lived. Here we see ancient hunter, large and aggressive, that roamed and terrorized the jungles of late Jurassic times as does the tiger today in an Oriental wilderness.

There were many carnosaurs living in all parts of the world during Jurassic times. They were all much alike—so much so, in fact, that they be included in a single family of dinosaurs, the Megalosauridae. *Megalosaurus* is the common European form, famous among other reasons, for being the first dinosaur ever to be described. *Ceratosaurus,* from North America, is distinctive in that it has a small horn on the nose, the only meat-eating dinosaur to be so equipped. *Spinosaurus,* a megalosaur that lived into late Cretaceous times in Egypt, has amazingly long vertebral spines, at times six feet in length. The reason for these great spines is not easy to fathom.

The culmination of carnosaurian evolution was reached during the Cretaceous period, with the development of the great tyrannosaurs, last and largest of the predatory dinosaurs. These giant carnivores may have been lineal descendants of the Jurassic megalosaurs, or they may have evolved from the same stock as did the megalosaurs, but along an independent and parallel line. This is a matter that can be argued either way upon the basis of present evidence.

For instance, there are some differences. The skull in the tyrannosaurs is quite solid, and has none of the internal mobility that characterizes the allosaur skull. And the long bones of the hind foot are closely appressed so that they form in effect one solid structure, thereby giving additional strength to a foot that in life had to support tons of weight. But generally speaking these last and largest of the carnosaurs differed from their Jurassic predecessors mainly in size and proportions. *Tyrannosaurus* was the largest of all carnosaurs, a reptile about fifty feet in length that stood some eighteen feet tall to the top of the head (*Pl.* 38). In life this dinosaur must have weighed all of eight tons—r m more.

In *Tyrannosaurus* almost everything is bigger and heavier than an Jurassic *Allosaurus.* The animal is bigger, as just mentioned; th an vidual bones are larger and heavier. The sacral attachment b dir pelvis and backbone is longer and stronger than in the earlier ve saurs. The skull is actually and relatively enormous, being mo is four feet in length. The teeth in the jaws of *Tyrannosaurus* are cla daggers, with sharp, serrated cutting edges. *Tyrannosaurus* q mi viously was well equipped for predation on a large scale.

And it is interesting to see that predation in this dinosaur, in close and slightly earlier relative, *Gorgosaurus,* was concentr an a most entirely in the jaws. The forelimbs are reduced to ridi jung small appendages, with but two functional fingers in each har dern furnished with relatively small claws. It seems strange that t Th and very efficient clawed hands of *Allosaurus* and other me Jura should have been abandoned by the Cretaceous tyrannosaurs, can is the case. In the tyrannosaurs the great, cruel jaws were Meg

These dinosaurs were the largest land-living predators of all time, and for many millions of years, during the final stages of the Cretaceous period, they were dominant on all of the continents.

The great predatory dinosaurs of Jurassic and Cretaceous times grew into giants at the time when the varied plant-eating dinosaurs also were developing as giants. It was an age of giants—perhaps because world climates and a great abundance of vegetation were favorable to giants on the land. Long ago the contenders in the age-old struggle between the hunted and the hunters were dinosaurs; today, on a smaller but more refined and vigorous scale, they are, in their most impressive forms, the antelopes and lions in Africa, the wild cattle and tigers in Asia, and the deer and panther in America.

Figure 13. World map showing the distribution of theropod dinosaurs

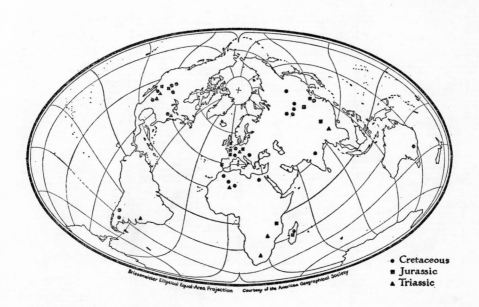

Brissemeister Elliptical Equal-Area Projection   Courtesy of the American Geographical Society

• Cretaceous
■ Jurassic
▲ Triassic

CHAPTER SIX

GREATEST OF THE GIANTS

A BIT OF HISTORY

Among all the dinosaurs the huge sauropods, the greatest of the giants, are perhaps the "typical" dinosaurs as far as most people are concerned. To the public at large *Brontosaurus* (more properly *Apatosaurus*), one of the best known of the sauropods, is literally *Mr. Dinosaur* himself, and when the word "dinosaur" comes up, the picture of a giant reptile with a massive body, heavy limbs, a long neck, a long tail, and a very small head is probably the image most frequently seen in the mind's eye. In life the sauropods must have been big and impressive, for the skeleton of one of these ancient reptiles, the bare framework without the added bulk of muscles and skin, is indeed awesome to one who sees it for the first time. The sight of such a skeleton stimulates the imagination, and leads to speculations about the world of long ago.

Everything about the sauropods must be expressed in superlatives. Even the prosaic business of digging their skeletons out of the ground is fossil hunting on a scale much bigger than anything attempted by most paleontologists. To remove a sauropod from the enclosing earth is a task to be approached with a full realization of the immense amount of work and trouble and expense that will be involved before the job has been completed. To take out a sauropod skeleton is something like getting a very large bear by the tail; once begun, the job is not easily concluded, and there are many problems. It is hardly to be wondered at that the fossil hunters who first began to dig out the bones of the giant sauropod dinosaurs were not quite aware of what they were up against. This has helped to make a lively story out of the history of sauropod digging.

Bones of sauropod dinosaurs were dug up in England more than a century ago, and all who saw them were mightily impressed. Professor Owen gave the giant bones a name—*Cetiosaurus*, meaning "whale reptile"—to indicate their massive dimensions. Though impressive, each in itself, the isolated bones of *Cetiosaurus* gave little idea as to what the whole animal might have been like. A complete skeleton was needed. It remained for Marsh and Cope, those bitter antagonists in early American paleontology, to make the first massive excavations of skeletons belonging to the dinosaur giants, thereby revealing the complete anatomy of these reptiles. As might be expected, any projects involving Marsh and Cope were punctuated by scientific fireworks that enlivened the work of discovery, excavation, study, and description.

In 1868 Professor Marsh went out west for the first time, traveling on the still-unfinished Union Pacific Railroad. The railroad in those days ran along the northern side of Como Bluff in eastern Wyoming (the tracks have now been relocated some miles to the south of the bluff), and at that place Marsh disembarked from the train of cars. There was a little lake at the foot of Como Bluff, and he wanted to collect some axolotls, which are large salamanders, that reportedly were living in the lake. At the station, which then formed a small dot on the landscape between the lake and the bluff, Marsh saw some large bones that had been collected nearby by Mr. W. E. Carlin, the station agent. For some inexplicable reason, Marsh showed what was for him a most atypical lack of interest in the bones, and went on about his business of axolotls.

Then, about a decade later, things began to happen. Early in 1877 some large dinosaurs were found near Canyon City and also near Morrison, Colorado. The Canyon City find was reported to Cope, the Morrison discovery to Marsh, and within a few weeks collectors were busy at the two localities, taking out giant bones for the two rival paleontologists.

Hardly had the work at Morrison got well under way when Marsh received a letter from Laramie Station, Wyoming, written by two men who merely signed themselves as "Harlow and Edwards." These worthies informed Marsh that they had found a large number of great bones nearby. Then they continued their letter as follows:

"We are desirous of disposing of what fossils we have, and also, the secret of the others. We are working men and are not able to present them as a gift, and if we can sell the secret of the fossil bed, and procure work in excavating others we would like to do so.

"We have said nothing to any-one as yet. . . .

"As a proof of our sincerity and truth, we will send you a few fossils, at what they cost us in time and money in unearthing.

"We would be pleased to hear from you, as you are well known as an enthusiastic geologist, and a man of means, both of which we are desirous of finding—more especially the latter."

Their frankness was rewarded. The enthusiastic geologist and man of means followed this lead with his characteristic vigor, first asking Harlow and Edwards to ship some bones to him. He then sent his assistant, Dr. S. W. Williston, to Wyoming, to see just what this was all about. Williston discovered, first of all, that Harlow and Edwards were none other than Mr. Carlin, the station agent at Como, and Mr. W. H. Reed, section foreman on that stretch of the Union Pacific line. Secondly, Williston found that there was an incredible quantity of giant bones weathering out of the slopes of Como Bluff. He wrote to Marsh in great excitement that the bones "extend for *seven* miles and are by the ton. . . . The bones are right by the station but there are only 4 or 5 persons that know about them. . . . The bones are very thick, well preserved, and easy to get out." That was enough for Marsh. Even though it was now late in November, he instructed Williston to begin excavating, and Williston did so.

He and his assistants labored through the cold and the snows of a Wyoming winter, and on into the following summer. The work went on, summer and winter, fall and spring, for several years, and bones were dug out literally by the ton, to be shipped off to New Haven. Williston left the job in the summer of 1878, to return to New Haven, and the erstwhile section foreman, Bill Reed, was left in charge of the project. In 1879 Marsh sent a former English clergyman, Arthur Lakes, a graduate of Queen's College, Oxford, to Como, to work with Reed. Lakes was one of the men who had found the dinosaur bones at Morrison, Colorado, in 1877 and had been digging for Marsh there ever since. Reed and Lakes almost immediately took a hearty dislike to each other. Perhaps the Englishman thought that Reed was a bit of a rough character; certainly Reed considered that Lakes was an effete gentleman who wasted a lot of time making notes and drawing pictures (leaving by the way an invaluable record of those early days at Como Bluff). But they managed to make a go of it by not working together.

The news of dinosaur bones on such an unprecedented scale at Como Bluff was bound in time to reach Cope, despite the efforts of Marsh and his men at secrecy. So Cope, whose men were all this time digging out tons of dinosaur bones at Canyon City, immediately became envious and jealous. He sent one of his field parties to Wyoming in 1879, to try its luck along Como Bluff. Marsh's boys regarded Cope's boys as poachers; Cope's boys, on the other hand, took the view that Wyoming was a big place, and not the private domain of any one man. There were disagreements and, as has been previously mentioned, at least one pitched battle between the rival collectors, to enliven the work of the summer. In the long run Cope accomplished very little at Como Bluff; in practice if not in theory it proved to be Marsh's domain, and from this region he amassed a superb collection of dinosaurs, and made for himself a scientific and popular reputation that went around the world.

In 1883 Bill Reed, who had most successfully supervised six years of work at Como Bluff, quit dinosaur digging to raise sheep. Marsh's efforts were continued for several years thereafter by two of Reed's assistants, E. Kennedy and Fred Brown. Finally this herculean task came to a close in the middle eighties, but not until 480 large boxes and crates of bones had been shipped to Yale University. Then Como Bluff lay fallow for a time.

In 1891 Professor Henry Fairfield Osborn, who had been teaching at Princeton University, came to New York to establish a program of vertebrate paleontology at the American Museum of Natural History and to help found the Department of Zoology at Columbia University. Osborn decided that at the museum he needed to interest the public in fossil bones, and what could attract more interest than some large dinosaur skeletons, particularly the skeleton of a giant sauropod? In 1897 he accordingly sent Walter Granger of the Museum to Como Bluff, to look into things there. Granger found that the old Marsh quarries were pretty poor picking—they had been cleaned out. He therefore scoured the countryside several miles to the north of Como Bluff, and one fine day he found what he wanted. In the middle of an open plain was a small, solid cabin, built by a sheepherder as his own domicile. Granger found to his amazement that the cabin was built out of huge dinosaur bones! And all over the ground around the cabin were more bones, weathering out of the rocks in which they had been entombed for so many millions of years.

Here was the place to dig, and here the Museum parties dug, year in and year out, until 1903 (Plates 41, 43, 44). Once more, as in the palmy days of Marsh and his assistants, great quantities of bones were taken from the ground, this time to be shipped to New York instead of New Haven. Professor Osborn got the dinosaurs he wanted to exhibit in the Museum halls, and today the great skeleton of *Brontosaurus* from Bone Cabin Quarry dominates the hall in which it is displayed, as popular a museum piece as it was fifty years ago.

"Harlow and Edwards" were being hardheaded realists when they told Marsh in their letter that they wished to do business with him because he was reputedly an "enthusiastic geologist and a man of means." It takes enthusiasm and money to get a big dinosaur out of the ground: enthusiasm to stick with a long, hard job through heat and sandstorms and rains, money to pay for the enormous number of manhours that go into the work. One man who had enthusiasm (although he was not a geologist), and money in almost undreamed-of amounts, was the little giant of steel, Andrew Carnegie.

Carnegie had built a new museum in Pittsburgh, and he wanted to have it filled with awe-inspiring objects. The giant dinosaurs caught his fancy; he had the means to bring some of them to Pittsburgh, and that was just what he proposed to do. It so happened that the successful operation of his plan depended primarily upon one man—Earl Douglass.

Earl Douglass was a native of Utah who had become associated with the Carnegie Museum early in the history of that institution. He had grown up in the spectacular country along the Green River in the days when that picturesque and inaccessible section of eastern Utah was almost unknown to the outside world. Major John Wesley Powell had made several boat trips down the Green River in the adventurous days after the Civil War, and he had written some accounts of his exploits. So had some of his companions. Of course, the ranchers who lived in this country knew it well. Even so, in the early days of the present century it was a rather isolated and unknown area to most of our population.

Douglass began to prospect for dinosaurs along the Green River, in the vicinity of Jensen, Utah. Olaf Peterson, another Carnegie Museum man, had found some dinosaur bones there back in 1892, at a time when he was working for the American Museum of Natural History in New York. During the summer of 1909 Douglass tramped the hot, tilted hills north and east of Jensen, day in and day out, and it was discouraging business. He prospected for weeks on end, and had little to show for his efforts until, on the nineteenth day of August, he found the articulated tail of a giant sauropod dinosaur, exposed in some dipping sandstones near Split Mountain. He followed the bones into the rock, chipping them out one by one, and soon became convinced that he had stumbled onto a complete brontosaur skeleton. The news went to Pittsburgh, and work began in earnest.

It was a great find and a most productive quarry for the Carnegie Museum. The work, begun in 1909, continued through the years under the direction of Douglass until 1922, and in that time vast quantities of dinosaur bones were excavated and shipped to Pittsburgh, where with much labor they were cleaned and studied. The few tail vertebrae that Douglass had found did lead into a complete skeleton, the skeleton of the sauropod *Apatosaurus louisiae*, named after Mrs. Carnegie. Many other dinosaurs came from this quarry, one of them being a very fine skeleton of another sauropod that was christened *Diplodocus carnegeii*. Andrew fell in love with this dinosaur—perhaps he liked its name as well as its dimensions. At any rate he ordered it to be cast, bone by bone, and plaster replicas of the skeleton were made, to be donated to large museums all over the world.

The great quarry developed by the Carnegie Museum was on public land, and for the first few years of its development Douglass secured yearly permits from the Department of Interior. Then it was decided that perhaps the property could be protected properly and worked to advantage if Douglass would file a mineral claim to it, which he did. The claim was disallowed because the bones that were being taken out could not be rightly regarded by the government as minerals. Nevertheless everyone concerned thought that this unique area should be protected in some way.

So it was that on October 4, 1915, President Woodrow Wilson set aside eighty acres of land, including the Carnegie quarry site, as Dinosaur National Monument, the nucleus of what has become one of the most interesting and spectacular areas in our present National Parks system.

From 1915 until 1922 the Carnegie Museum worked the quarry

under a special arrangement with the Department of Interior. Since then the government has developed the quarry site, and it is now being made into a permanent outdoor exhibit *in situ* where visitors will be able to see brontosaur skeletons and other dinosaurs exposed in the rock, just as they were found (Plate 42).

Such is the story of the discovery of a few giant sauropods that have been found in North America. The account might be extended at length, to tell how these giant dinosaurs have been discovered and dug out of the ground in other North American localities, in Europe and in Asia, in South America and especially in East Africa, where expeditions from Germany and later from England exhumed some very large and very famous sauropod skeletons. But the story won't be thus prolonged. It is high time to get on with the description of what the fossil bones of the giant sauropods are like, and of what they tell us about the life and times of these great dinosaurs.

ON BEING A GIANT

It is not so easy to be a giant in real life as it is in the folk tales and the fairy stories. The giants of legends are merely people projected to immense size, great, overwhelming men who march through the forests as if through a patch of weeds, who may crush a house or wreak havoc in a village with their seven-league boots. For them there are no laws of physics nor are there any knotty problems of physiology to limit their size or their actions.

For the dinosaurs, and particularly for the sauropods, the greatest of the giants (Plate 47), it was quite a different thing. They had reached the ultimate in size among land-living animals, for the simple reason that bones and muscles and ligaments and tendons could not support the weight of animals any larger than they were. The downward pull of gravity, which is of so little consequence to a fly, and which is so important to us, was an overwhelmingly constant factor in the daily life of a sauropod dinosaur. A man may tumble down a bank two or three times his own height with no ill effects and he can readily jump a stream, but one of the giant sauropods could not fall over a bank of even less than his height without serious injury, nor could he jump across a stream or over a fallen log, any more than can an elephant. Indeed, the sauropod, like a modern elephant, could never get all four feet off the ground at once.

His ponderous bulk must always have been adequately supported, and for this the legs were developed as massive, pillar-like structures. The bones of the limbs are extremely heavy and dense—as strong in structure as bone can be—so that they were capable of resisting massive compression along their axes and powerful angular forces exerted against their length. The limbs of the sauropod, like the piers of a great bridge, held the dinosaur up and kept him from collapsing to the ground. Compare if you will a giant dinosaur with a modern whale, which, if stranded on a beach, immediately suffocates because of its great weight. The skeleton of the whale is not strong enough when that animal is out of the water to hold the giant mammal up; thus the lungs are cruelly crushed, the whale is unable to breathe, and in short order it helplessly expires.

Of course, the heavy leg bones of the dinosaur were surrounded by great muscle masses that gave life and movement to the limbs, so that they were much more than mere supporting piers. Add the muscles and their attendant nerves and blood vessels to the bones and connective tissue, and the limbs of the giant dinosaurs become dynamic

Figure 14. The Upper Jurassic sauropod dinosaur *Camarasaurus*. This figure illustrates the open but strong structure of the vertebral column, and the heavy limbs for supporting the great weight of the body

structures, the locomotor organs that millions of years ago carried the great reptiles in wide wanderings across the continents.

The hind limbs of the giant sauropod dinosaurs are particularly straight, and this is reflected in the post-like form of the bones—the upper bone of femur and the two lower bones, the tibia and fibula. In life these bones obviously were pretty much aligned along one axis, when the limb was extended, in which respect the hind limb of the sauropod dinosaurs may be compared with the hind limb of a modern elephant. There was once a common legend that elephants have no joints in their legs. The joints are there, all right, but for an elephant it is advantageous not to bend the leg any more than necessary, thereby keeping the axis of the leg aligned against the downward pull of gravity. So it must have been for the sauropod dinosaurs.

The forelimbs in the sauropods were not quite so nicely adjusted for the carrying of weight as were the hind limbs, for it would appear that the elbows were always somewhat bent, even when the limbs were held at their straightest. But bones and muscles and ligaments were all massive, so that even though the elbows were a bit akimbo the forelimbs were quite capable of supporting the front portion of the

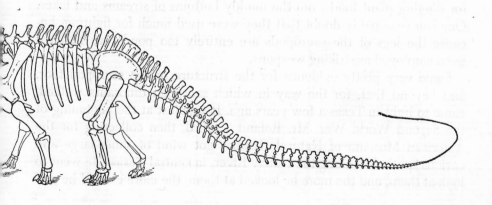

body in these giant dinosaurs. The front legs in the sauropods are almost always considerably shorter and smaller than the hind legs, a clear indication that these giant dinosaurs, though adjusted through millions of years of evolution to a four-footed pose, none the less retained vestiges of their descent from ancestors that walked on strong hind legs and had small, arm-like front legs. It is thus obvious that the sauropods were *secondarily* four-footed animals, and that their pose and their method of walking about on all four feet were clearly adaptations to great weight. During their evolution from bipedal ancestors there came a time when the weight of these dinosaurs became so great that the hind legs alone were no longer able to carry the load.

Among land-living animals broad padded feet go along with massive pillar-like limbs. Witness once more for comparison the elephant, with round feet shaped something like nail kegs, each foot soled with a thick spongy cushion, a sort of spread-out heel, to take up the shock of several tons of weight. There is conclusive proof that the feet in the sauropod dinosaurs were generally similar to the feet of modern elephants, and for similar reasons. The toe bones in the sauropod foot are short and heavy, as they are in the elephant's foot, and it would appear that, as in the elephant, there was in life a very thick and expanded pad behind and beneath the bones of the foot, to take up the shock of impact as each foot was put down on the ground.

In the sauropods each hind foot is commonly provided with three large claws on the first, second, and third toes. The two remaining toes have no claws, and probably they were buried in the mass of the foot, with little or no external evidence of their presence. In the front foot there is often a single large claw on the thumb, with the other toes enclosed inside the massive foot. The purpose of these claws on the feet can only be guessed at; perhaps the giant dinosaurs used them for digging plant food from the muddy bottoms of streams and lakes. One can reasonably doubt that they were used much for fighting, because the legs of the sauropods are entirely too ponderous to have been employed as striking weapons.

Some very pretty evidence for the structure of the sauropod foot, and beyond that, for the way in which sauropod dinosaurs walked, came to light in Texas a few years ago. It was just at the beginning of the Second World War. Mr. Roland T. Bird, then collecting for the American Museum of Natural History, got wind of some large and curious "potholes" along the Paluxy River, in central Texas. He went to look at them, and the more he looked at them, the more excited he got.

A pothole is commonly a large round hole in the rock along the bottom or at the edge of a stream, and is formed by stream currents and eddies washing sand and pebbles and large stones around and around in a small circle, thereby wearing out a deep depression in the rock. The holes that Bird saw along the bed of the Paluxy River seemed rather queerly shaped to have been formed in the usual way; it was hard to make them out very clearly, because they were partially filled with sand and mud, washed in by the river. Mr. Bird, his excitement rising by the minute, for he had begun to suspect what the alleged potholes might be, hastily procured a shovel and a broom and went to work on one of them. Within a few minutes the form of the depression was completely exposed, and sure enough, it was the footprint of a huge sauropod dinosaur. It didn't take long to ascertain that this was only one of several footprints, that there was fossil trackway in the rock, the record of an excursion by a sauropod, millions of years ago. It was too late in the season to do much about it, but Bird made plans for the next year.

Those were the days of the W.P.A., when educational institutions could get manpower with federal funds for large projects. Bird made arrangements for a large W.P.A. crew to be on the job with him the next year, the project to be sponsored jointly by the American Museum of Natural History and the University of Texas.

That next year they went to work with a will. The crew made a sandbag dike to divert the waters of the Paluxy from a portion of its channel. When everything was reasonably dry, the men labored hard and long to remove great quantities of shale that covered the hitherto unexposed portions of the trackway, and within the course of a few weeks' time they had uncovered a magnificent dinosaur trail. There were washtub-sized tracks made by a great sauropod dinosaur, and along with them large bird-like tracks of one of the carnivorous meat-eating dinosaurs. It was quite plain that the meat eater had been following the giant herbivore, for in some cases he had stepped *into* the footprints of his prey. All was there in the rocks, just as it had been made in the mud during the distant days of early Cretaceous times, a petrified drama of the geologic past (Plate 90). The sauropod tracks were very deep, as clear evidence that they had been made by animals of great weight. Evidently the tracks were made in soft sediments, because the mud had been squeezed up in large rolls around the edges of each footprint. Moreover, the tracks must have been made in shallow water, perhaps three or four feet deep, because there were no marks made by a dragging tail. (At another locality, not far away, Bird found tracks in which the tail drag was visible.) Yet the water was shallow enough so that virtually the full weight of the animal was pressed down upon the feet as the dinosaur splashed along on his flight from the dreaded hunter behind him. Which means that the water was not up to the belly of the sauropod.

Bird and his men excavated the tracks, and today they may be seen in Austin, Texas, and in New York.

The sauropod tracks from Texas furnish definite proof that in these ancient dinosaurs each foot was provided with a gigantic "heel pad." The tracks of the hind feet, each of which can be filled with some fifteen gallons of water, show this quite clearly. Furthermore, these footprints show the marks made by the three claws. The tracks of the front feet are, as might be expected, much smaller than those of the hind feet, and in these particular footprints there are no indications of a claw on the thumb.

It is especially fortunate that Bird was able to excavate a whole trackway rather than a few isolated footprints, for this trackway shows clearly the manner in which one of the giant sauropods walked. Briefly, this dinosaur walked along most efficiently, with the feet well under the

---

Figure 15. Above. A herd of sauropod dinosaurs walking through rather shallow water would have made the footprints in the Cretaceous rocks at Glen Rose, Texas. Notice that the tails are afloat, but the water is not deep enough to have buoyed up the bodies. Therefore deep footprints were made. *Below.* A longitudinal section of a print of a hind-foot. Note the roll of mud pushed up around the margin of the track

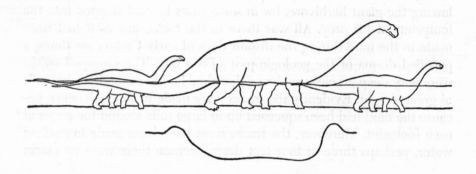

body. Indeed, the tracks of the right and left sides are separated from each other only by about the width of a single footprint.

This settles once for all a controversy that persisted during many years about how sauropod dinosaurs walked on land, or whether they walked on land at all. Some students of ancient reptiles used to think that the giant sauropods were so heavy that they could never come out of the water so that the body would be completely supported by the limbs. They thought that the sauropods, like whales, needed to have the body buoyed up by the water. The Texas tracks take care of that argument; sauropods obviously did walk around out of the water without a bit of trouble. Other authorities used to think that the sauropods could not have held the legs in a vertical position, with the feet well in beneath the body near the mid-line. These scholars were making the mistake of comparing sauropod dinosaurs with some of their modern reptilian cousins, none of which is confronted with the problem of weight that plagued the sauropods, rather than with the unrelated elephants which none the less have a weight problem similar to that of the ancient dinosaurs. The Texas tracks show that the sauropod dinosaurs did walk like elephants, not like lizards.

If you want to get an idea as to just how big the giant sauropod dinosaurs were, go to a museum where there is a big brontosaur skeleton and look up at the pelvis. It is truly one of the most impressive objects of the animal world. The skull of a big whale is longer, but somehow nothing bony seems so massive and solid as the pelvis of a brontosaur. It brings home in no uncertain way the fact that the structures for the support of one of these great dinosaurs were of necessity tremendously strong and extraordinarily well designed for their function.

Structurally the pelvis was a segment of the skeleton of particular importance in the sauropod dinosaurs, as it was in all the other dinosaurs for that matter, for it formed the principal connection between the massive body and the stout limbs that held the body off the ground. In the bipedal dinosaurs the pelvis was, as we have seen, an actual pivot upon which the body was balanced, the weight of the body in front of the pelvis being counterbalanced by the weight of the long, heavy tail behind the pelvis. In the quadrupedal sauropods this pivotal function had been lost, yet the pelvis had in no way suffered any reduction in size or importance because of the transition from a partially upright two-legged pose to a horizontal four-footed pose. It seems evident that in the giant dinosaurs the pelvis and the hind limbs carried by far the largest fraction of the body weight.

It is certainly a structure well adapted to support tons of reptilian flesh and viscera. The upper bone of the pelvis on either side, the ilium, is a thick plate, long and deep, that affords ample surface on its inner side for the expanded articulations of five sacral vertebrae. To the broad outer surface of the ilium there were attached heavy muscles that gave power and movement to the hind leg. Below the ilium on each side the two other bones of the pelvis, the pubis and the ischium, are heavy bones that in life formed the bases for strong leg muscles. Thus the pelvis as a whole, which was constructed to give a remarkably firm anchorage for exceedingly large and strong leg muscles, was a basic part of the power plant that moved thirty or forty tons of brontosaur ponderously but nevertheless surely and successfully across the face of the earth.

The pectoral or shoulder girdle is not so massive in the sauropod dinosaurs as the pelvis, for, as has been pointed out above, the forelimbs in these dinosaurs are much smaller than the hind limbs. The principal bone in the pectoral girdle, the shoulder blade or scapula, is very long, flat, and is expanded at its lower end, where it is attached to the large, semicircular coracoid bone. Between and somewhat back of the right and left coracoid bones are a pair of large sternal bones. Taken together the shoulder blades, coracoids, and sternal bones of the two sides make a sort of sling around the front part of the body, held to the body by very large muscles and forming in part a base for other muscles that moved the front legs.

Figure 16. The bones of the gigantic Upper Jurassic sauropod dinosaur *Apatosaurus*, drawn to the same scale. About one-twentieth natural size. A. The femur or upper bone of the hind limb, a straight and a very strong bone. B. The pelvis as seen from the back. Note the massive, buttress-like construction of the sacrum and the attached ilia, above. C. A cervical or neck vertebra as seen from the front. The spine of the vertebra is divided to form a gigantic V, a housing for the elastic cable (the *ligamentum nuchae*) that served to support the neck and head. D. The same vertebra as seen from the left side. Notice the large openings and depressions in the bone, giving it lightness. E. A back or dorsal vertebra, as seen from the rear. Note the heavy spine for muscle attachments, and the complex articulating surface for the next vertebra. F. The same vertebra from the left side

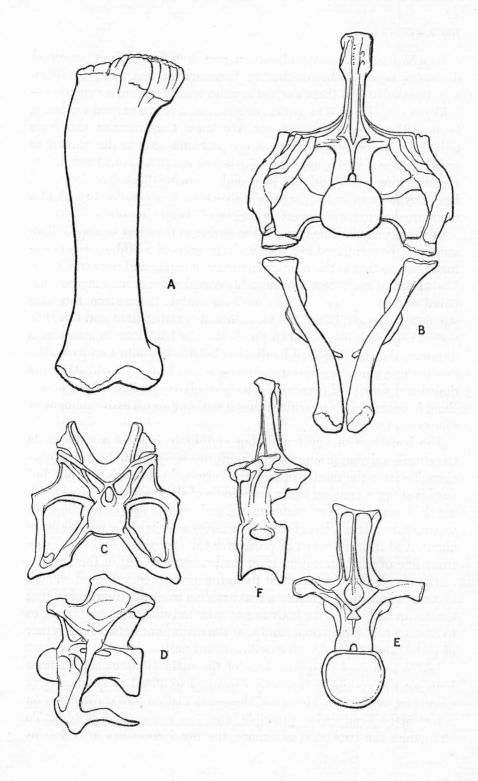

It seems almost inevitable when one is talking about sauropod dinosaurs, or about any of the big dinosaurs for that matter, to compare the skeleton in these ancient reptiles with man-made structures—bridges or steel beams or girders or buttresses. It is a natural tendency, because the comparisons are apt. We know the problems that have to be solved when a bridge is put up, problems such as the support of weight across a free span, the avoidance of excessive "dead weight" in the structure itself, and the like; and, knowing these problems and how they are met in the man-made structure, it is possible to look at a dinosaur skeleton with a certain degree of comprehension.

We have seen that the legs and the girdles in the great sauropod dinosaurs may be compared in a way with the piers of a bridge, remembering of course that in the reptile they were dynamic and not static piers. The sauropod backbone, a remarkably complex structure, may be compared with the span of a steel cantilever bridge. It has strength where strength is needed, but at the same time it is rather light and airy, like a steel truss. If a line is drawn just below the backbone in a sauropod dinosaur, the skeleton may be divided by this line into two parts. Below the line almost everything is massive and heavy, to withstand the downward thrusts of tremendous weight; above the line almost everything is lightened, to provide strength without an excessive amount of unnecessary weight.

The backbone of any land-living vertebrate is truly a remarkable structure—a dynamic support that performs several simultaneous functions. To state the matter briefly, the vertebral column is a strong but flexible support running along the middle of the back, capable of holding the body up without undue tiring, and capable also of bending this way and that. It is a base for many muscles that help the animal move about. And it forms a sort of protective tube for the spinal nerve, the trunk line of communication from the brain to the rest of the body.

The effective performance of these functions is complicated enough in a small animal; it becomes a real problem in giants. Remember that the downward pull of the body in a four-footed animal is at right angles to the axis of the backbone, and that the main joint between each pair of vertebrae is aligned with this downward pull.

In the sauropod dinosaurs each of the main joints or articulations between the vertebrae is greatly expanded to afford as great an area of contact as possible. Moreover, these articulations are constructed on a sort of ball-and-socket principle, and this made them flexible. To strengthen the backbone still more, the usual accessory articulations between the vertebrae, the surfaces known to anatomists as zyga-pophyses, and of which there are two at the front and two at the back of each vertebra, are also widely expanded. In addition to these joints there are supplementary joints between the vertebrae which are not found in other animals; these are known as the hyposphenes and hypantra. Finally, the spines that project up from the vertebrae are very long, particularly in the region between the front and hind limbs and over the hips. This gave attachments for extremely strong muscles and tendons that ran along the top of the back and bound it together, something in the manner of a series of overlapping, interlocking, flexible cables. By such adaptations the backbone in the sauropod dinosaurs developed as a powerful and flexible truss, capable of withstanding the enormous stresses to which it was daily subjected.

What about the problem of excessive weight in the backbone itself? This was nicely taken care of among the sauropod dinosaurs by a sort of hollowing out of the bones in those regions where stresses were not involved. Here one can bring in the comparison of a steel truss with its V-shaped struts, or a flying buttress on a medieval cathedral. Strength and lightness were achieved simultaneously. Large cavities in the sides of the sauropod vertebrae are particularly characteristic of the skeleton in these dinosaurs.

Now we come to the comparison with a modern derrick. The neck in the sauropods is very long—say twenty feet in a big brontosaur. This was in effect a long lever with its fulcrum between the shoulders, like the long boom of a derrick. In life this boom was raised up and down, carrying on its end the head, which was the business end that controlled much of what the big dinosaur did during his lifetime, and like the boom of a derrick the long sauropod neck had a strong supporting cable to help hold it up, and to raise and lower it. This cable was an enormous ligament that ran from the shoulders to the back of the skull; and it is interesting to see in the sauropods that along the entire length of the neck the upwardly projecting spines of the vertebrae are split lengthwise with the two halves of each spine divergent, forming a big V, so that all of the spines together, one behind the other, make a long, bony trough down the top of the neck. This trough housed the living cable, the ligamentum nuchae, that gave power and movement to the neck.

The flexible boom that was the sauropod neck has at its free end a head which in comparison to the great bulk of the dinosaur is relatively small and fragile. But the comparison of head to body must be kept in mind, because when seen by itself a sauropod skull is of fair size as animal skulls go, a skull bigger than the skull of a horse or a bison, but many times smaller than the skull of a modern elephant or a hippopotamus. For an animal sixty feet and more in length, the sauropod skull is definitely small. It is of very light construction, with exceptionally large openings for the eyes and for the accommodation of the bulging jaw muscles (Plate 48). This leaves little room within the skull for the housing of the brain, which means that these dinosaurs in life had one of the smallest brains in relation to body weight that can be found among the grand parade of backboned animals through time. In short, *Brontosaurus* had a brain no bigger than your fist. He and his sauropod cousins were virtual walking automatons, going through life on their reflexes and instincts.

The jaws of the sauropod dinosaurs are not very strong, and they have along their margins a limited number of weak peg-shaped or perhaps spoon-shaped teeth. These teeth obviously were for plucking soft leaves or for biting off pliant rushes and other aquatic plants. They could hardly have served any other purpose.

How did the brontosaurs take in enough food, especially bulky green plants, with those weak teeth and jaws to fill and nourish the giant bodies or to furnish sufficient energy for moving the great legs back and forth? This question is often and quite unnecessarily regarded as a puzzler. Since we make size comparisons between brontosaurs and mammalian giants like whales and elephants, it is easy to fall into the error of making similar physiological comparisons. Here we are in a different realm from that of mechanics and structure, because we know from the comparative study of modern reptiles and mammals that they show remarkable differences in their life processes. It has been determined that the basic metabolism, the general rate of keeping alive, is for a lizard only a small percentage of what it is for a mammal of similar size, like a rodent. Small mammals that may be compared in size with most modern lizards do have a high metabolic rate; nevertheless the comparison is a valid one. Therefore we can suppose that a giant dinosaur required during the course of a day only a small fraction of the plant food that would be consumed by an equal weight of elephants. There is no mystery as to how the sauropods gathered enough food with their small jaws and teeth to keep alive and active.

Another sauropod problem concerns breathing. The nostrils in these reptiles are placed high up on the skull. Indeed, in the long, attenuated sauropod *Diplodocus,* from western North America, the nostrils are on the very top of the skull, while in the giant of giants, *Brachiosaurus,* from East Africa, the nostrils are even elevated to project above the skull roof. Elevated nostrils such as these among modern air-breathing animals indicate life in the water. Consider the crocodile, with the nostrils occupying a pair of protruding bumps like little volcanic craters, on the front of the muzzle, and the hippopotamus, with a similar arrangement. Or consider the whale, with the nostrils on the top of the skull. If the analogies are valid, it seems reasonable to think that the giant sauropods often waded in deep water—that they thrust the head at the end of the long neck above the surface, to peer about and breathe, while the body was submerged and safely hidden from predatory eyes. Yet an objection has been made to this seemingly valid reconstruction of sauropod habits, for it has been claimed that the giant reptiles would not have been able to pull air into the lungs and expel it while the body was submerged. The pressure of the water, it is claimed, would not have permitted the lungs to expand and thus draw in the air. A man, when down a few feet below the surface, cannot breathe through a

---

Figure 17. World map showing the distribution of sauropod dinosaurs

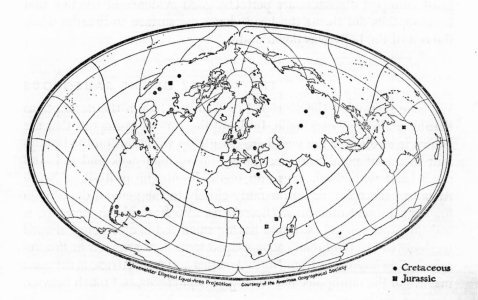

Bricemeister Elliptical Equal-Area Projection   Courtesy of the American Geographical Society

• Cretaceous
■ Jurassic

tube that extends above the water, because of the weight of the water; he must get his oxygen from a tank, under pressure. The only answer to this is that the sauropods were not men, and what men cannot do, perhaps they could. It is very likely that they could breathe with the body submerged, just as a modern whale can rise almost vertically, stick his nose out of the water, and breathe very happily, while the lungs are quite a few feet below the surface.

Footprints give some clues on this problem. R. T. Bird, who, it will be recalled, excavated the beautiful sauropod trackways in Texas that showed quite clearly how the giant reptiles walked in shallow water, found at another Texas locality some footprints of the same sauropods that seem to indicate how these dinosaurs moved along in fairly deep water. These latter trackways show only shallow prints of the front feet. It would appear that the sauropods were floating along, probably swinging the tail from side to side to help propel themselves through the water, and putting down one and then the other front foot for an additional push against the bottom. The hind feet evidently were trailing along and did not push against the bottom. If a sauropod were floating and "poling" himself along in this way, it seems possible that the body was almost or even completely submerged, and if the body was submerged the lungs were at least some distance beneath the surface. During this time the dinosaur must have been breathing.

All in all there are good reasons to think that the high nostrils in the giant sauropod dinosaurs are perfectly good evidence of the fact that these reptiles did thrust the head above the surface to breathe while the rest of the body was down under.

THE VARIETY OF THE SAUROPODS

We have seen what the sauropod pattern was like in the descriptions that have already been made. In detail the various sauropods that are known from all over the world are essentially variations on the brontosaur theme of ponderous size, heavy limbs, long neck and tail, and small head with weak jaws and teeth. *Brontosaurus* itself, a North American sauropod, conforms fairly closely to the general description for the sauropod dinosaurs. *Diplodocus,* also from North America, is a slender, attenuated sauropod having small rod-like or pencil-shaped teeth instead of the broad spoon-shaped teeth that are seen in *Brontosaurus.* *Brachiosaurus,* from North America and from Africa, is the most massive of the sauropods, not so long as *Diplodocus,* but much heavier.

In life this dinosaur may have weighed as much as fifty tons. It is different from the other sauropod dinosaurs in that the front legs are very large, so that the shoulders were high and the back sloped from shoulders to hips, giraffe-fashion. *Cetiosaurus* is a large sauropod from England. *Dicraeosaurus* is a *Diplodocus*-like sauropod from East Africa. And there are many other named genera.

There is no need to worry too much about the different names. They are indicative mainly of differences in details among the greatest of the giants. Think rather of the great bodies, half submerged in the waters of ancient swamps; think of broad, padded feet pushing down with great force against the earth; think of long necks swinging up high, so that the weak jaws could pluck leaves from the upper branches of the trees. Such was the pattern of reptilian success that continued with little change through 100 million years or more of earth history.

CHAPTER SEVEN

IGUANODONTS AND SUCH

ANCESTRAL ORNITHISCHIANS

The fossil record seems to show that during the many millions of years constituting late Triassic times the ancient saurischian dinosaurs (the early predators and the ancestors of the giant sauropods) may have been the only dinosaurs in a reptilian world. They were the first dinosaurs, they were eminently successful, and seemingly no other dinosaurs roamed the land to compete with them for living space.

Where were the ornithischian dinosaurs during these initial years of dinosaurian evolution? Indeed, were there any ornithischians, or were these particular dinosaurs yet to appear for the first time? Such questions are not easy to answer, because the evidence of the fossils is at this day incomplete and unsatisfactory.

At first sight it might seem reasonable to think that a fossil is a fossil, and with such a tangible, solid thing as a petrified bone or a group of associated bones in hand the evidence for the animal they represent would be well established. But it is not so simple, because some bones are not particularly diagnostic and are therefore anything but easy to interpret, while other bones may be quite unlike anything known, so that comparisons are difficult if not impossible to establish, thereby making solutions of the relationships of such fossils a matter of educated speculation as much as anything else. These are some of the problems we are up against when we try to look into the origins of the ornithischian dinosaurs.

According to the fossil record the ornithischians are strictly Jurassic and Cretaceous reptiles; they would seem to have made their first appearance at a later date than did the saurischians. Such is the evidence as we know it, obviously imperfect and incomplete. In spite of a century of work in field and laboratory the origin of the ornithischian dinosaurs still eludes us, so that the problem of when they got their start on what was to be a most interesting and complicated maze of evolutionary highways and byways is a moot point.

The first undoubted ornithischians are found in rocks of early Jurassic age in various parts of the world. Yet, strangely enough, these ornithischians are not particularly primitive; they suddenly appear, full blown and highly specialized. To see a truly primitive ornithischian it is necessary to journey up through time into the lower Cretaceous sediments of England, where we encounter a small dinosaur known as *Hypsilophodon,* probably the most archaic of the known ornithischians. Once again, as was the case among some of the saurischians described in earlier pages of this book, we are dealing with a structurally primitive type that lived along with its highly specialized relatives; this is not to be wondered at, for it often happens in the world of living things, and even in the man-made world. Thus in the realm of Nature, when we look at an opossum we see one of the most primitive of mammals, still surviving and doing well in this day and age; and in the realm of Man, when we sit in front of a fireplace we enjoy the inefficient warmth and comfort of a very ancient type of heating apparatus that because of its charm has survived into our modern world.

Hypsilophodon, the first described specimen of which was found on the southwestern shore of the Isle of Wight, at a locality having the delightful and improbable name of Cowleaze Chine, is one of the smaller dinosaurs, a reptile some five or six feet in length. It is therefore comparable in size to some of the early saurischians of Triassic age, and indeed is somewhat smaller than *Coelophysis,* the Triassic saurischian described in an earlier chapter as a well-known example of a comparatively primitive member of its reptilian order.

Hypsilophodon, like the early saurischians, has a thoroughly bipedal type of skeleton, with large hind limbs and small forelimbs, with the body pivoted at the hips, with a long tail serving in part as a counter-balance to the body, and with a relatively small skull carried at the end of a rather sinuous neck. In this simple recitation of general characters we are repeating what has already been said in describing the general form of *Coelophysis* and its close relatives. Beyond this the resemblances end, because when we begin to look at the details we can see that *Hypsilophodon* is a very different reptile from the early saurischian dinosaurs. The similarities in size, pose, and broad skeletal aspects between this primitive ornithischian and the primitive saurischians are indications of their derivation from a common thecodont ancestor; the differences of details, large and small, that will now occupy our attention are indications of the basic distinctness of the dinosaurs as two quite separate reptilian orders, a dichotomy that must have taken place far back in the early stages of the Triassic period.

In the first place, there is the crucial difference between *Hypsilophodon* and the primitive saurischians in the structure of the pelvis, the difference so fundamental and important that it has been used in the naming of the two dinosaurian orders. In *Hypsilophodon* as in *all* of the ornithischian dinosaurs, the pubic bone of the pelvis is parallel to the ischium, a position very similar to that of the pubis in birds. Furthermore, the pelvis in this dinosaur is characterized by a prominent forwardly projecting process of the pubis, the *prepubis,* and in addition a prominent forward projection of the ilium. Consequently the ornithischian pelvis of *Hypsilophodon* is in lateral view a sort of four-pronged affair, the front portion of the ilium and the prepubis forming the anterior prongs, the back part of the ilium and the combined pubis and ischium forming the posterior prongs.

Although the pelvis of *Hypsilophondon* is bird-like in the relationships of ischium and pubis, the bones of the skeleton are less avian than they are in the primitive saurischians, for they have lost much of the hollow nature that is so typical of the early theropod skeleton. In fact, as compared with the early coelurosaurs the skeleton of *Hypsilophodon,* especially the bones of the legs, seem rather heavy—almost "clumsy." The femur, the upper bone of the hind limb, is stout, and on the middle of its shaft is a pointed process with the point directed downwardly. This is the *fourth trochanter,* a prominent feature of the femur in many ornithischians, that served for the attachment of certain leg muscles. The hind foot in this dinosaur is not nearly so bird-like, as is the case in the primitive saurischians; rather it is a broad, heavy foot, with three principal toes and with a large, forwardly directed great toe. The fifth toe is retained as a mere remnant of bone which in life was certainly completely hidden beneath the skin.

The small forelimbs, no more than half the length of the hind limbs, were obviously grasping organs, as in the primitive saurischians, and could not have been used to any great degree for locomotion.

There are five fingers, all complete, but they are not so elongated as in the primitive saurischian hand, and the claws are not enlarged. This is a type of hand that might very easily have evolved into a wide, strong structure, adapted for walking—which is just what happened in a great many of the more advanced ornithischian dinosaurs. It is not difficult to imagine even *Hypsilophodon*, with its comparatively short forelimbs, as going down on all fours at times, especially when searching the ground for food. Kangaroos do this today, and they have forelimbs that proportionately are smaller than the forelimbs in *Hypsilophodon*.

The small skull in *Hypsilophodon* is rather deep, and is not so elongated as the skull in the early theropod dinosaurs. The teeth are limited to the sides of the upper and lower jaws, except for a few small teeth in the *premaxillary* bones, in the front part of the upper jaws. These

---

Figure 18.   The skeleton of the Cretaceous ornithopod *Hypsilophodon*, as figured by Hulke in 1873. Although the pose is not good in the light of modern knowledge, this illustration does give some idea of what a primitive ornithischian skeleton is like. About one-fifteenth natural size

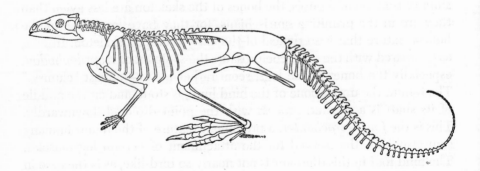

premaxillary teeth, which in most of the ornithischians have completely disappeared, are clearly vestigial remnants from a primitive ancestor. The teeth in the sides of the jaws are specialized beyond the simple shearing blades of the thecodonts or of the early saurischians, and each tooth is expanded fore and aft, and its edges are marked by prominent crenulations. Moreover, there are three prominent ridges on the outside of each tooth, running from the tooth base to its cutting edge. Obviously such teeth are adapted for a definite kind of diet, probably a vegetarian one, since teeth of this type are found in many plant-eating dinosaurs (and other plant-eating reptiles) and are not at all fitted for the cutting and tearing of meat.

That *Hypsilophodon* was a plant-eating dinosaur is further indicated by the structure of the jaws. In front the upper and lower jaws have the form of a beak that in life was without much doubt encased in a horny covering. Moreover there is an extra, new, crescentic bone known as the *predentary*, on the front of the lower jaw, that formed in life the base for the lower horny beak. This bone is so very characteristic of the ornithischian dinosaurs that they are often called the "predentate" dinosaurs. In addition, as an adaptation for a diet of plants, the *quadrate* bone of the skull, the bone that forms the articulation with the lower jaw, is elongated downwardly, so that the joint between skull and jaw is carried below the level of the teeth. This "offset" joint has the mechanical advantage of bringing all of the teeth together at about the same time, an adaptation that is frequently seen in plant-eating vertebrates.

Finally, and this is of particular interest, *Hypsilophodon* shows remnants of an armor plating, a double row of bony scutes down the middle of the back. Here we see an inheritance from its thecodont ancestors, for the thecodonts are notoriously well armored.

Perhaps the foregoing enumeration of characters will give some idea of what *Hypsilophodon* is like; of what may be expected in an ancestral ornithischian dinosaur. In life *Hypsilophodon* was, like so many primitive dinosaurs, a rather lightly built and agile reptile. It has even been suggested that this dinosaur may have been a tree climber, that it may have clambered along slanting branches to find its protection among dense foliage, out of reach of its dinosaurian enemies (Plate 51). Whether such a mode of life can be accepted for *Hypsilophodon* is a debatable question, but perhaps it is significant that the toes of the hind feet are long and supple, and the thumb is set somewhat apart from the other toes, as if it might have been suited for grasping branches.

Another argument in favor of the idea that this dinosaur sought safety in treetops is the fact that the hind limbs, while strong and well adapted for carrying *Hypsilophodon* in the semierect bipedal posture so characteristic of primitive dinosaurs, are still not elongated for rapid running, and therefore not particularly efficient for enabling the dinosaur thus to escape from predatory reptiles. The long tail may have been of some aid in helping *Hypsilophodon* to maintain its balance while perched upon the limbs of trees.

It may be remembered that *Hypsilophodon* has a rather small skull, but among the ornithischians as a group the size of the skull varies widely, and some of these dinosaurs have extraordinarily large skulls. The several openings in the skull, so constant among the saurischians, are variably developed in the ornithischians, and there is a strong trend toward reduction or even elimination of the openings in front of the eyes, and frequently of reduction of the temporal openings behind the eyes. Adaptations for feeding upon plants, as illustrated by the jaws of *Hypsilophodon*, are universal within this order of dinosaurs, and include, in addition to the offset joint of the jaw and the cutting teeth, already mentioned, a high bony process, the coronoid, arising on the outer surface of the lower jaw, and extending up along the side of the skull. This process is for the attachment of muscles that close the lower jaw, and increases the efficiency of chewing.

The vertebrae in front of the pelvis join each other with a sort of ball-and-socket arrangement which adds strength and flexibility to the column with the convex surface on the front of each vertebra and the articulating concave surface on its back face. These are called opisthocoelous vertebrae. The vertebrae are further strengthened by ossification of the tendons of the back muscles, to form a sort of bony latticework along the back. The bones of the wrist are often rather long, and the joint between the lower leg and the foot comes in the middle of the ankle, as it does among the saurischian dinosaurs.

Having looked at *Hypsilophodon*, a primitive ornithischian dinosaur, and having reviewed briefly the salient ornithischian characters that are for the most part already established in *Hypsilophodon*, we may now turn our attention to the evolutionary patterns among the Ornithischia. If the reader wishes to turn back to the first chapter of this book, he will see a diagram that shows how the ornithischians developed along four main evolutionary lines during Jurassic and Cretaceous times. These lines, the ornithischian suborders in most systems of reptilian classification, are generally designated as the Ornithopoda—the ornithopods, or

duck-billed dinosaurs, and their relatives; the Stegosauria—the stegosaurs, or plated dinosaurs; the Ankylosauria—the ankylosaurs, or armored dinosaurs; and the Ceratopsia—the ceratopsians, or horned dinosaurs.

Hypsilophodon is a primitive ornithopod, and it would seem that
this particular dinosaur and its close relatives approximate in many
ways the central ornithischian stem, its "close relatives" being other
hypsilophodonts and the rather similar camptosaurs. From the hypsilophodonts and the camptosaurs (which in formal terms may be regarded
as constituting two dinosaurian families) there evolved the more specialized types of ornithopod dinosaurs; the large iguanodonts, the bizarre
and truly enigmatic pachycephalosaurs, and the varied and highly successful trachodonts, or duck-billed dinosaurs.

Camptosaurus is a reptile of late Jurassic age, the remains of which
have been found in the Morrison formation of western North America.
This is the geologic horizon that has yielded so many interesting dinosaurs—the giant swamp-dwelling sauropods like *Brontosaurus* and
Diplodocus, the powerful predators like *Allosaurus* and *Ceratosaurus,*
and other varied types. In the days of his life, *Camptosaurus* was sur-

---

Figure 19. The Upper Jurassic ornithopod dinosaur *Camptosaurus* in bipedal
and quadrupedal positions. About one-sixteenth natural size

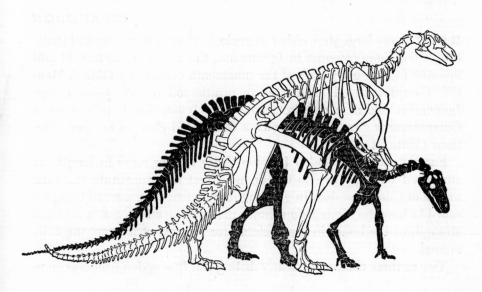

rounded by many giants, which must have made things interesting for this dinosaur, because it was not large and it certainly was an inoffensive reptile.

The skeletons of *Camptosaurus* from the Morrison beds show a considerable range in size. The smallest ones are only four feet or so in length, while the largest skeletons may be more than fifteen feet long. Perhaps these skeletons represent several species of camptosaurs of different sizes; perhaps they indicate growth stages in a single species. Be that as it may, the known skeletons of *Camptosaurus* show a striking uniformity of structure, so that there is little besides size that differentiates one from another.

Camptosaurus shows the various ornithischian characters that already have been listed, and there is no point in enumerating the details of its anatomy—this would be mere repetition of what already has been said. Briefly this dinosaur can be characterized as a bipedal type with the diagnostic ornithischian form of pelvis. The hind limbs are very heavy, indicating great power. The small forelimbs are stout, and the hands, each provided with a full complement of fingers, are broad. Thus it would appear that *Camptosaurus* very likely was able to get down on all four feet with ease, as it may have done frequently while feeding. The skull is relatively small and of the generalized ornithischian type that already has been described. We see in this ornithopod a plant-eating dinosaur, perhaps less agile than *Hypsilophodon*, perhaps more definitely a ground-living type than its primitive relative.

IGUANODON

It is not a very large step, either in geologic time or in anatomical structure, from *Camptosaurus* to *Iguanodon*, the dinosaur discovered and described in the early days of the nineteenth century by Gideon Mantell. *Camptosaurus* is primarily an ornithopod of late Jurassic age, *Iguanodon* one of early Cretaceous age. *Iguanodon* is in essence a *Camptosaurus* grown large—with a few added changes or specializations (Plate 54).

For instance, *Iguanodon* is some thirty feet or more in length, as compared with the five to ten or more feet that constitute the total length of *Camptosaurus*. In growing into a giant from a small *Camptosaur*-like ancestor, *Iguanodon* shows the necessary increase in size and strength of the bones in the skeleton for support of a large, ungainly animal.

Two or three characters clearly distinguish *Iguanodon* from its camptosaurid ancestors. For example, the pubic bone, the lower bone of the pelvis that runs backwardly in these dinosaurs, parallel to the ischium, is in *Iguanodon* somewhat reduced as compared to its condition in *Camptosaurus*. Again, *Iguanodon* has more teeth in the sides of the jaws than does *Camptosaurus*—teeth that are crowded into several longitudinal rows ranging along the length of the jaws. These numerous teeth form a dental battery in which replacing teeth are constantly erupting to take the place of teeth that have been worn out and are dropping from the jaws. Furthermore, the forelimbs in *Iguanodon* are even larger proportionately than they are in *Camptosaurus;* evidently *Iguanodon* was capable of fairly efficient quadrupedal locomotion, even though it probably spent most of its time as a bipedal dinosaur. And finally, *Iguanodon* is particularly noted for the fact that it has a large, spike-like thumb.

As related in Chapter Two, when *Iguanodon* was first discovered the early students of dinosaurs thought that it was a rhinoceros-like quadruped, with a horn on its nose, and so it was that when Sir Richard Owen and Waterhouse Hawkins constructed the full-scale model of *Iguanodon* for the Crystal Palace grounds in London, they made it look something like an oversized reptilian rhinoceros, with a covering of scales like the tiles on a roof. The model is still there to be seen, and in spite of the fact that we know now that it is all wrong the restoration is remarkably life-like and effective. As one looks across a moat at the huge animal, partly hidden by the trees and other vegetation that cover the little island on which it stands, along with the restorations of other prehistoric animals, this dinosaur seems to come to life—as if it were about to push clumsily through the trees and bushes in an effort to escape from prying eyes (Plate 8).

In 1877 a magnificent series of *Iguanodon* skeletons came to light in a coal mine near Bernissart, Belgium, as mentioned in Chapter Three. These skeletons, together with other skeletons found in England, afford very full knowledge as to the anatomy of *Iguanodon,* so that this is one of the most completely known among the dinosaurs. What one skeleton of the series lacks another supplies. And the skeletons show differences in size and other variations that might be expected in a group of animals belonging to a single population.

THE DOME-HEADED DINOSAURS

Some very strange ornithopods, known as pachycephalosaurs, have been found in late Cretaceous sediments in western North America and eastern Asia. At the present time our knowledge of these dinosaurs rests upon scanty evidence: a few skulls and partial skulls, and portions of skeletons. It is all too little, and all too tantalizing, and one can only hope that much more material will be discovered in the future.

The pachycephalosaurs, based upon a very small form, *Stegoceras* (let's not confuse this with the well-known plated dinosaur *Stego-saurus*), and from a large type, *Pachycephalosaurus,* are ornithopods in which the skeleton is, as far as we can tell, of the generalized bipedal type. It is the skull that makes these dinosaurs look so strange to us, for in the pachycephalosaurs (plate 55) the skull roof is thickened and expanded into a great bulging dome formed of solid bone, which may reach a thickness of more than ten inches. The growth of this bony dome has crowded out the upper temporal opening (one of the very characteristic features of most dinosaurs) and has altered the shape of the entire back portion of the skull. There are knobs and short spikes around the domed skull roof and on the nose.

Why should these dinosaurs have had such outlandish skulls yet such generalized ornithopod skeletons? It is not an easy question to answer. Did the thick dome afford special protection to the brain of the pachycephalosaurs?

The discovery of *Pachycephalosaurus* was a bright and interesting event in the history of paleontology. This dinosaur was found by a group of dedicated amateur paleontologists in Ekalaka, Montana, a group composed of high-school students, their teachers, their parents, and their friends, who spent many happy spare hours in exploring the Cretaceous badlands in the vicinity of the town. These enterprising people have discovered and collected various dinosaur bones during the course of the last decade or two, including a complete skeleton of a duck-billed dinosaur, but *Pachycephalosaurus* was their great prize. When they found the skull, which at this date is the only known fossil of *Pachycephalosaurus,* they realized that the specimen was new to science and of inestimable value. They very generously presented it to the American Museum of Natural History, where this unusual dinosaur could be studied in detail, where its description could be published and distributed to the scientific world, and where it would be carefully kept in perpetuity as a scientific treasure. Would that there were more part-time paleontological enthusiasts as generous and as enlightened as the members of the Carter County Geological Society, in Ekalaka, Montana!

CHAPTER EIGHT

DUCK-BILLED DINOSAURS

HADROSAURUS AND CLAOSAURUS

The evolution of the ornithopod dinosaurs from camptosaur ancestors progressed along varied lines during the Cretaceous period: along the line that led to the iguanodonts, in a sense overgrown camptosaurs; along the line that led to the puzzling dome-headed pachycephalosaurs; and above all, along the line that culminated in the hadrosaurs or duck-billed dinosaurs, a large family of ornithopods known from numerous skulls and skeletons, and characteristic of the Upper Cretaceous deposits in North America and eastern Asia. Among the dinosaurs only the ceratopsians, or horned dinosaurs, to be considered on subsequent pages of this book, show a degree of evolutionary variety approaching or equal to that of the hadrosaurs. Among the dinosaurs no other group, not even the horned dinosaurs, presents so many challenging problems of interpretation of varied anatomical characters as do the duck-billed dinosaurs. All of which makes the duck-bills a fascinating group to study, and at the same time a group that leads the paleontologist into frustrating experiences.

It will be recalled that the first dinosaur skeleton to be discovered in North America was a hadrosaur, found at Haddonfield, New Jersey, in 1856, and studied and described by Joseph Leidy, the pioneer American paleontologist. Although a few fragments of dinosaurs had been found on this continent and described prior to the discovery of *Hadrosaurus,* our knowledge of North American dinosaurs had its true beginnings with Leidy's work on this headless skeleton from the marl pits just across the Delaware River from Philadelphia. The original *Hadrosaurus* was the first of a very considerable series of skeletons that have been unearthed in North America, especially in the western states and provinces, during the century elapsing since Leidy's time; though it was the first duck-billed skeleton to be discovered, it is one of the latest of the hadrosaurs, geologically speaking.

For a logical beginning of hadrosaurian history, let us look at the oldest North American hadrosaur, *Claosaurus,* based upon a partial skeleton on display at the Yale Peabody Museum. This fossil was found in western Kansas, in the Niobrara formation, by collectors working for Professor Marsh in 1871, during those lusty days when the collecting of dinosaurs in western North America was an adventurous and colorful undertaking. The specimen was immediately shipped back to New Haven, and in 1872 Marsh described it as a species of *Hadrosaurus.* But in the same year he came to the realization that this fossil could hardly be included within the same genus as *Hadrosaurus,* so he quite rightly renamed it *Claosaurus.*

Claosaurus is much smaller than the other hadrosaurs of North America, the skeleton being ten or twelve feet in length—perhaps a third the length of hadrosaurs such as *Anatosaurus* or *Corythosaurus.* Otherwise the skeleton of this reptile is of the characteristic hadrosaurian type, and any qualitative differences to be seen between the bones of *Claosaurus* and those of the later and presumably more advanced hadrosaurs are very slight to all but the most critically discerning eye. One minor difference is that *Claosaurus* does possess the remnant of a first toe in the hind foot, a feature whereby it resembles the camptosaurs and iguanodonts and differs from other hadrosaurs, in which this digit has been lost. Because *Claosaurus,* like the original *Hadrosaurus,* lacks a skull, we unfortunately are in the dark as to what the head of this dinosaur might be like. Some fragments of jaws, however, are preserved, and they show that *Claosaurus* has small teeth, proportionately broader and more primitive than the teeth in the later hadrosaurs. Of course, it would be nice to know something about the skull of *Claosaurus,* because this hadrosaur is, by reason of its geological age and its anatomical characters as far as we know them, a logical ancestor for the later hadrosaurs of North America. A skull of this dinosaur would very probably help to bridge the gap between the specialized hadrosaur skulls, of which we have such abundant knowledge, and the more primitive camptosaur-like types. We can only make the best of this situation by consoling ourselves with the thought that the paleontologist is in the fortunate position of having some reasonable expectations that something new may come out of the ground—and every now and then something new does turn up to help solve some of the puzzles that have plagued him. So perhaps some day next year, or ten years from now, or perhaps in the next century, a good skull of *Claosaurus* will be discovered in the Niobrara beds of western Kansas.

In the meantime we can best build up a picture of a characteristic hadrosaurian dinosaur on the basis of one of the geologically younger forms, of which complete skeletons are known. Among the skeletons of hadrosaurs displayed in North American museums are two fine specimens of the genus *Anatosaurus,* on display at the American Museum of Natural History in New York (Plate 57), the two skeletons of the same genus at the United States National Museum in Washington, and still other skeletons at the Denver Museum, the University of Michigan Museum, and the Yale Peabody Museum. The Yale specimen, by the way, is the first dinosaur *skeleton* to have been mounted for display in an American museum (which is not to be confused with the *plaster restoration* of the skeleton of the original *Hadrosaurus* from New Jersey, which was set up in the Philadelphia Academy of Natural Sciences by Waterhouse Hawkins in 1868). *Anatosaurus,* although one of the last of the hadrosaurs, living during the very latest stages of Cretaceous history, was in some ways a "conservative" type of duck-billed dionsaur, and therefore is useful for our present purpose.

THE HADROSAURIAN PATTERN

Most of the hadrosaurs were large dinosaurs, and none of them was particularly small. The skeleton of *Anatosaurus,* for example, is thirty or forty feet in length, and in life this dinosaur probably weighed as much as five or six tons, perhaps more. The hind limbs are very strong and heavy, and the front limbs are comparatively slender and light. In this respect *Anatosaurus* displays the bipedalism that is so characteristic of all of the ornithopod dinosaurs, a bipedalism that reflects

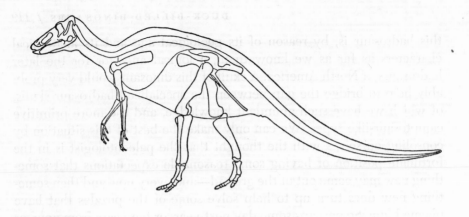

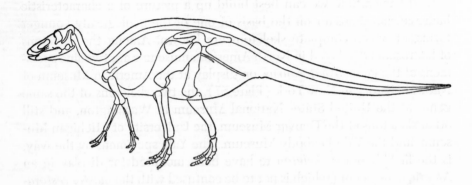

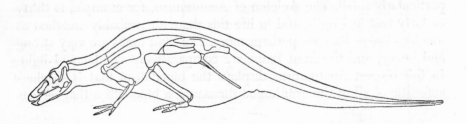

Figure 20. The Upper Cretaceous hadrosaurian *Anatosaurus* in a bipedal walking pose (above); in a quadrupedal walking pose (middle); and in a resting pose (below)

their ultimate ancestry in small, agile progenitors. It is quite evident, however, that the habit of walking about on the hind legs was not so extremely developed in the great hadrosaurs as it was in their contemporaries, the giant carnivorous or meat-eating dinosaurs, because the forelimbs in the duck-billed types are of such size that they would have been quite functional for walking about in a quadrupedal fashion, and the hands, instead of being the grasping organs that so typify the meat-eating dinosaurs, are long, compact organs, with the fingers terminating in broad, flat bones rather than in claws. Thus we gain an impression of a dinosaur that frequently got down on all four feet, especially when it was feeding, but one that habitually would stand up on its long, strong hind legs to walk or to run. *Anatosaurus* was obviously an adept swimmer, as indicated by a deep, strong tail and by other anatomical characters that will shortly be discussed.

The hadrosaurians are called duck-billed dinosaurs for a good reason, because the front of the skull and the lower jaws in these reptiles are elongated and broadened to form a sort of "beak," shaped very much like a gigantic duck bill. This broad, flat bill, so nicely exemplified in the skull and jaws of *Anatosaurus*, was evidently a structure for probing and shoveling in mud on the bottom of lakes and streams, or perhaps even along the shores of the sea. The "bill" of *Anatosaurus* is devoid of teeth, and it seems likely that in life both its upper and lower portions were covered by a horny sheath.

Because of the elongation of the anterior bones of the skull, and the front of the lower jaw to form the bill, the eye in *Anatosaurus*, as in all of the hadrosaurs, occupies a position far back in the skull, in a way somewhat comparable to the position of the eye in a modern herbivorous mammal such as a horse or a cow. Likewise, as in many modern plant-eating mammals, the back of the skull in *Anatosaurus* is rather deep, which in part is an adaptation allowing for the attachment of strong muscles to activate the jaws.

Indeed, the jaw mechanism in *Anatosaurus* and in the other hadrosaurs may be compared with the jaw mechanism in present-day plant-eating mammals, and the comparison will show that in these ancient dinosaurs there had evolved a system of joints, bony levers, and powerful muscles that performed in different ways the same functions that are accomplished by the joints, the levers, and the muscles in the jaws of modern horses or cattle or elephants. Among plant eaters the problem is to bring all of the cheek teeth together at about the same time, so that the teeth can function as an efficient mill for crushing and grinding fairly tough and hard plant fibers. This is done by having an offset joint between the skull and the lower jaws, a joint that is not in line with the grinding surfaces of the teeth. In the hadrosaurs, as in so many plant-eating dinosaurs, the offset joint was

Figure 21. The mechanics of jaw movements in the hadrosaurian dinosaur *Corythosaurus*. This figure shows the direction of pull of the strong adductor muscles (A.E., Ps.) that closed the jaws; of the muscles (A.P., Pt.) that pulled the lower jaw forward and back; and the muscle (D.M.) that opened the jaws

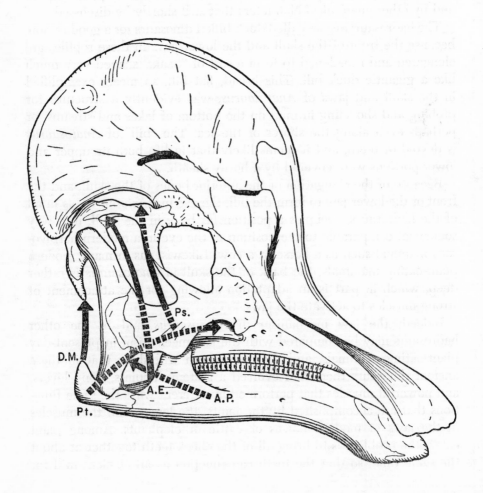

attained, as it was in their camptosaur cousins, by a lengthening of the quadrate bone on each side of the skull, the bone that forms at its lower end the bearing on which the lower jaw moves, thereby carrying the articulation for the jaw below the tooth line. (In modern mammals—including all who read this—the same effect is reached by having the joint between skull and jaw elevated far above the tooth line.) Furthermore, *Anatosaurus* and all of its hadrosaurian relatives have a long coronoid bone that projects up from the outer side of the lower jaw to form a lever at right angles to the axis of the jaw. Strong muscles that attach to this bone are important for closing the jaw with power and speed. (In modern mammals there is a coronoid process on the jaw for the same purpose.)

The teeth of *Anatosaurus* are most remarkable, and exceedingly difficult to describe (Plate 63). The reader is advised to look at Figure 22, time and again, while reading this description. In effect, there is a battery of imbricated, interlocked teeth on each side both above and below—four batteries of grinding teeth, two to each side, that oppose each other. Each battery may contain several hundred teeth, so that there can be a thousand or more teeth in the mouth of a hadrosaur such as *Anatosaurus*. The teeth are prisms, arranged in alternating rows and tightly pressed together, so that in their totality they form a sort of pavement of teeth. The outer side of each upper tooth and the inner side of each lower tooth is covered with a lozenge-shaped or elongated coating of enamel, which is harder than the dentine, of which the rest of the tooth is composed. The upper teeth kept pushing down throughout the life of the animal; the lower teeth constantly pushed up; and as the fully erupted teeth above and below came together they wore against each other and against the food, with a constant grinding action. The difference in hardness between enamel and dentine increased the effectiveness of the grinding surfaces. As each tooth was ground down to a remnant of its complete size, it was succeeded by a new tooth coming down, or up, to take its place. This description almost surely is inadequate and confusing; the only way to understand the teeth in hadrosaurs is to see the originals, and as a next best step, to see good pictures of the originals. So look at the figure again, and study it for a while. If it is examined carefully and at some length, the arrangement and function of hadrosaur teeth should become reasonably clear.

The reason for such a complicated system of batteries of teeth is that the hadrosaurs evidently fed upon plants that contained large amounts of abrasive silica (sand is silica). The numerous teeth arranged in batteries, with constant replacement going on, provided a mechanism that overcame the effects of excessive wear. (Today horses and cows meet the same problem by having a limited number

Figure 22. Cross-section of the upper and lower jaws and teeth in a duck-billed dinosaur. *Abbreviations:* A—lower jaw; B—maxillary bone of the skull; C—contact of upper and lower teeth; D—much worn teeth; E—partially worn teeth; F—successional teeth that will replace D and E; H—groove in lower jaw; I—inner side of jaws

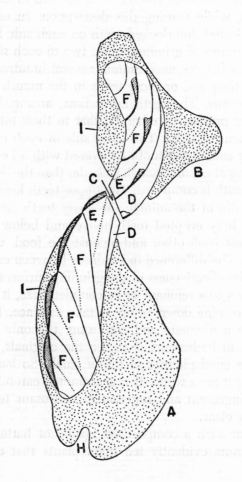

of very long cheek teeth that erupt constantly as they are worn down by the siliceous herbage on which the animals feed. In young horses and cattle most of the length of the cheek teeth is buried within the jaws; in old age the teeth are almost completely erupted and are short, which means that a large part of each tooth has disappeared through wear.)

The elongated, highly specialized skull with its complex batteries of teeth is carried at the end of a rather long, sinuous neck. In *Anatosaurus* and the other hadrosaurs there are about fifteen vertebrae comprising the neck, as compared with the ten vertebrae that are usual in most of the dinosaurs, and these added to the vertebrae of the back make a total of about thirty to thirty-four vertebrae in front of the pelvis. The transverse processes of the vertebrae in the back, which in most reptiles extend straight out on each side, in the hadrosaurs, as in other ornithischian dinosaurs, extend obliquely upward.

The pelvis in *Anatosaurus* is attached to the spinal column by a long sacrum, composed of eight vertebrae. In most of the hadrosaurs this sacral attachment involves seven or eight vertebrae, and thus there is a strong union at this crucial pivot, which of course is essential in a giant bipedal dinosaur weighing many tons.

As mentioned above, the tail of *Anatosaurus* and of all of the hadrosaurs is deep and long. It is obviously a strong tail, and during the life of the animal was evidently a powerful scull for swimming, probably used by the dinosaur in much the same fashion that a crocodile or an alligator uses its tail for propulsion through the water. In many of the hadrosaurs there is a strong lattice of crossed tendon bones on the back over the pelvis and over the base of the tail, and these, the ossified tendons of powerful back and tail muscles, must in life have increased greatly the strength of the spinal column (Plate 62).

Articulating with the strong ornithischian pelvis is the long, heavy femur, or upper leg bone, and below it the almost equally long and heavy tibia with its parallel, rod-like fibula. The hind foot, which is very heavy, is limited to three heavy toes that terminate in broad, rounded hoofs, rather than claws. It has already been said that the forelimb in *Anatosaurus* is slender but of such size as to have been an aid in occasional quadrupedal locomotion. There are four fingers in the hand.

In the American Museum of Natural History in New York, and in the Senckenberg Museum in Frankfurt am Main, Germany, there are remarkable fossilized mummies of the hadrosaur *Anatosaurus* (Plate

58). Both of these mummies were discovered in Wyoming many years ago by Mr. Charles Sternberg, one of the early collectors of fossil vertebrates, and were acquired from him by the institutions in which they now repose. In each of these dinosaurs most of the skin has been preserved through petrification. Consequently we need not make conjectures as to the external appearance of *Anatosaurus,* except so far as the color of the skin is concerned, for the structure and texture of the skin are shown with great clarity and in detail in these two remarkable fossils.

Anatosaurus was covered with a leathery skin, not unlike the skin that covers much of the body in modern crocodiles and alligators (Plate 59). There are no bony ossicles in the skin of *Anatosaurus*— no large scutes such as those that range in rows down the back of a crocodile; rather the skin consists of a "ground area" of small tubercles, somewhat like what one sees in the skin of the modern Gila monster (that poisonous lizard living in Arizona and other southwestern states), with interspersed clusters of large flat tubercles arranged at fairly regular intervals over the body. It is interesting to note that there are webs of skin between the fingers in *Anatosaurus,* which is what might be expected in a water-loving reptile. There are seemingly no webs between the toes. Another detail shown by these mummies is the presence of a fold of skin, a sort of frill, that extends down the middle of the back from the head almost to the end of the tail. The function of such a fold is not clear to those who try to interpret the habits of dinosaurs long since extinct, but certainly to our eyes it adds an elegant touch to the general appearance of these duck-billed hadrosaurs.

From such evidence we are able to get a truly intimate glimpse into the past—to see what a dinosaur that lived 80 or 90 million years ago looked like in detail. As mentioned above, only the color of the animal need be guessed at. Perhaps the clusters of large flat tubercles indicate a color pattern on *Anatosaurus*—perhaps not. The conservative approach is to suppose that these dinosaurs, like most big crocodiles, were of fairly dull coloration, and not flashily colored as are many of our small lizards and snakes.

How is it that these two mummies were fossilized and preserved through millions of years of earth history? In both specimens the skin is tightly stretched over the abdominal region and over some other parts of the body, as if the animal had become a dry cadaver after its death. This dry cadaver was then probably buried by drifting sands so that it was not subjected to the oxidizing action of ground waters. But there was enough ground moisture to carry minerals that infiltrated the skin, and thus in time the skin, as well as the bones, was petrified. All of which was a fortunate chain of circumstances for the modern paleontologist.

It is an interesting fact that quite a number of duck-billed dinosaurs show large patches of fossilized skin in association with the skeleton. In most instances, however, it would appear that the preservation of the skin may have been accomplished under wetter conditions than what has been assumed to have been the case for the two mummies of *Anatosaurus*.

THE FLAT-HEADED HADROSAURS

Having made a somewhat detailed excursion into the anatomy of *Anatosaurus*, it is now possible to make a sweeping survey of the various other hadrosaurs. This will be done mainly by looking at the skulls, for it is by a study of the head that one may follow the various trends of hadrosaurian evolution. The duck-billed dinosaurs are all much alike in the body, the differences being largely those of size and of a few minor and rather subtle details of structure. But in the development of the skull these dinosaurs show a wide range of evolutionary development.

Anatosaurus is, as has been said, a conservative type of duck-billed dinosaur, even though in geologic age it is the last surviving member of this group of dinosaurs. It is one of the "flat-headed" hadrosaurs, so called because the skull is low and flat, without any bony growths or excrescences on its top. It is a member of one branch of hadrosaurian evolution that stands in sharp contrast to the various "crested" hadrosaurs, the duck-billed dinosaurs in which the skulls are diversely decorated with bony crests of different forms. More of them later.

For the moment, let us consider briefly the several flat-headed types. *Anatosaurus* is found not only in the latest North American Cretaceous sediments of *Lance* age, but also in the somewhat earlier *Edmonton* beds of Alberta, an indication that this genus of duck-billed dinosaurs was sufficiently successful to have lived through quite a few million years of geologic history. In the Edmonton, too, is *Edmontosaurus*, a dinosaur very much like *Anatosaurus*, but of greater size. In fact, *Edmontosaurus* is very probably the largest of all hadrosaurs, a very ponderous reptile forty feet or more in length.

Far to the south of the Edmonton sediments, as they are exposed along the Red River in Alberta, are the correlative *Kirtland* beds of New Mexico, containing fossils very similar to the ones found in Canada, and in the Kirtland formation is the duck-billed dinosaur *Kritosaurus,* a type that is also found in the even older *Belly River* sediments of Alberta. *Kritosaurus* is a flat-headed hadrosaur in which the nasal bone is expanded upwardly in its back portion to form a low median ridge on the front of the skull. Or to put it in simpler language, *Kritosaurus* has a sort of Roman nose, which gives it a distinctive, if not a patrician, appearance.

As for the other supposedly flat-headed hadrosaurs in North America, there is not much that can be said about their relationships, because in them the skull is either unknown or imperfectly known. Consequently dinosaurs that have been described for as long a time as *Hadrosaurus* and *Trachodon* are placed in this group largely because they are *inferred* to have had skulls without crests. It is an inference only, and to this day there has never been enough material found in the Cretaceous beds of eastern North America to show, for example, whether *Hadrosaurus* was truly a flat-headed or a crested type. As in the case of *Claosaurus,* mentioned at the beginning of this chapter, we shall have to wait patiently until some future day when a skull will turn up somewhere in New Jersey, to indicate just where *Hadrosaurus* belongs in the evolutionary tree of the duck-billed dinosaurs.

While the duck-billed dinosaurs were evolving along different lines of adaptation in North America, there was a similar development of related hadrosaurs in eastern Asia, the evidence for which is indicated by fossils found in Mongolia, in eastern China, and in the northernmost island of the Japanese archipelago. Several partial skeletons have been described, and like *Hadrosaurus* and some of the other North American forms these are tantalizing fossils because they so frequently lack skulls or have only fragmentary skulls that fail to give us the evidence we need in order to determine precise relationships.

Bactrosaurus, one of the better known of the Asiatic hadrosaurs, is an enigmatic specimen in that the skull is of the flat-headed type, while the skeleton shows characters that might be expected in a crested form. Here is one of those cases of conflicting evidence that not infrequently confuses the paleontologist. For the time being, and until better fossils are known, let us consider *Bactrosaurus* as one of the flat-headed hadrosaurs, something like *Anatosaurus,* but perhaps not so large, and with a less-elongated skull in which the bill is not so broad and flat as in the American flat-headed duck-bills.

Mandschurosaurus, Tanius and *Nipponosaurus* are all known from various skeletons in which the skulls are not completely preserved, yet the evidence would seem to indicate that these may be flat-headed hadrosaurs. (*Mandschurosaurus* is almost certainly a flat-headed type. The fossils of *Tanius* and *Nipponosaurus* found to date are, like the known materials of *Bactrosaurus,* equivocal, and a positive judgment as to the relationships of these hadrosaurs cannot as yet be made.) The localities at which these fossils have been discovered indicate how widely the duck-billed dinosaurs ranged through eastern Asia during late Cretaceous times. *Mandschurosaurus,* for example, has been found in northern Manchuria, in Mongolia, and in Indo-China. *Tanius* is known from several specimens from the province of Shantung, in northern China. *Nipponosaurus* is based upon a partial skeleton that turned up in a coal mine on the island of Sakhalin.

In addition there have been some remains of crested duck-bills found in Asia: *Saurolophus* from Mongolia, *Tsintaosaurus* from Shantung, and *Jaxartosaurus* in Asiatic Russia, not far from the fabled city of Samarkand. We shall now turn to a discussion of the crested hadrosaurs, in the course of which these Asiatic types will be included.

THE CRESTED HADROSAURS

To a casual museum visitor a display of crested hadrosaur skulls is at first glance confusing and puzzling. Here, indeed, is remarkable variety within a single group of dinosaurs! How is one to arrange such a rich array of types to show the proper interrelationships of these dinosaurs, each with the others, and how is one to interpret their evolutionary history? Many trained paleontologists have applied themselves to the problem of the crested hadrosaurs during the course of several decades, and their cumulative studies have established considerable order among these fossils, and at the same time have left a few problems still unsolved.

First of all, it seems apparent that the crested hadrosaurs can be grouped in two large subdivisions, which can be called the Saurolophinae, or solid-crested forms, and the Lambeosaurinae, or hollow-crested forms. The first of these two groups (subfamilies in a formal system of classification) is small; the second is large. The formation of the crest in the first group is relatively simple; in the second group it is rather complex.

Four genera make up the solid-crested hadrosaurs: *Prosaurolophus* from the Belly River beds of Alberta; *Saurolophus* from the overlying and therefore younger Edmonton formation of the same region, and from correlative sediments in Mongolia; *Tsintaosaurus* from Upper Cretaceous beds of Shantung, China; and *Jaxartosaurus* from Russia. These dinosaurs may be thought of as flat-headed types in which certain bones have become enlarged to form crests on the top of the skull.

In *Prosaurolophus* the skull is in many respects like the skull of *Anatosaurus*, but the bill is relatively smaller, being shorter and not so widely flared in front. The nasal bones in *Prosaurolophus* extend up and back to a position above the eyes, where they meet an up-

Figure 23. Evolution of the hadrosaurian dinosaurs as shown by the development of the skull. The shaded areas show the varied development of the premaxillary and nasal bones

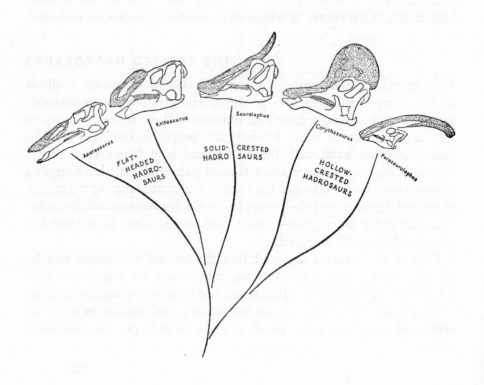

growth of the frontal bones, the bones that form a part of the top of the brain case, to form a low crest.

In *Saurolophus* the crest, formed of the nasal bones buttressed on the sides by the frontal bones, extends back and up as a long, sharp prong or spike above the skull roof. In *Tsintaosaurus* the nasal crest attains its most extreme development among the saurolophines, for it extends up as a long, slender, vertical or even forwardly inclined rod from a position immediately above the eyes. The upper end of the crest is expanded into a sort of fore-and-aft blade, instead of having the form of a blunt point as is the case in *Saurolophus*. In *Prosaurolophus* and *Saurolophus* the crest is solid, with no internal cavities of consequence, but in *Tsintaosaurus* the nasal crest is hollow and tube-like, with a closed internal cavity somewhat expanded in its lower portion.

What might have been the function of the crest in the so-called solid-crested hadrosaurs? One might suppose that the crest in *Saurolophus* was a sort of horn, although the surface of the bone does not indicate that there was any kind of a horny covering, as would be expected if the crest served as a true weapon of combat. Rather it would appear as if the crest were covered with skin. Indeed, it has been suggested by Chinese and Russian paleontologists that the nasal crest in *Tsintaosaurus* not only was covered with skin but also supported a flap or vane of skin that extended in front of the bony rod and as far forward as the middle region of the beak.

Our interpretations as to the function of the crest in these dinosaurs must remain largely within the realm of speculation. As for *Prosaurolophus*, the crest is so comparatively small that any guess as to its possible function is even more speculative than in the case of *Saurolophus* and *Tsintaosaurus*. Perhaps one positive thought can be brought out of this guessing game: the crests in the saurolophines do give the twentieth century paleontologist a handy character for recognizing and classifying these dinosaurs.

The late Cretaceous sediments of Alberta, Canada, specifically the Belly River beds and the overlying Edmonton beds as they are exposed along the Red Deer River, have yielded an astonishing array of crested hadrosaurs—a varied series of related dinosaurs that is perhaps without equal. It is indeed remarkable that so many different dinosaurs, all closely related within the confines of a single subfamily, should occur in so limited a geographic area. There can be no doubt that these dinosaurs abounded throughout western North America, in addition to the area that is now Alberta, during late Cretaceous times. They must have wandered across the Cretaceous lands in great numbers and in varied form, much as today the many kinds of antelopes drift across the African veldt in great herds. The comparison is a valid one, because the hadrosaurs were the large plant eaters of their day just as the great hoofed mammals are the plant eaters of the present continents. Let us look at this parade of crested hadrosaurs that within the past half-century have emerged from their resting places in the cliffs and banks of the Red Deer River. They may be lined up as follows:

Procheneosaurus—a rather small hadrosaur in which the premaxillary and nasal bones are somewhat expanded to form a hollow crest that juts up bulbously above the roof of the skull.

Cheneosaurus—a moderate-sized hadrosaur with a hollow crest on the skull formed by the nasal and premaxillary bones and generally shaped like the crest in *Procheneosaurus.*

Lambeosaurus—a large hadrosaur in which the premaxillary and nasal bones are greatly expanded to form a hollow, hatchet-shaped crest above the skull roof, with a sort of accessory spine extending back, beyond the back limit of the skull.

Corythosaurus—a large hadrosaur in which the premaxillary and nasal bones are enormously expanded to form a hollow, helmet-like crest that covers the entire top of the skull.

Hypacrosaurus—a very large hadrosaur in which the premaxillary and nasal bones are greatly expanded to form a hollow, helmet-like crest, similar to, but more "swollen" than, the crest in *Corythosaurus.*

Parasaurolophus—a very large hadrosaur in which the premaxillary and nasal bones are remarkably expanded into a long, hollow, curving tube that extends far back over the shoulder region from the top of the skull. This great tube is almost twice the length of the skull.

Please note that in each of these crested hadrosaurs not only the shape but also the hollow nature of the crest has been emphasized. This is the crux of the matter, for in all of these hollow-crested hadrosaurs the nasal passage running from the nostrils to the throat loops up into the crest. In the simple types, such as *Procheneosaurus,* the looping of the nasal passage is correlatively simple, but as the crests become increasingly large and ornate the nasal passage becomes increasingly elongated and complicated.

In *Corythosaurus*, for example, the nasal passage bends upwardly into the crest, where it makes a wide curve of 180 degrees, like a Mississippi River meander, and then descends through the back of the palatal region into the throat. Similar courses for the nasal loop can be traced in other helmeted hadrosaurs, such as *Lambeosaurus* and *Hypacrosaurus*. In *Parasaurolophus* the nasal loop is even more extended, for it runs from the nostrils to the end of the long crest, following a passage in the upper part of the crest, and then turns the corner to return through a passage in the lower part of the crest parallel to the upper passage, where finally, after having reached that part of the crest above and immediately in front of the eye, it descends to the throat. Such are the facts concerning the crest in the lambeosaurs or hollow-crested hadrosaurs. What do they mean?

Paleontologists, anatomists, and physiologists have been struggling with this problem for many years, producing a spate of theories that can be argued about ad infinitum, but very little that is capable of proof. What are some of the ideas that have been advanced in attempts to interpret the development of the hollow crests and their contained looped nasal passages?

To begin with the most improbable, it was suggested many years ago by Baron Nopcsa, a Hungarian paleontologist (who incidentally was involved in a good deal of political intrigue during the First World War, and at one time was chosen by the Central Powers to be the King of Albania), that the crests in these hadrosaurs were sexual characters. He supposed that the crested forms were males, the flat-headed forms, females. It would be a pretty thought except that the crested and the flat-headed types usually occur in sediments of different ages, which raises insuperable obstacles to the perpetuation of duck-billed dinosaurs.

Along somewhat more realistic lines of reasoning, several students in the past supposed that the crests might have served as air intakes, as "snorkels" while the hadrosaur was feeding in shallow water with the head submerged. This might do very well for such types as *Lambeosaurus* and *Parasaurolophus*, except it has now been definitely established that in these hadrosaurs the tube has no openings whatsoever at its free end by which air might have been drawn into the lungs. Furthermore, the helmeted crests of *Corythosaurus* and *Hypacrosaurus* do not fit into the requirements of this theory.

A more tenable theory is the one that supposes the nasal loop in the crest to have been some sort of an air lock—a sort of valve or trap to keep water from flooding through the nasal passage when the head was submerged. There is indeed some merit to this idea, except that such an air trap would not have been very effective, and it would have been quite unnecessary. As for its effectiveness, it would work

Figure 24. Internal anatomy of the crest of *Corythosaurus*

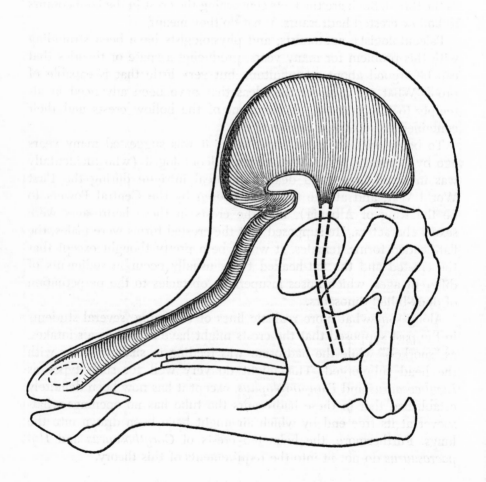

only if the head were held in such positions beneath the water that air would be trapped in the upper part of the loop, and if the head were not pushed to such a distance beneath the surface that the water pressure would drive the air bubble out of the nasal loop. It would have been unnecessary because almost all air-breathing aquatic vertebrates have ways of closing the nostrils to keep the water out of the nasal passages. We see valves formed by small sphincter muscles around the nostrils in modern water-living vertebrates like crocodiles, otters, hippopotamuses, and many others that might be named. And the mummified remains of hadrosaurs that have already been mentioned give some indication that these dinosaurs probably did have nostrils that could have been closed by the action of sphincter muscles. So why should these hadrosaurs go to the elaborate bother of developing great crests on the top of the skull to house air traps that at best would not have been particularly effective?

If the looped nasal passages were not air traps, could they have been sand traps? Some modern lizards, the so-called "horned toad" of southwestern United States, has a looped nasal passage that serves to keep sand out of the lungs. But why should the hadrosaurs, which were so obviously aquatic reptiles, have had a sand trap in the nose? And here again, would not muscles that closed the nostrils have served to keep the sand out, just as in the modern camels the nostrils can be closed when the sand blows?

Another idea that has received a great deal of attention is that the nasal loops within the crests of the hadrosaurs formed accessory air storage chambers, so that when the dinosaur was submerged it had an extra reservoir of air to help it stay down longer than might otherwise have been possible. Two things are wrong with this theory. In the first place, it would be very difficult to inspire air into the lungs from a closed air chamber in the nasal crest on the skull, because the dinosaur would be creating a vacuum in that chamber. The lungs would have to act like a suction pump, and that would take a great deal of power of inspiration. Second, and this is particularly important, the volume of air that might have been stored in the nasal loop within the skull crest would have been so very small in comparison with the capacity of the lungs that such an accessory air reservoir would have been of little use to the animal. What is the need of having an additional tenth or twentieth of the lung capacity on hand as a reserve? It does not make much sense.

This brings us to the idea that the crests may have been largely for the purpose of improving the sense of smell. Such crests would have increased the area of mucous membrane in the nasal passage, which in turn would have allowed for large areas of sensitive olfactory nerve endings. Many modern mammals that have a keen sense of smell possess elaborate scrolls of bone, the "turbinals" within the nasal region of the skull. These scrolls greatly increase the surface of the mucous membrane and the effectiveness of the olfactory nerves. Perhaps the duck-billed dinosaurs accomplished this by the evolution of the crests.

If so, why did some of them have large crests and others no crests at all? Perhaps the crested types had a better sense of smell as compared with the noncrested forms. But then why did the crests take such a variety of elaborate shapes? This is one of those fascinating paleontological puzzles to which we shall probably never have a satisfactory answer. In the meantime it is a great deal of fun to speculate about the problem—to see if we can guess at the reasons why some of the animals that lived long ago are so different from anything we know today. This is one of the nice things about paleontology: it is a science that leaves something to the imagination.

SIGHT AND HEARING

If the duck-billed dinosaurs, or at least some of them, had a keen sense of smell, as has been suggested in the preceding remarks, this in no way led to any diminution in their vision (as is so often the case among animals that have well-developed olfactory powers) because the bony orbits of the skull indicate by their size that these dinosaurs had large and well-developed eyes. It seems likely that the hadrosaurs depended very largely on their visual sense and that they could see things clearly and at great distances, just as do a great many modern birds. Indeed, an interesting and probably a valid comparison can be made between the hadrosaurian eye and the eye of a large modern bird, such as a bird of prey, for in both the eye is large, and in both there is a ring of bony plates, the sclerotic plates, enclosed within the bony orbit. These sclerotic plates are found in many vertebrates and probably represent something inherited from primitive fishes. They are quite characteristic of many fossil and modern reptiles and birds, but they are not found in mammals. The purpose of the plates is a matter of debate; it has been supposed that they may have protected the eyeball. The sclerotic plates in the hadrosaurs appear as if they might have been movable upon each other, like the mechanical iris diaphragm of a camera, yet experiments with living reptiles do not seem to indicate any movement of their plates. However that may be, the ring of sclerotic plates in the duck-billed dinosaurs indicates that these reptiles had very large eyeballs. This evidence, together with impressions in the skull of large optic lobes and of large optic nerves, shows that the hadrosaurs must have had an extraordinarily keen sense of sight. They very likely had to maintain a constant and alert watch for the great meat-eating dinosaurs that were ever on the prowl in the Mesozoic world.

Did the dinosaurs make any noise? Did they have voices—did they

---

Figure 25. Sight and hearing in a duck-billed dinosaur. The sclerotic plates encircled the eyeball. The long rod-like stapes transmitted vibrations of the tympanic membrane or eardrum, to which it was attached, to the inner ear

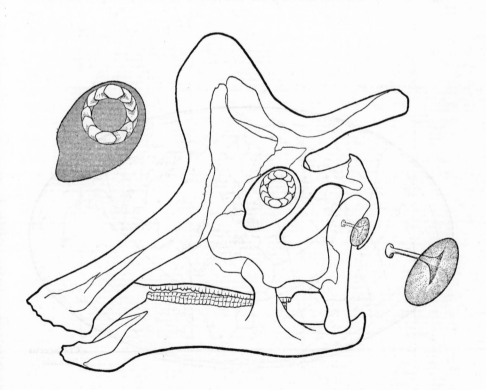

roar or bellow? These questions are frequently asked. The answers seem to be available, but they must be reached by indirect methods. Which brings us to the problem of hearing in the hadrosaurs.

At the back of the skull on each side in all of these dinosaurs there is a large notch between the squamosal and quadrate bones, as shown in Figure 25, that would very nicely have held a large eardrum or tympanic membrane. And recently a bony stapes, the bone that in reptiles transmits vibrations from the eardrum to the inner ear, has been found in a skeleton of *Corythosaurus* at the American Museum of Natural History. This stapes is a long, slender, rod-like bone that neatly spans the gap between the brain case and the notch where the eardrum is supposed to have been. Such evidence seems almost irrefutable; it seems to indicate without much doubt that the duck-billed dinosaurs had a keen sense of hearing.

If this be the case, it can be assumed that they probably had strong voices, too. In this respect they may be compared with modern

---

Figure 26. World map showing the distribution of the ornithopod dinosaurs

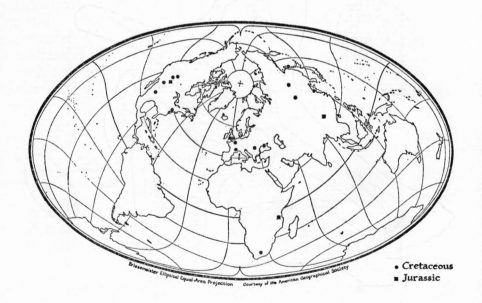

Briesemeister Elliptical Equal-Area Projection   Courtesy of the American Geographical Society

• Cretaceous
■ Jurassic

crocodiles and alligators, which hear very well, and which are capable of bellowing and roaring in stentorian tones. In fact, the bellowing of a bull alligator can easily be heard across a mile or more of swamp and forest, and during the mating season these reptiles can be very noisy. Therefore, it is reasonable to assume that the duck-billed dinosaurs also probably were able to bellow or roar, and, like our modern crocodilians, they may have made the Cretaceous welkin ring with their racket, on moonlight nights during the mating season.

THE SUM OF THE EVIDENCE

These various bits of evidence when taken together and added to the testimony of the bones and of the petrified mummies help us to gain a considerable understanding of the duck-billed dinosaurs—of what they were like and how they lived. Certainly the accumulated facts and the logical deductions from these facts seem to show that the hadrosaurs were alert and lively animals, especially for reptiles. They must have spent a great deal of their time in the water, partly in deep water where they could swim freely, and partly in shallow water, where they could feed upon various aquatic plants. At the approach of danger, in the form of *Gorgosaurus* or *Tyrannosaurus* or some of their carnivorous cousins, the hadrosaurs could make a dash for deeper water, to swim away from their land-based enemies. It was a successful way of life. The hadrosaurs prospered, and during the latter portion of the Cretaceous period they lived in great numbers along the streams and lakes and along the seacoasts of North America and of Asia. Perhaps they lived elsewhere too—on that point the geologic record is incomplete. Be that as it may, these were among the most numerous of the dinosaurs. They had a short but very full evolutionary history, and they left their huge bones by the thousands in the rocks of the earth's crust as clues to their past greatness.

THE OLDEST ORNITHISCHIAN

We now turn from the remarkably varied ornithopods, a suborder that contains such different types as the comparatively primitive camptosaurs, the small hypsilophodonts, the ponderous iguanodonts, and the truly fantastic hadrosaurs, to the stegosaurs, a suborder that is limited in the extent of its fossil record and in the limits of its evolutionary history as well. The stegosaurs adhere within fairly narrow limits to a single structural pattern, and in this respect are rather similar to the gigantic sauropod dinosaurs that were described in Chapter Six or the armored ankylosaurs that will be described in the next chapter, for in these several dinosaurian groups the number of genera is rather restricted, and all of them are, except for differences in certain skeletal proportions and matters of detail, much alike.

The stegosaurs are known from perhaps less than a dozen valid genera, the oldest one of which is found in the Lower Jurassic sediments of Europe and the youngest ones in Lower Cretaceous rocks of

Eurasia, Africa, and North America. They are known from a respectable number of skeletons, and of course various skulls and isolated bones, but most of the fossils belong to the single genus *Stegosaurus*. These are the most narrowly documented of the dinosaurs.

The oldest of the plated dinosaurs, geologically speaking, and the most primitive, *Scelidosaurus,* has the distinction of being perhaps the oldest known ornithischian dinosaur. What we know about this dinosaur is unfortunately all too little, for *Scelidosaurus* is based upon a single partial skeleton, discovered in 1850. Yet meagre though the evidence may be, it must suffice, and luckily it is sufficiently good to give us a fair idea of what *Scelidosaurus* was like (Plate 64).

This dinosaur was found in the seaside cliffs near Charmouth, in Dorset, one of the southern counties of England, where in the stretch of coast line between Lyme Regis on the west and Bournemouth on the east is a magnificent sequence of Mesozoic rocks that contain many fossils. The oldest rocks are to the west, where Upper Triassic sediments are exposed, and where the dark cliffs of Lower Jurassic shales rise above the beaches at Lyme Regis and Charmouth, and the youngest rocks are to the east, where the famous and beautiful chalk cliffs of Cretaceous age form the gleaming white ramparts that through the centuries have protected England along the narrow part of the Channel. All of these rocks are predominantly of marine origin,

Figure 27. The skeleton of the Lower Jurassic stegosaur *Scelidosaurus*. About one thirty-fifth natural size

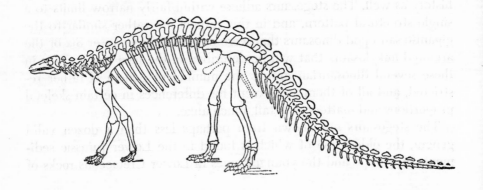

and although they contain for the most part numerous fossils of former denizens of the sea, the remains of an occasional land dweller may sometimes be found here, the record of an animal that died along the shore and perhaps floated out on the tides to be deposited and covered up in the shallows.

Scelidosaurus, the fossil skeleton of which is in the British Museum, is about twelve feet in length, making it a dinosaur of very modest proportions. It is a quadrupedal reptile, in which the hind limbs are considerably larger than the forelimbs, so that the hips are elevated to form the highest point of the body. The body itself is heavy; the legs are stout and the feet are broad. The skull is small. The jaws are weak, and it seems quite obvious that *Scelidosaurus* fed upon soft plants. This dinosaur was protected in life by rows of bony scutes or armor plates that range longitudinally from the head down to the tip of the tail. Along the middle of the neck, and also along the middle of the top of the tail, are vertical plates that stand up something like great saw teeth to give *Scelidosaurus* an interesting and a rather rough profile. In many of these features, such as the arched back, the vertical plates, the heavy limbs, and the small skull, *Scelidosaurus* is prophetic of what was to appear in greatly exaggerated form among the later plated dinosaurs, as we shall shortly see.

MORE HISTORY

Since the Jurassic of the Dorset coast has been mentioned, let us digress briefly to notice Mary Anning, one of the Victorians who was prominent in the early history of paleontology. Perhaps it might have been proper to have said something about her back in Chapter Two, but she was not particularly concerned with dinosaurs, and for this reason she was not there considered. She did participate very largely in the early discoveries of fossil marine reptiles along the Channel coast.

Her father had a shop in Lyme Regis, where he sold fossil sea shells to the early nineteenth century visitors who visited the beaches in the vicinity of that charming little town. His daughter assisted him, and at an early age she became well acquainted with the cliffs at Lyme Regis and Charmouth and on to the east. When she was still a very young girl her father died, but with commendable courage she carried on his work, searching the cliffs for fossils, especially after storms had freshly eroded the rocks. Then, in 1811, she found the first associated skeleton of an ichthyosaur at Lyme Regis. This inspired her to further efforts, and in the course of time she unearthed a considerable number of fossil skeletons, which she sold to wealthy patrons and to scientific institutions. She became famous in her day, and in the history of paleontology for her discoveries, but she died before the skeleton of *Scelidosaurus* came to light at Charmouth. Dr. Gideon Mantell, who visited her in 1832, remarked that she was "a prim, pedantic, vinegar-looking, thin female, shrewd, and rather satirical in her conversation." Perhaps this unflattering description reflects some of the vinegar of which Mantell had so abundant a supply.

STEGOSAURUS

To get back to our story, let it be said that if our knowledge of *Scelidosaurus* leaves more than a little to be desired we can perhaps feel compensated by the wealth of available material when we come to look at that very familiar dinosaur *Stegosaurus*, skeletons of which are to be seen in a number of North American museums. The first *Stegosaurus* was one of that great parade of dinosaurs collected in the Morrison formation at Como Bluff, Wyoming, by Professor Marsh's field men, and of course the original description was written by Marsh —in 1877. He found *Stegosaurus* to be a paleontological puzzle, as attested by a letter he wrote in the same year to Sir Richard Owen, the great English anatomist and paleontologist, and director of the British Museum of Natural History. Said Marsh, "Just now I can only send you a Note on some very strange Reptiles, which I shall soon describe in detail. *Stegosaurus* is one of the strangest of animals." To-day we have at hand a great deal more material of *Stegosaurus* than did Marsh, and in some respects we still find this ancient reptile a paleontological puzzle. This is nothing new. As has already been made amply evident in this book, many dinosaurs are puzzles and continue to be puzzles, no matter how many fossils are discovered and studied, and we shall never quite surmount the disadvantage of being separated from these reptiles by a great gap in time.

Among the dinosaurs, *Stegosaurus* is one of the most bizarre in its appearance. Here is a permanently quadrupedal dinosaur in which the front legs are almost ridiculously short as compared with the hind limbs, with the result that this reptile is a "high behind" of extreme proportions, with the hips elevated far above the level of the shoulders. Here is a dinosaur with a skull remarkably small in comparison with

Plate 57. One of the largest and latest of the duck-billed dinosaurs, *Anatosaurus* (or *Trachodon*), from the Upper Cretaceous of North America. The upright skeleton is about seventeen feet tall

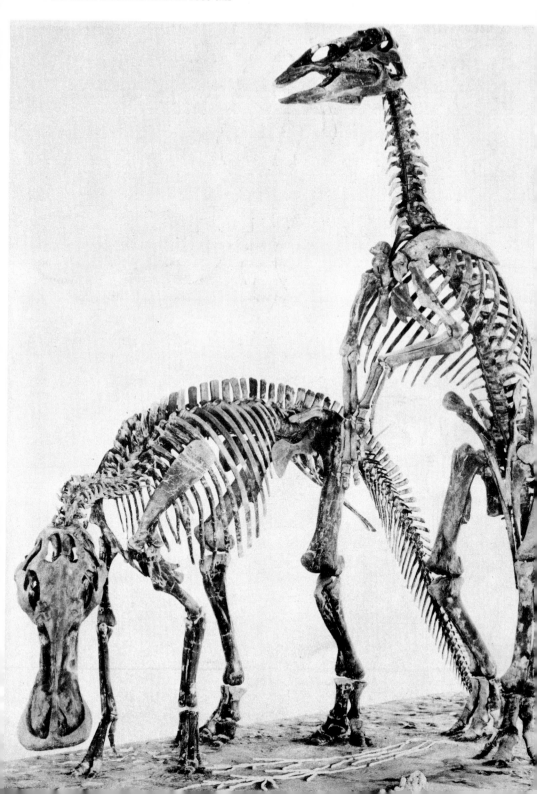

Plate 58. A fossil "mummy" of the duck-bill *Anatosaurus*. Note the fossilized skin stretched over the ribs, the shoulder blade, and the forelimb

Plate 59.   Detail showing the surface pattern of the skin in the "mummy" of *Anatosaurus*. It was evidently a thick, leathery skin like that of a modern crocodile

Plate 60. A tropical landscape in Wyoming during late Cretaceous times. The dinosaurs are *Anatosaurus*. By Charles R. Knight

Plate 61. The duck-billed dinosaur *Corythosaurus,* from the Upper Cretaceous beds of Alberta. The skeleton is about twenty-six feet long. Note the tendon bones along the back

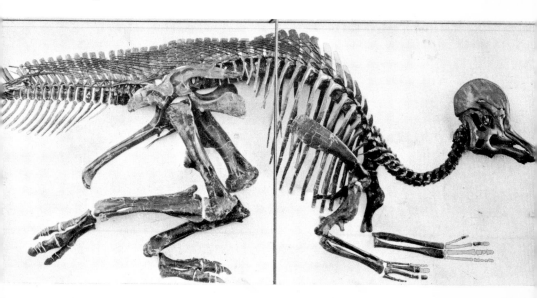

Plate 62. The tendons of the back and tail were frequently calcified in the duck-billed dinosaurs and their relatives, as seen in this specimen from Montana

Plate 63. An inside view of the left lower jaw of a duck-billed dinosaur, showing the complex dental battery composed of rows of interlocking teeth

Plate 64. *Scelidosaurus*, the earliest ornithischian in the geologic record, was found in the Lower Jurassic rocks of England. This dinosaur was about thirteen feet long. By Neave Parker

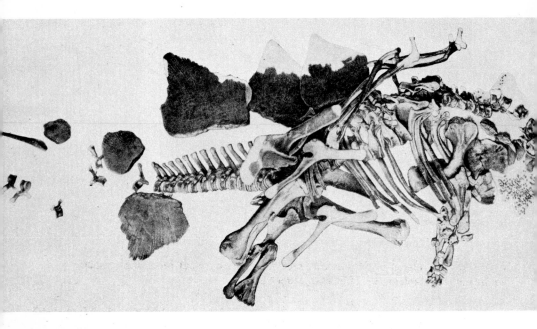

Plate 65. A skeleton of *Stegosaurus* as found in the Upper Jurassic Morrison beds of North America. This specimen shows an alternating arrangement of the large plates along the back

Plate 66. A skeleton of *Stegosaurus* set against a somewhat formalized Jurassic landscape. The skeleton is about twenty feet long

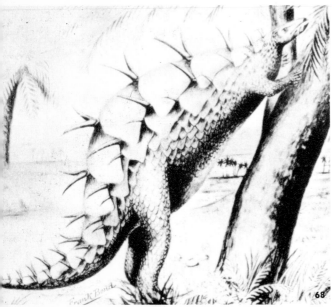

Plate 67. *Stegosaurus,* as restored by H. N. Hutchinson and J. Smit, 1893. *Plate 68.* As restored by W. C. Knight and Frank Bond, 1899. *Plate 69.* As restored by F. A. Lucas and Charles R. Knight, 1901. *Plate 70.* A model by Charles R. Knight, 1903

Plate 71. As restored by
E. Ray Lankester, 1905.
Plate 72. A model by Richard Swann Lull, 1910. Plate
73. Second restoration by
Hutchinson and Smit, 1911.
Plate 74. As restored by
Charles R. Knight, 1928

Plate 75. The bony plates covering the back of *Nodosaurus,* an armored dinosaur from the Upper Cretaceous of North America. The specimen is about twelve
feet long

Plate 76. The armored dinosaur *Polacanthus*, from the Lower Cretaceous beds of southern England. This dinosaur was about fourteen feet long. By Neave Parker

Plate 77. Model of the armored dinosaur *Ankylosaurus*, from the Upper Cretaceous of North America. This reptile was about fifteen feet in length

Plate 78. Looking down on the armor-plated back and the skull of *Palaeoscincus,*
an Upper Cretaceous fifteen-foot-long ankylosaur from North America

Plate 79. A restoration of *Palaeoscincus* that may help to clarify the preceding
plate. By E. Rungius Fulda

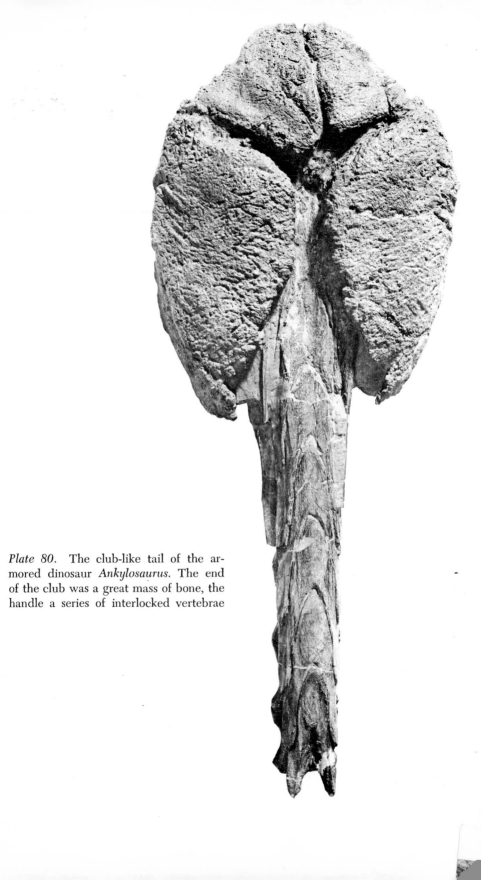

Plate 80. The club-like tail of the armored dinosaur *Ankylosaurus.* The end of the club was a great mass of bone, the handle a series of interlocked vertebrae

the body—even in an assemblage of reptiles among which small skulls are quite common. Here is a dinosaur with strange plates and spikes on the body.

The skeleton of *Stegosaurus* is about twenty feet in length, and perhaps eight feet in height at the hips (Plate 66). When the skeleton is viewed from the side, the spinal column is seen to form a great arc, rising from the head and the shoulder region to its high point at the pelvis, and then descending as a moderately long tail to the ground. This dinosaur is characterized by its very long-spined vertebrae, to which, in the thoracic region, are attached strongly arched ribs, thus providing *Stegosaurus* with a framework for a most capacious body cavity. A plant-eating animal—and there cannot be much doubt that *Stegosaurus* fed upon vegetation—needs a roomy body to hold great quantities of bulky plant food, as is painfully evident to anyone who for the first time has placed himself astride a large and corpulent horse. The manner in which the highly arched ribs of this dinosaur provide extra room for lungs, stomach, and intestines is an object lesson of form and function in the animal world.

Of course, *Stegosaurus* possesses the diagnostic ornithischian pelvis, in which the upper bone, the ilium, is very much prolonged toward the front, to overlap the last half-dozen ribs on each side. The shoulder blade in this reptile is elongated, as is so frequently the case among the dinosaurs, and its lower end, the coracoid portion, is very greatly expanded.

A considerable part of the length of the hind limb in *Stegosaurus* may be attributed to the unusually long, straight femur, or upper limb bone, which resembles in proportions the femur of an elephant. It is almost twice the length of the lower leg bones, the tibia and fibula, and this makes the knee joint in *Stegosaurus* very low, again an elephant-like character in the Jurassic dinosaur. And still once again, as in the elephant, the hind limb of *Stegosaurus* is articulated as a straight, almost pillar-like support, certainly an efficient way of carrying the weight of a heavy body. The forelimb bones are short and stubby, as has been mentioned, and in life were carried with the elbow everted outwardly, a characteristic reptilian pose.

Both front and hind feet in *Stegosaurus* are short and broad, an adaptation for the support of great weight, and it seems extremely likely that in life there were heavy, adipose cushions behind and beneath the bony toes, to absorb the shock of several tons of weight being transmitted through the foot against the hard earth. In the hand the outer two fingers are reduced, and it is probable that in life they were not visible externally. In the foot there are three large functional toes, the three middle ones. Fingers and toes terminate in broad, flattened hoofs.

Stegosaurus is particularly noteworthy because of its so-called armor, consisting of a series of large, more or less vertical, triangular bony plates that run in a long double row down the middle of the back, and because of some paired bony spikes on the end of the tail. The two pairs of spikes on the tail (not three pairs as was once supposed and as will be seen in some of the earlier restorations of *Stegosaurus*) make sense to us, for it seems quite obvious that these weapons, which in life were certainly encased in horny coverings, could have inflicted painful wounds on any reptile that ventured too close to the flailing tail of *Stegosaurus*. But the function of the great plates on the back is not so obvious.

That these plates were carried in a vertical position is made clear by their broadened bases, which gave them strong support in the body tissues, and by fossils in which the plates are found in position. That they formed a double row is also indicated by at least one specimen in which the plates occur in complete series. But the arrangement of these plates within the double row is a matter of some dispute. It was thought for many years that the plates were paired, which is a logical view, but no two plates are of quite the same size and shape. Then, a good many years ago, the paleontologists of the United States National Museum found a *Stegosaurus* skeleton with the two rows of plates nicely arranged in an alternating fashion (Plate 65). This led C. W. Gilmore, one of the great authorities on dinosaurs, to believe that such was the disposition of the plates in life; but as opposed to this view it can be argued that although the plates of each row are in order, one row slipped forward or back with relation to the other row during the process of fossilization, to make this alternating arrangement of constituent plates. So the matter stands today. Unfortunately, no other skeletons have been found with the two rows of plates all in order, so their arrangement as paired or alternating plates cannot be definitely proved at this time.

Whether the plates were paired or alternating in life is largely an academic question. The more important problem is that of their function. They have been called "armor plates," but how might two rows of vertical plates down the middle of the back have formed any very effective protection for *Stegosaurus?* Of course, they would have protected the spinal column and the spinal nerve from injury from above, but certainly the flanks of this dinosaur were wide open to attack, covered only by a leathery skin. Were the plates some kind of "frightening device" to make *Stegosaurus* look bigger than it really was? We can only guess at the answers. We can be sure that these enormous plates must have been something of a physiological drain on the reptile, at least during that period of its life when they were growing, and attaining their full size.

Stegosaurus is almost as famous for its small head as for its gigantic plates and long, sharp spikes on the end of the tail. The skull is, in effect, an elongated camptosaur-like skull with small, weak teeth, these limited in number to about twenty-five on each side, above and below, with only a single set of replacement teeth present at one time. Quite a contrast, this, to the great dental batteries that we saw in the jaws of the duck-billed dinosaurs! Evidently *Stegosaurus* fed upon soft vegetation that did not require much cutting, chopping, or mashing. The front of the jaws, as is so usual in the ornithischian dinosaurs, formed a sort of beak, which in life undoubtedly had horny coverings.

One of the remarkable features of *Stegosaurus* is the very small brain, no larger than a walnut, and the relatively large sacral nerve plexus, an enlargement of the spinal nerve in the pelvic region that is at least twenty times as great in volume as the brain. The significance of the minute brain and the remarkable enlargement of the sacral plexus will be discussed in Chapter Thirteen.

It is of course quite understandable that a fossil so strange in appearance as *Stegosaurus* should inspire scientists and artists to attempt reconstructions of its appearance in life, and it is interesting to see how these restorations have developed and become increasingly stabilized as more and more material has been made available through discoveries of fossils. Perhaps a brief review of the progressive refinement of *Stegosaurus* restorations will be helpful in showing how our knowledge of a particular fossil may grow through time; how our efforts to clothe the bones with muscle and skin may progress from the first crude impressions through ever better representations, with perhaps a few side excursions into fantasy, until a final result is reached that is probably not very far short of the truth.

The first figure of *Stegosaurus* was not a restoration of the animal as it may have appeared in life, but rather a reconstruction of the skeleton in a natural pose, made in 1891 under the direction of Professor Marsh. So far as the pose of the skeleton is concerned, this figure is excellent; little fault can be found with it even upon the basis of our modern knowledge of the fossil. But Marsh erred in showing a single row of plates down the middle of the back, even though at that time a fossil had been found showing the double row of plates. He erred further by indicating four pairs of spikes on the tail.

With this figure as a basis, an artist by the name of J. Smit made a restoration of *Stegosaurus*, as he thought it might have appeared in life, for a book, published in 1893, entitled *Extinct Monsters*, by the Reverend H. N. Hutchinson, an English author (Plate 67). It seems probable that Smit's drawing was supervised by Hutchinson. The restoration shows the single row of plates down the back as first indicated by Marsh, and the four pairs of spikes on the tail, these reduced to spines of almost pin-like proportions. Hutchinson and Smit gave *Stegosaurus* a sprawling alligator or lizard-like pose, sadly out of keeping with the anatomical evidence of the skeleton.

In 1899 Dr. W. C. Knight of the University of Wyoming supervised a restoration of *Stegosaurus* (the artist was Frank Bond) with the plates down flat, forming a huge, pavement-like armor over the back and the sides, with pairs of spikes protruding from between the plates, all over the body (Plate 68). It looks like an effective arrangement for defense, but there is not the slightest shred of evidence for such a concept. And the way in which this dinosaur is depicted as rearing up into the treetops is again an indication of a fertile imagination rather than an assessment of anatomical evidence.

Perhaps the first reasonably good restoration of *Stegosaurus* in the flesh (Plate 69) was made by the great artist Charles R. Knight under the direction of Dr. F. A. Lucas, in 1901. Here we see a drawing that indicates the knowledge and background of a first-class scientist and the skill of an excellent artist. This figure shows a double row of paired plates down the back, and four pairs of spikes on the tail.

In the same year Lucas supervised another restoration of *Stegosaurus*, the drawing being done by G. E. Roberts. There is little merit in this figure—artistically it is poor, and the body of the animal is much too long—but it has the distinction of being the first restoration showing alternating plates, with the tail spikes reduced to two pairs.

Then in 1903 Knight made a model of *Stegosaurus* (Plate 70) that is probably as fine a restoration of this dinosaur as has been done. It shows alternating plates and the two pairs of tail spines, and in pose and in general appearance it is convincingly lifelike.

The next restoration, made in 1905 under the direction of E. Ray Lankester (Plate 71), is a distinct step backward. It represents an impossible beast, which is all the more surprising because Lankester was one of the great zoologists of his time. Why a man of his learning and insight should approve of such a weird effort is hard to understand. The bird-like beak, the swollen body, the *five* pairs of spikes on the tail have nothing to commend them. The only thing to be said for Lankester's restoration is that he does attempt to indicate a color pattern, a matter of imagination rather than of scientific knowledge.

In 1910 Professor R. S. Lull of Yale University made a model of *Stegosaurus* to go with the skeleton that had been set up at the Yale Peabody Museum under his direction. He elevated the animal on its legs more than had previous scientists and artists, and he indicated paired plates and four pairs of spines on the tail (Plate 72). This model, even though made by one of the great authorities on dinosaurs, does not measure up to the model made by Knight in 1903.

In the following year Hutchinson and Smit tried another restoration of *Stegosaurus* (Plate 73) which was something of an improvement over their effort of 1893. The pose is not bad, but they show the back portion of the tail devoid of plates, for what reason it is hard to say, and they stick to the older idea of four pairs of spikes on the tail.

The most recent restorations of *Stegosaurus* are those by Knight in the Chicago Museum (Plate 74), by Neave Parker, done under the direction of Dr. W. E. Swinton, and by Z. Burian, done under the direction of Dr. Joseph Augusta. All of them are excellent, although a small objection can be made to the clawed toes in Burian's painting.

THE WIDE EXTENT OF THE STEGOSAURS

Although *Stegosaurus* is commonly regarded as a dinosaur particularly characteristic of the Morrison formation of western North America, this reptile very probably was not confined to the continent of North America. Its plates have been found in England, an indication that *Stegosaurus* may have roamed widely across the Northern Hemisphere during late Jurassic times. A very closely related type, *Dacentrurus* or *Omosaurus*, occurs at various localities in Europe, and eggs attributed to this European stegosaur have been discovered in the Upper Jurassic sediments of Portugal.

Kentrosaurus is an African stegosaurian, its bones having been excavated in East Africa, along with the remains of *Brachiosaurus*, other brontosaurs, and still other dinosaurs, all of which show close relationships to the Morrison dinosaurs, of North America. These Tendaguru dinosaurs, for such is the name of the Upper Jurassic sediments in the vicinity of Lake Tanganyika where the fossils occur most abundantly, indicate a development of great dinosaurs in East Africa during late Jurassic times that may be correlated closely with the wide radiation of Morrison dinosaurs over large segments of North America.

The skeleton of *Kentrosaurus* is very similar to that of *Stegosaurus*. Perhaps it is not so large, and it would seem that *Kentrosaurus* had smaller and fewer plates and more spines than did its American cousin. *Chialangosaurus* is a recently described stegosaurian from eastern Asia. Stegosaurian bones have also been found in Argentina. When all of the evidence is considered, it seems quite clear that the stegosaurs were of world-wide extent during the late phases of Jurassic history.

Figure 28. World map showing the distribution of the stegosaurs and the ankylosaurs

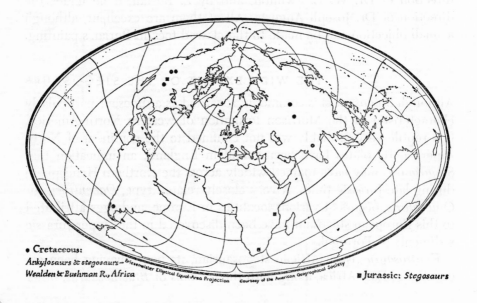

• Cretaceous:
Ankylosaurs & stegosaurs - Briesemeister Elliptical Equal-Area Projection   Courtesy of the American Geographical Society
Wealden & Bushman R., Africa

■ Jurassic: *Stegosaurs*

THE EARLY EXTINCTION OF THE STEGOSAURS

Among the dinosaurs the stegosaurs—*Stegosaurus, Omosaurus, Kentrosaurus,* and their cousins—make up the one major group that did not persist until the end of Mesozoic times. All of the other suborders of dinosaurs, the carnivorous theropods, the giant swamp-dwelling sauropods, the duck-billed ornithopods, the armored dinosaurs, or ankylosaurs, and the horned dinosaurs, or ceratopsians (these last two groups still to be discussed), continued vigorously and in most cases abundantly until the very close of the Cretaceous period, at which time they all became extinct at once, geologically speaking. But the stegosaurs passed on at a much earlier date, for their range in time does not extend beyond the early stages of Cretaceous history.

Why the stegosaurs should have become extinct so much earlier than the other dinosaurian suborders is a matter for speculation. The possible answer to this puzzle will not be attempted at this place, for on subsequent pages the large problem of the extinction of dinosaurs will be discussed at some length. Let it be sufficient now to record the fact.

CHAPTER TEN

ARMORED DINOSAURS

THE NATURE OF THE ANKYLOSAURS

Perhaps it is a mere coincidence that the stegosaurians, or plated dinosaurs, should have become extinct just as the armored dinosaurs (often called the ankylosaurs) first became evident in the changing picture of Mesozoic life, or perhaps there is some connection, some relationship of cause and effect, in the fact that as the stegosaurs disappeared during early Cretaceous times the ankylosaurs appeared in various parts of the world. Could it be that the waning of the stegosaurs was brought about by the waxing of the ankylosaurs, that the armored dinosaurs, better fitted for the role of upland plant eaters than were the plated dinosaurs, crowded these latter from the face of the earth? Conversely, is it possible that the stegosaurs were on their way out anyway, from causes that subtly escape our interpretive eye, and that in vanishing from the land they opened up a "niche" that was most efficiently occupied by their ankylosaurian cousins? Who is to say? The fact is that the stegosaurs, so successful during

Jurassic times, were succeeded by the ankylosaurs that reached the culmination of their evolutionary development in late Cretaceous times.

If the great plates that so characterize the stegosaurs are not easy to interpret in a logical way, the armor of the nodosaurs, the most advanced of the armored dinosaurs, in the form of heavy, contiguous, pavement-like plates of bone (undoubtedly covered by horny layers in life), is to our eyes quite obvious as to purpose. In short, the anatomical structure and the adaptations of the nodosaurs make sense to us.

There are some striking resemblances between the stegosaurs and the armored dinosaurs, especially the nodosaurs: in the general pose of the skeleton, for example. In both groups of dinosaurs the spinal column is highly arched, with the highest point of the arch above the pelvis, and in both groups this configuration of the backbone is a result of long hind limbs and short forelimbs in a quadrupedal animal. Yet there are differences, for the arching of the back is not so extreme in the armored dinosaurs as it is in the plated dinosaurs, which in turn can be attributed to the fact that the difference between length of hind limbs and length of forelimbs is less in the nodosaurs than is the case in the stegosaurs. For example, the humerus, or upper arm bone, of a nodosaur is perhaps two-thirds or three-fourths the length of the femur, or upper leg bone, whereas the upper arm bone in a stegosaur is only half the length of the upper leg bone. It is safe to assume that the ornithischian ancestor of both of these types was a bipedal dinosaur that walked on strong hind limbs and that used its short forelimbs less for locomotion than for an aid in feeding or for other purposes. When the stegosaurs and the nodosaurs evolved as distinct types from their relatively primitive dinosaurian ancestor, the front limbs in the two groups followed different paths of development. In the stegosaurians there was not a great deal of relative increase in forelimb length, although the limbs became stout to help support the weight of the body. In the nodosaurs, on the other hand, there was a double increase in size of the forelimbs, both in length and in robustness. Therefore, to our way of thinking, the fore and hind limbs of the nodosaurs seem more "harmoniously developed" (if we may use such a phrase) for quadrupedal walking than are the limbs of the stegosaurs.

Again, these two groups of dinosaurs are rather similar in their possession of short, broad feet, but this is hardly a matter for astonishment, since heavy limbs and elephant-like feet are the usual thing in land-living animals that individually weigh many tons. Look at the other giant quadrupedal dinosaurs, the great sauropods that were described in Chapter Six and the horned dinosaurs that will be described in the chapter immediately following this one. Or, in our modern world, look at elephants and hippopotamuses and rhinoceroses. It is all a matter of the functional relationships between weight and the strength in bones, ligaments, and muscles.

Once again, the stegosaurs and armored dinosaurs show resemblances to each other in the low carriage of the head and to a lesser degree in the rather small size of the skull. The low position of the head is of course the result of the low shoulder region in both groups. As for the small skull, some ankylosaurs do have very small skulls, as do the stegosaurs, but in the nodosaurs the skull is of considerable size. The group shows a progressive increase in the size of the skull as we follow its evolution through late Cretaceous times.

In the nodosaurs the skull is covered, almost buried as it were, by an armor plate of thick dermal bones. This bony helmet, fitting tightly over the skull, obliterates the upper temporal openings in the skull roof behind the eyes, so characteristic of other dinosaurs, and it likewise completely covers or reduces to very small size the lateral opening that normally is seen behind the eye on each side of the skull. The eye itself is very small, as if its borders had been restricted by the heavy armor plate that makes the nodosaurian skull such a solid, massive object. And in most armored dinosaurs the skull is very broad and low.

The teeth are extraordinarily small, almost like tiny fluted beads that form weak rows along the borders of the jaws. It seems quite evident that the armored dinosaurs lived upon vegetation, and very soft vegetation at that.

The body is capacious, as is common in animals that feed upon bulky plant food, and it is comparatively flat from side to side, even though the back is arched from front to rear. The ribs are greatly arched in much the same fashion that they are arched in the stegosaurs, to make the capacity of the thorax and abdomen considerably greater than it otherwise might be. At the back the spinal column is attached to a long pelvis by from six to nine vertebrae, a long and strong sacrum. Moreover, the ilium is very long and heavy, and very wide, too, and the outer surface of this upper bone of the pelvis, instead of being more or less vertically placed, as is usual in the reptiles, is quite horizontal, so that it forms a long, broad roof in the pelvic region. In short, the ilium and its attached sacrum in the nodosaurs is a massive structure, conforming to the expanded body and serving as an immensely broad capital to the pillars of the hind limbs, a capital that affords wide attachments for heavy leg muscles and simultaneously serves as a support to transmit the heavy thrust of the massive body armor through the hind limbs to the ground. In contrast to the great enlargement of the ilium or upper pelvic bone, the two other pelvic bones on each side, the ischium and the pubis, are much reduced, the latter to such a degree that it must have been of little functional use.

The armor, so variously developed in the different genera, covers the entire body (Plate 75). In many of the armored dinosaurs there are spikes on the body and masses of bone on the tail that must have served as effective weapons for defense. There is no doubting the fact that the armored dinosaurs were well protected for life in a world where gigantic predators roamed the continents.

EARLY ARMORED DINOSAURS

The word picture that has been presented in these preceding paragraphs attempts to describe in fairly general terms the "typical" armored dinosaurs or nodosaurs that lived during late Cretaceous times when these reptiles had reached a high point in their evolutionary development, and when all of the dinosaurs, for that matter, were enjoying the last expression of their dominant rule on the earth's continents. But it must be remembered that the armored dinosaurs had a history and they had a beginning—somewhere within the confines of the suborder Ornithischia.

It seems evident that the armored dinosaurs and the plated dinosaurs, that is, the ankylosaurs and the stegosaurs, evolved quite independently of each other. So they did, but recent discoveries by Russian paleontologists working in eastern Asia indicate that perhaps these two groups of dinosaurs may have a common ancestral relationship, that perhaps they arose from the same stem, or even that perhaps the armored nodosaurs may at the beginning of their history have been an offshoot from the plated stegosaurs. The evidence for this view comes from the fossil bones of the syrmosaurs, typified by *Syrmosaurus*, from Mongolia.

Syrmosaurus is a dinosaur some twelve to fifteen feet in length, in which the body is covered by an armor made up of separate, pointed plates, arranged symmetrically over the surface of the back, the neck, the tail, and the outer sides of the limbs. This armor, comparatively primitive in that the armor plates are not bound together into a continuous, flexible cuirass as in the later nodosaurs, is none the less effective, and it must have afforded to the reptile beneath it a considerable defense against the teeth and claws of enemies. The skull is small and the teeth are weak, as in the stegosaurs. Also, as in the stegosaurs, the blade of the ilium, the large upper bone of the pelvis, is vertical, whereas, as the reader will recall, this bone is horizontal and much expanded in the characteristic late Cretaceous nodosaurs. In contrast to some of these stegosaur-like features, the back portion of the long tail in *Syrmosaurus* is fused into a rather solid structure, a sort of long rod, at the end of which is a horizontally arranged bony blade, something like the blade of a crude ax. Now, this is just the type of tail that is found in some of the advanced nodosaurs, as we shall presently see. *Syrmosaurus* shows a mixture of stegosaur-like and nodosaur-like features, and because of this it has been suggested that this Mongolian dinosaur may be a connecting link between the scelidosaurs, the most primitive of the stegosaurians, and the typical nodosaurs. Perhaps so, but it is a problem that still needs a great deal of study.

The best fossils of *Syrmosaurus* come from the upper part of the Lower Cretaceous sequence in Mongolia, which is about as old as any of the known fossils of armored dinosaurs. There is a genus from Europe, known as *Acanthopholis,* of about the same geologic age. It

Figure 29. A restoration of the lower Cretaceous armored dinosaur *Syrmosaurus*

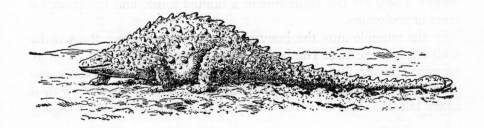

is not very well documented, for the fossil materials are fragmentary and scattered, but from what is available this dinosaur would seem to be a rather primitive ankylosaur, having a comparatively narrow body covered with plates, and with some spines, perhaps on the shoulders.

A much more completely known European dinosaur of about this same age is *Polacanthus* (Plate 76), the remains of which have been found on the Isle of Wight. This dinosaur, some fourteen feet in length, is characteristically nodosaurid by virtue of its low, flattened body, its long, heavy tail, its strong limbs (the hind limbs being much larger than the forelimbs), and also of its small skull with weak teeth. The armor is certainly distinctive. Along the back, from the neck to the hips, is a double row of truly enormous spines, seven or eight pairs of them, of which the two spines in the shoulder region are the largest. Behind these spines the region over the hips is protected by a flat, solid shield of bone. And then, behind the pelvic buckler are paired stegosaur-like plates running down the tail. A prickly individual indeed for the giant meat-eating dinosaurs to cope with!

A related nodosaur is *Hoplitosaurus* from the Lower Cretaceous beds of western North America.

A VARIETY OF NODOSAURS

And now we return to the typical late Cretaceous nodosaurs that already have been described in general terms within the first part of this chapter. There is no need to repeat what has been said about the skeleton; what goes for one goes pretty much for all of them. It is in details of the skull, the armor, and the tail of these dinosaurs, found especially well preserved in western North America and in Mongolia and adjacent parts of Asia, that the differences between them are most readily apparent. In a broad way (and let's keep this consideration of the late Cretaceous nodosaurs as simple as possible in order that we may not get completely bogged down in confusing details) the last of the nodosaurs may be divided into two large groups. These are the nodosaurs in a limited sense, and the panoplosaurs or scolosaurs.

In the panoplosaurs the bony armor plates that cover the narrow skull are of large size. The body armor is composed of rows of large, rounded bony scutes or plates between which is a pavement or mosaic of small, polygonal plates. The entire body is thus covered with a heavy but flexible armor. There may be spines in the shoulder region, sticking up vertically as in *Scolosaurus*, or laterally as in *Palaeoscincus* (Plate 78). These are both genera from western North America. The tail is completely armored by rings of plates, and numerous spines may protrude from this armored tail. If some of the armored dinosaurs that we have previously considered were well protected for defense against their enemies, they were still poor seconds to these superbly protected panoplosaurs.

And if the panoplosaurs were well adapted to defend themselves, they were equaled by the nodosaurs, with which they were contemporaneous. In the nodosaurs the comparatively large, broad skull is covered by a mosaic of small armor plates. There are pointed spines

---

Figure 30. Side and top views of the skeleton of the upper Cretaceous armored dinosaur *Ankylosaurus*. The bony club at the end of the tail, typical of most ankylosaurs, is not shown in this skeleton. About one fiftieth natural size

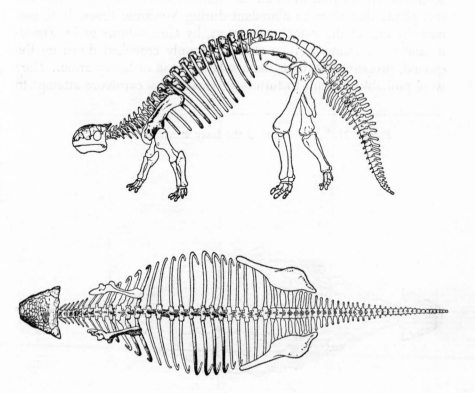

on the back corners of the skull, giving the head of these dinosaurs a faint Mephistophelean appearance when seen from above. The body armor is no less complete than it is in the panoplosaurs, but in the nodosaurs there are very large armor plates over much of the back. Furthermore, these dinosaurs are furnished with continuous rows of long spikes down each side of the body, giving these large reptiles a very bristly appearance indeed. The tail, too, is armored, but instead of being provided with spikes there is a huge club of bone on the end of the tail. The entire back portion of the tail is strongly co-ossified to support this massive war club, which looks as if it must have been a very fearful weapon (Plate 80).

THE ROLE OF THE ARMORED DINOSAURS

These descriptions will, it is hoped, have given some idea as to what the armored dinosaurs are like. Their role in the Cretaceous world seems clear to us; they can be compared in a way with modern armadillos, but of course on a greatly magnified scale. They were harmless reptiles that lived on the uplands where they fed upon the soft plants that were so abundant during Mesozoic times. If threatened by one of the giant meat eaters, by *Gorgosaurus* or by *Tyrannosaurus,* for example, they almost certainly crouched down on the ground, presenting to their foe a solid defense of heavy armor. They were probably difficult to turn over, should any carnivore attempt to

---

Figure 31. A top view of the bony armor of *Ankylosaurus*

get at the vulnerable, soft belly, and woe betide the enemy that attempted such a tactic, for the heavy tail was an effective weapon! The large spiked tail that one sees in many of the nodosaurs must have been capable of inflicting deep, painful wounds. The great club of other nodosaurs must have been quite literally a bone crusher. In medieval days bishops and other churchmen who felt the urge to join in battle carried maces and flails (which were considered by some strange logic to be more appropriate for holy men than vulgar spears and bows and arrows), and these maces and flails were terrible weapons that crushed skulls and broke bones and caved in chests. So it was with the nodosaurs; they had their maces and flails with which they could keep an overambitious predator at a safe distance. Theirs was a successful design for survival in late Cretaceous times. The nodosaurs prospered in various parts of the world, until like all of the other late Cretaceous dinosaurs they were caught up in the great wave of extinction that during the transition from Cretaceous to Cenozoic times spelled the doom of the reptilian rulers of the Mesozoic scene.

CHAPTER ELEVEN

HORNED DINOSAURS

THE FIRST DISCOVERIES

In 1887 a young man by the name of Whitman Cross, working for the newly established United States Geological Survey, was exploring and studying the sedimentary beds around Denver, Colorado, in an attempt to fix the geologic age of these rocks. In the course of his work, Cross, who in subsequent years was to become an outstanding authority on the Survey and one of the leading lights of North American geology, was confronted with a pair of large fossil horn cores, which had been found by a geological colleague, Mr. George L. Cannon, on the banks of Green Mountain Creek, near Denver. The fossil horn cores were sent to Professor O. C. Marsh at Yale University, and that great paleontologist with very little hesitation pronounced them to be the horns of an ancient bison, *Bison alticornis* he called it, of probable Pliocene age. But this identification did not suit Cross because he was convinced by his field studies that the Denver beds, in which the fossil horn cores had been found, were of Cretaceous age.

How could a bison, one of the latest and most advanced of mammals, have been found in Cretaceous sediments?

During the next year John Bell Hatcher, one of Marsh's fossil collectors, and one of the truly great collectors of dinosaurs and of other fossil vertebrates in the history of American paleontology, was exploring along the Judith River in Montana, where in Cretaceous sediments he found a part of a skull with horn cores quite similar to those of *"Bison alticornis."* After having worked along the Judith River, Hatcher went to Wyoming, where in the town of Douglas he met a rancher by the name of Charles A. Guernsey. Mr. Guernsey had made a collection of fossils on his ranch, and among the various specimens he showed to Hatcher on that occasion a fragment of a very large horn core. In a letter to Marsh, Hatcher said, "On enquiry Mr. Guernsey informed me that the specimen had been taken from a skull several feet in length which had been found by his ranch foreman . . . in the bottom of a deep canyon about 35 miles north of Lusk."

Actually, the story is just a bit more exciting than one would guess from Hatcher's matter-of-fact letter to Marsh. According to Guernsey, some of his cowboys during a roundup had found a great fossil skull "with horns as long as a hoe handle and eye holes as big as your hat" sticking out of a bank on the side of a deep gulch. After the roundup Guernsey and his foreman, Mr. Edmund B. Wilson, hastened to the locality and attempted to dig out the great skull. They managed to undermine it so that suddenly it broke loose and crashed to the bottom of the gulch, almost taking Guernsey with it. Needless to say, the skull reached the end of its fall in several pieces, of which the horn cores and the lower jaw were picked up by Guernsey and carried back to his ranch house.

When he got back to New Haven that fall, Hatcher at once recognized the similarity between the horns of *"Bison alticornis,"* the specimen he had seen in Mr. Guernsey's collection, and the fossils from the Judith River beds. Suddenly everything clicked into place, and suddenly Marsh and his Yale colleagues realized that a new group of dinosaurs had been discovered—great dinosaurs with immense horns!

The discovery of the first horned dinosaurs, or ceratopsians, was more momentous than could at once be realized by the little band of New Haven paleontologists, for it revealed an entirely new vista in the paleontology of the dinosaurs, and initiated a series of explorations in the field and studies in the laboratory that were to bring to light a profusely abundant record of dinosaurs, showing a remarkable variety of specializations.

The horned dinosaurs are of particular interest not only because of their wide anatomical range but also because of their very rapid evolutionary development. These were the last dinosaurs to appear in the geologic record; their earliest and most primitive representatives arose during late Cretaceous times, and from this beginning the horned dinosaurs went through the entire course of their evolutionary history within the limits of this part of the Cretaceous period. They are also of great interest because of their seeming geographic restrictions, for if the geologic record is now read correctly the horned dinosaurs were confined during their history to North America (and perhaps only to western North America at that) and to eastern Asia. They seem to furnish us a nice case history of rapid evolution in a comparatively limited geographic area.

But let us begin at the beginning.

CERATOPSIAN ANCESTORS

Psittacosaurus is a dinosaur that is generally classified by most authorities as one of the ornithopods—a relative of *Hypsilophodon* and its cousins, which were described in Chapter Seven, and of the duck-billed dinosaurs that formed the subject matter for Chapter Eight. *Psittacosaurus* is being discussed at this place in connection with the horned dinosaurs, because if it is not a direct ancestor of the ceratopsians it certainly cannot be very far removed from their ancestral line.

Skeletons of this small bipedal dinosaur, perhaps five or six feet in length, have been found in Mongolia and in Shantung Province, China. As is the case in other primitive ornithischian dinosaurs, the hind limbs in *Psittacosaurus* are much longer than the forelimbs, actually in a ratio of about two to one. This is a structural pattern that we have seen time and again among primitive dinosaurs, and it indicates quite clearly the bipedal ancestry of these reptiles. *Psittacosaurus* has many of the adaptations that go along with bipedalism: strong hind feet for running over the ground, front feet adapted as grasping hands, and a long tail to counterbalance the body in front of the pivotal hip joint. There is a certain amount of reduction in the outer fingers of the hands, an indication that *Psittacosaurus* can hardly be on the exact line of development leading to the horned dinosaurs, in which all fingers are present. Nevertheless this is a minor point of divergence.

This last statement can be made with good reason, because the skull of *Psittacosaurus* is almost exactly what one would expect in an ultimate ceratopsian ancestor. It is a very deep skull, the front part of which is narrowed into a sort of parrot-like beak; hence the name *Psittacosaurus*—"parrot reptile." The lower jaw, too, is narrowed in its front part into a sharp beak. The nostrils and the eyes are placed rather high on the sides of the skull; the teeth are limited in number; and on the side of each jugal bone, that lower bar in the reptilian skull connecting the cheek region with the back of the skull, there is a strong point or spike, laterally directed. The parrot-like beak, the jugal with a lateral point, the nostril and the eye high up on the side of the skull, and the limited number of teeth are all characters very suggestive of the first true ceratopsians.

The step from *Psittacosaurus* to the most primitive ceratopsians is a

---

Figure 32. Skeleton of *Psittacosaurus*, possibly an ancestor of the horned dinosaurs. Note the deep parrot-like skull. About one-tenth natural size

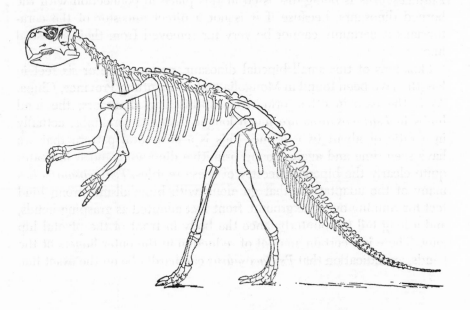

small one indeed, yet it is not a step that can be taken directly. For even though *Psittacosaurus* in most of its characters is so nicely ancestral to the horned dinosaurs, it is excluded from an actual ancestry by certain small points in its anatomy—by the loss of fingers in the hand, for example. We should not, however, take such minor departures as this very seriously, for if we did, the piecing together of the history of various groups of extinct animals would become an almost insuperable task. It must be remembered that the fossils we find are almost always *approximations* to the types that might be expected in a logical progression from ancestor through intermediate forms to ultimate descendant. What the fossil record shows us are the structural types, each very commonly with specializations that may bar them from positions in the direct line of evolution. If a direct evolutionary line were to be represented by a sequence, *A* to *B* to *C* to *D*, the fossil record more often than not may show something very close to *A*, leading to *B*, this in turn leading to something close to *C*, this leading to *D* or something very close to *D*. If these facts be recognized, if the validity of *approximate* ancestral types be accepted, then the validity of lines of descent need not be seriously questioned, even when some members of such lines are slightly removed to positions on one side or the other of the direct line. These thoughts are set forth to explain why *Psittacosaurus*, in spite of its somewhat specialized hand, can none the less be regarded quite correctly as close to the ancestry of the ceratopsians. Some close cousin of *Psittacosaurus*, as yet unknown to us, in which there had been no evolutionary loss of fingers would be a more satisfactory ancestor for the horned dinosaurs, but since such a reptile has not come to light *Psittacosaurus* will for the present have to serve our purposes as the grandfather of the ceratopsians. All in all, it is a pretty good grandfather.

THE FIRST CERATOPSIANS

The next step beyond *Psittacosaurus* brings us to *Leptoceratops*, a form known from some nice skeletons that have been found in the Edmonton beds of Alberta. Now it so happens that *Leptoceratops* is one of the later ceratopsians; it was living when the horned dinosaurs had attained a high degree of evolutionary specialization, when giant horned dinosaurs of various kinds roamed the late Cretaceous landscapes of western North America. None the less, *Leptoceratops* is a truly primitive type of ceratopsian that nicely bridges the gap between the ancestral form *Psittacosaurus* and the characteristic horned dinosaurs, all of which probably stem from a nice little ceratopsian known as *Protoceratops,* soon to be described. In *Leptoceratops* we see once again a "structural ancestor" living along with his descendants.

The skeleton of *Leptoceratops* is not very large, perhaps some six feet or so in length. In this dinosaur the forelimbs are of such size that the animal very probably assumed a quadrupedal or four-footed pose much of the time, yet even so the disparity in size between front legs and hind legs is still great. All of the fingers are present, but the outer ones, the fourth and fifth digits, are small. The skull is deep and has a beak, like the skull of *Psittacosaurus,* but in *Leptoceratops* the back part of the skull roof, composed of the parietal and squamosal bones, extends back over the neck in the form of a flat crest. This is a very significant feature of the skull of *Leptoceratops;* it marks the beginning of a spectacular evolutionary trend that was to be particularly characteristic of the horned dinosaurs.

We now turn our attention to a summer day in 1922, when a convoy of automobiles crossing the desert plains of Outer Mongolia came to a halt at some spectacular cliffs that rose from the desert floor to make a prominent landmark on a caravan trail that crossed Mongolia from east to west. These were the so-called "Flaming Cliffs" of Djadochta near Shabarakh Usu. The automobiles were the cars of the Central Asiatic Expeditions of the American Museum of Natural History, and the men who swarmed out of the vehicles when the stop was made were scientists engaged in a large and elaborate natural-history survey of the Gobi. The members of the expedition began to explore the cliffs, and before long fossil bones were being found—bones of a small dinosaur. And then a truly electrifying discovery was made, of fossil eggs near the top of one of the cliffs (Plate 81). Thus was *Protoceratops* first discovered, one of the most completely documented of all dinosaurs. In time a large series of skulls, skeletons, and eggs of this interesting dinosaur had been accumulated, not only in decades past by the Central Asiatic Expedition but also in recent years by Russian and Chinese paleontologists.

Protoceratops carries the story of ceratopsian evolution beyond the stage that is represented by *Leptoceratops,* and establishes quite definitely the structural pattern of the varied horned dinosaurs that lived during the closing phases of Cretaceous history.

Protoceratops is not so very different in size from *Leptoceratops;*

it is a small dinosaur, the skeleton of which is perhaps six or eight feet in length (Plate 83). It is a completely quadrupedal dinosaur, even though the front legs are considerably smaller than the hind legs. The feet are rather broad, as if to give firm support to the animal on dry land. The tail is rather long.

It is no wonder that *Protoceratops* was so completely quadrupedal in its pose, even though it is a small dinosaur, because in this reptile the skull is a remarkably large structure in comparison with the size of the body. In fact, the length of the skull is just a bit more than three-fourths the length of the back, from neck to pelvis, and any animal with a skull almost as long as the body is not suited to walking about on its hind legs. The great size of the skull in *Protoceratops* is in part the result of a differential evolutionary growth rate that caused the skull to become increasingly large during time at a faster rate than did the body, but it is also due in part to a great expansion of the crest, that flattened expansion of the parietal and squamosal bones on the back of the skull that we have seen in *Leptoceratops*. Whereas in *Leptoceratops* the crest or *frill*, as it is commonly called, is of rather modest size, in *Protoceratops* it is a large, flaring shield that extends back over the neck and the shoulders; and whereas the small frill in *Leptoceratops* is a solid shield, the large frill in *Protoceratops* is perforated by two openings or vacuities, one on each side.

It is the frill, adumbrated in *Leptoceratops*, completely developed in *Protoceratops*, that so characterizes and identifies the horned dinosaurs, for in these reptiles the horns from which the group takes its name may vary as to size and development, but, beyond the *Leptoceratops* stage, the frill is always there as an expanded shield that materially increases to the size of the gigantic skull. It is quite clear the frill began as an accommodation for the attachment of strong jaw muscles, and this was its primary function throughout ceratopsian evolution. But it also served for the attachment of strong neck muscles that controlled the movement of the head, and as an auxiliary function which certainly must have been useful, as a sort of buckler to protect the neck and shoulders, always a vulnerable region.

The front part of the skull in *Protoceratops* shows the form that had already evolved in its more primitive relatives. It is a deep, narrow skull, with a parrot-like beak and a mouth in which the teeth are restricted to the sides of the jaws. *Protoceratops* exhibits a primitive feature by virtue of the fact that in each premaxillary bone, on each

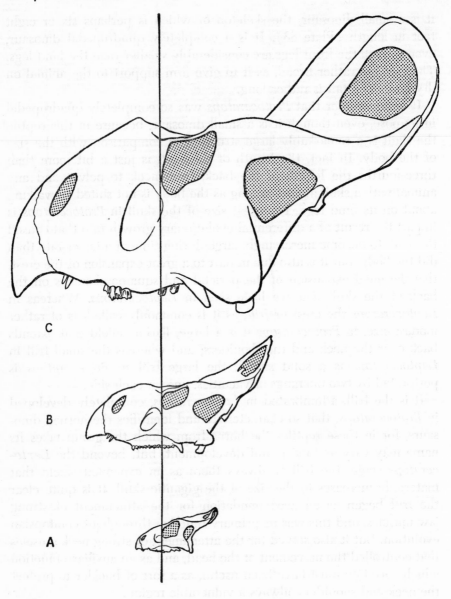

Figure 33. Growth stages in the primitive ceratopsian *Protoceratops*. A. Skull of a very young individual, newly hatched from the egg. B. An intermediate stage. C. An old adult. All are drawn to the same scale, about one-sixth natural size

side of the front of the skull, there are two small teeth. This is merely the retention of an ancient condition that had disappeared in *Leptoceratops* and even in so primitive a type as *Psittacosaurus*.

In one respect the front part of the skull shows a very significant advance, for in very large individuals of *Protoceratops* there is a distinct bump or point on the mid-line of the two conjoined nasal bones. This is the beginning of the nasal horn; it is the first indication of the many kinds of horns that were to decorate the skulls of the more advanced ceratopsians.

Some mention already has been made of the fact that *Protoceratops* is probably the most completely documented of all dinosaurs—and so it is. Not only are there numerous skeletons in museums of this dinosaur, but also there are many skulls that represent an unparalleled record of growth from the newly hatched baby dinosaur to the full-grown adult. This series of skulls shows that as *Protoceratops* grew up, the frill at the back of the skull became progressively ever larger in relation to the size of the rest of the skull. Thus does the growth of the individual mirror evolutionary development in a very general way.

The record of individual growth, or ontogeny, in *Protoceratops* extends back to include the eggs, which is most unusual among the dinosaurs, or among any of the fossil reptiles for that matter. The American Museum Expedition to Mongolia recovered more than seventy eggs from the Flaming Cliffs, and countless thousands of fragments of eggshells. And again, Russian and Chinese workers have since added to this record. The eggs are commonly about eight inches in length and are greatly elongated, as are the eggs of modern lizards. The shell has a pebbly surface, and in life was probably rather leathery, as is commonly the case among modern reptiles. Many of the eggs were found in clusters—obviously nests. It seems quite evident that the female *Protoceratops* did just what we see various modern reptiles do, reptiles such as sea turtles or crocodiles. She dug a big hollow in the sand, deposited as many as a dozen or fifteen or more eggs in this hollow, and then covered the eggs with sand, depending upon the heat of the sun to hatch them. Something went wrong at times, and some of the nests of eggs failed to hatch. Consequently we have a priceless paleontological record of fossil eggs, most of them completely filled with sand, a few showing traces of embryonic bone.

GIANT HORNED DINOSAURS

From *Protoceratops* on, the evolution of the horned dinosaurs was marked by three trends, which were:

1. Increase in size.
2. Various developments of the frill.
3. Various developments of horns on the skull.

The results of these trends in the evolution of the horned dinosaurs are nicely demonstrated by the ceratopsians that are found in Upper Cretaceous deposits of western North America. In Wyoming, Montana, and Alberta there are certain sediments that represent a sequence of deposition through late Cretaceous times, thus:

Lance and Hell Creek formations—Wyoming and Montana

Edmonton formation ⎫
Belly River series ⎭ Alberta

In going from the Belly River, the oldest of the sequence, through the Edmonton and finally the Lance, or the Hell Creek, it is possible to follow in detail the geologically brief but spectacular evolution of the horned dinosaurs. At an early stage in this history of the horned dinosaurs, in the Belly River beds, there is generally speaking a two-fold division of the ceratopsians, in one of which the skull carries a comparatively short frill, in the other, a rather long frill. These two lines of short-frilled and long-frilled ceratopsians continue, parallel to each other, through the Edmonton and Lance horizons. In both evolutionary lines there are varied developments of horns and an increase in the size of the dinosaurs through time.

To take the size increase first: it was not a constant evolutionary growth, but as is so often the case in evolving groups of animals, there was an initial spurt to giantism, followed by a very modest increase. For example, *Protoceratops* is a dinosaur perhaps six feet or so in length. *Monoclonius* of the Belly River has a length of about sixteen or eighteen feet, and it seems likely that this threefold increment in length (with a correlative increase in weight of perhaps twentyfold or more) took place very rapidly in terms of geologic time. From *Monoclonius* to the last of the horned dinosaurs the increase was quite moderate—from about eighteen feet to perhaps a maximum of twenty-four feet in the length of the skeleton—an addition of about a third in linear terms, with a correspondingly moderate increase in weight.

The real interest in later ceratopsian history is in the variety of patterns developed in the frills and the horns of the skull. *Monoclonius* (Plate 84) has been mentioned. This is a rather large ceratopsian with a comparatively short frill, the frill being perforated on each side by a large opening or vacuity, and with a long horn on the nose. There are small brow horns, one over each eye. The edge of the frill in *Monoclonius* is scalloped in a series of rounded bumps, and at the back of the frill are hook-like processes of bone. *Styracosaurus* (Plate 85) was a contemporary of *Monoclonius* in the short-frilled line. It, too, has a long horn on the nose, and virtually no brow horns at all.

Figure 34. Increase in the size of the ceratopsian dinosaurs as they evolved through late Cretaceous time

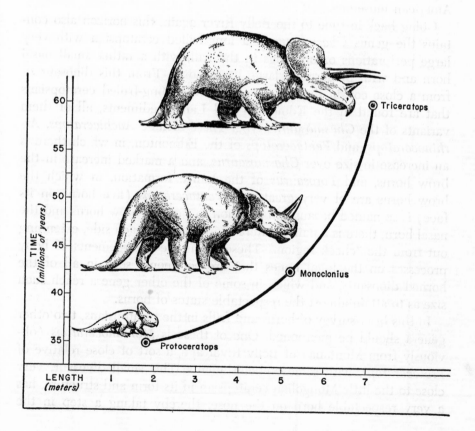

But in *Styracosaurus* there are very long spikes of bone all around the edge of the frill, culminating in two extremely long spikes at the back, pointing backwardly. These spikes give the impression of a long frill in *Styracosaurus*, but if the basic frill is looked at carefully, without the added decoration of the peripheral spikes, it becomes quite apparent that this is a short-frilled ceratopsian, not unlike *Monoclonius* in the general structure of the skull.

Perhaps the best known of the horned dinosaurs is *Triceratops* of the Lance and Hell Creek beds (Plate 86). This is a short-frilled ceratopsian, in which the frill is solid, in which the horn on the nose is relatively short, and in which the brow horns are enormously long. *Triceratops* is one of the largest of the horned dinosaurs, and one of the last. It must have roamed the tropical landscapes of what are now Wyoming or Montana in great numbers, perhaps in enormous herds. Certainly fossils are very common, with the result that many skulls and a goodly number of skeletons are to be found in various North American museums.

Going back in time to the Belly River again, this horizon also contains the genus *Chasmosaurus*, a long-frilled ceratopsian with very large perforations or openings in the frill, with a rather small nasal horn and with moderately large brow horns. From this dinosaur or from a close cousin there evolved the other long-frilled ceratopsians that are found in the Edmonton and Lance sediments, all of them variants of the *Chasmosaurus* type. These include *Anchiceratops*, *Arrhinoceratops*, and *Pentaceratops* of the Edmonton, in which there is an increase in size over *Chasmosaurus*, and a marked increase in the brow horns, and *Torosaurus* of the Lance formation, in which the brow horns are of very great size. *Pentaceratops* (five horns on its face) is so named because, in addition to the two brow horns and the nasal horn, there is a pair of lateral horns, one on each side, extending out from the "cheek region." These horns are enlargements of bony processes on the jugal bones that are commonly seen in all of the horned dinosaurs, and which in some of the other genera reach such size as to attain almost the respectable status of horns.

In this brief survey of horns and frills in the ceratopsians, two other genera should be mentioned. One of these is *Montanoceratops* (obviously from Montana) of Belly River age, a sort of close relative of *Protoceratops*, with some embellishments. This small dinosaur, very close to the little Mongolian ceratopsian in its form and structure, has a very respectable horn on the nose, thereby taking a step in the

direction of its large relatives. The other of the two genera is a large
ceratopsian, *Pachyrhinosaurus*, from the Edmonton formation. This
dinosaur, only recently discovered and described, seems not to have
had any horns on the skull, but rather a great thickened boss or
rough plate of bone that covered the top of the skull from above the
eyes forward to the region of the nose. It represents a separate line of
ceratopsian evolution about which much remains to be learned.

SOME PROBLEMS

Having made ourselves acquainted with the several horned dinosaurs
that inhabited western North America during late Cretaceous times,

Figure 35. Evolution of the ceratopsian dinosaurs as shown by the development
of the skull. The varied development of horns (solid black) and frills (shaded)
is shown

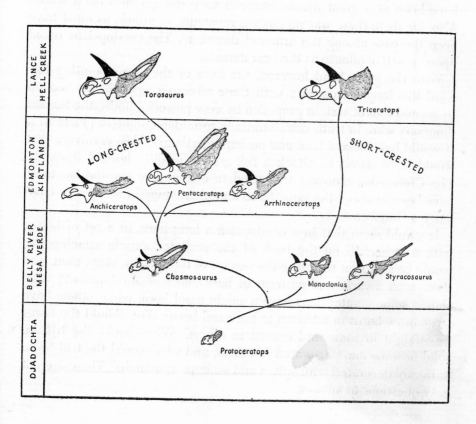

let us now inquire into the meaning of their evolutionary development. To begin this inquiry, let us look at a typical horned dinosaur, such as *Monoclonius* or *Triceratops,* with an analytical eye for a glimpse into the possible habits or the mode of life of these long-extinct reptiles.

Evidently the ceratopsians were active reptiles that roamed the uplands of their environment in search of succulent plant food. Very probably they traveled in groups, possibly in rather large herds, as do many modern groups of plant-eating mammals. They were probably fairly inoffensive animals, but when they were threatened by the giant predatory dinosaurs of late Cretaceous times, dinosaurs such as *Gorgosaurus* and *Tyrannosaurus,* they must have fought off their attackers with vigor and power. For them there was no escape to the haven of deep water, as was possible for the giant brontosaurs or for the active, duck-billed dinosaurs. Nothing about the ceratopsians indicates that they ever ventured into water of any depth, and as a matter of fact such heavily built, large-headed dinosaurs as these would probably have been at a great disadvantage if they did get into deep water. Also, for them there was no passive resistance to attack, as must have been the case among the armored dinosaurs. The ceratopsians relied upon an active offense as the best defense.

With the great head lowered, the horn or the horns pointing forward like long spears, and with these offensive weapons backed up by several tons of weight propelled by very powerful limbs, the horned dinosaurs were in truth extraordinarily formidable fighters (Plate 87). It would have been a bold and perhaps a rather reckless carnivore that would have dared to attack a full-grown, healthy horned dinosaur. The Cretaceous dinosaur that tried to challenge a ceratopsian must have been in about the same fix as a modern animal that tries to challenge a rhinoceros.

It would seem that in a ceratopsian a long horn, or a set of horns, with a large frill on the back of the skull for muscle attachments, would be sufficient to ensure the success of the species. Why, then, was there such a variety of patterns of horn and frill development? Why should some ceratopsians have a single nasal horn, while others have large brow horns in addition to the nasal horn? Why should the horns be straight in some and curved in others? Why should the frill be solid in some and perforated in others, and why should the frill be so variously decorated with spikes and scallops and knobs? These are not easy questions to answer.

Plate 81. Collecting a nest of *Protoceratops* eggs on the **Flaming** Cliffs at Shabarakh Usu, Outer Mongolia, in 1922

Plate 82. A group of *Protoceratops* eggs from the Cretaceous beds of Mongolia. The largest egg is about eight inches in length

Plate 83. The ancestral horned dinosaur *Protoceratops,* from the Cretaceous of Mongolia, shown with a reconstruction of a nest containing eggs. Each skeleton is about six feet long

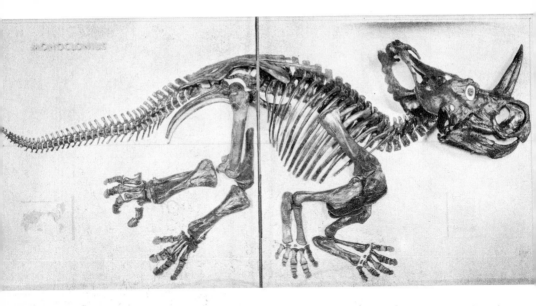

Plate 84. The horned dinosaur *Monoclonius*, from the Cretaceous beds of Alberta. The skeleton, about sixteen feet long, is shown in the position in which it was found

Plate 85. *Styracosaurus,* another ceratopsian dinosaur from the Cretaceous beds of Alberta. The skeleton is about eighteen feet long

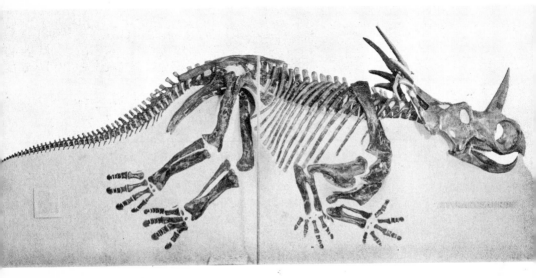

Plate 86. One of the last of the horned dinosaurs, *Triceratops,* from the Upper Cretaceous beds of western North America. The huge skull is about seven feet long; the skeleton twenty-four feet in length

Plate 87.   Restoration of *Triceratops.* By Charles R. Knight

Plate 88. Dinosaur footprints as exposed in the Triassic rocks of the Connecticut Valley

Plate 89. Triassic dinosaur footprints in the Arizona desert. Note the general similarity of these tracks to those found in the Connecticut Valley. They were made by primitive theropods

Plate 90. A trackway of huge sauropod footprints in Lower Cretaceous rocks in Texas. Note the round fore-foot prints, the immense hind-foot prints, and to the left, the three-toed tracks of a carnivorous dinosaur

Perhaps our only answer is to compare the horned dinosaurs with the modern horned antelopes of Africa, to see if structures in the recent mammals give any clues to structures in the ancient dinosaurs. Again, on the face of it, one would think that a simple set of straight or slightly curved horns would be sufficient for a modern antelope. But in Africa there is a great and almost bewildering array of antelopes with horns of all shapes and sizes. There is the gemsbok, with very long, straight horns; the sable antelope, with magnificent curved horns that sweep far back; the eland, with tightly spiraled horns; the kudu, with beautiful openly spiral horns; the gazelle, with small horns; the redunca, with forwardly curved horns; the gnu, with downwardly and forwardly directed horns; and many others that might be mentioned. What are the advantages of one type of horn over another? Unfortunately we still have much to learn even about living animals, and the answer to this problem of antelope horns is still to be found. Perhaps

---

Figure 36. World map showing the distribution of the ceratopsian or horned dinosaurs

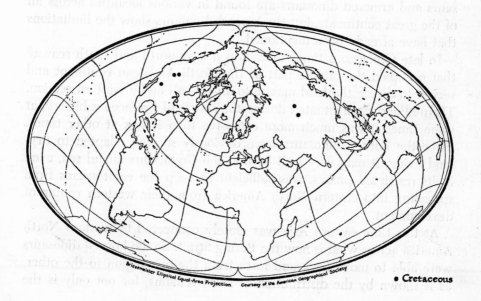

• Cretaceous

the antelopes of Africa represent animals that have evolved as separate populations in which differences became established long ago and were perpetuated. Perhaps the differences in antelope horns are largely an indication that all horns are useful, and the shapes are of less importance than the presence of the horns. And perhaps this line of reasoning may be applied to the horned dinosaurs. Whatever the cause, the fact is that the horned dinosaurs lived in great profusion and variety during late Cretaceous times.

The geological record seems to indicate that the horned dinosaurs were limited to western North America and to northeastern Asia. Many times a limited distribution like this in the geological record should be viewed with suspicion; it is more likely than not indicative of the fact that the record is still very incomplete, that there are fossils still to be found. As for the horned dinosaurs, there are undoubtedly fossils still to be found, but the present writer is willing to wager that they will be found in western North America and eastern Asia. The limitation of fossils of horned dinosaurs to these regions may very truly reflect the limitations of their ranges when these reptiles were alive.

If horned dinosaurs lived in other parts of the world, why have not their bones been discovered, along with the bones of other dinosaurs with which they might logically be expected to have lived? Giant meat-eating dinosaurs and great brontosaurs, duck-billed dinosaurs and armored dinosaurs are found in various localities across all of the great continents, but the horned dinosaurs show the limitations that have already been mentioned.

In late Cretaceous times there was a long north and south seaway that occupied the middle part of the North American continent and served to divide the land mass into an eastern and a western section. The midland sea fluctuated during the course of Cretaceous history; at some times it was much more extensive than it was at other times. Since the horned dinosaurs were obviously so well adapted to dry-land living, it may very well be that the Cretaceous inland sea, even in its restricted phases, was sufficient to keep the ceratopsians from spreading into eastern North America from their western center of development.

At this time eastern Asia was closely connected to western North America across what is now the Bering Strait. So the horned dinosaurs were able to move back and forth from the one region to the other, as is shown by the distribution of fossil remains, for not only is the primitive ceratopsian *Protoceratops* found in Mongolia, but also some of the more advanced types, such as *Styracosaurus*. Perhaps there was a barrier of some form to the west on the Asiatic continent, so that the ceratopsians there may have been prevented from spreading to the west, just as the ceratopsians in North America may have been prevented from spreading to the east.

That is the way it looks, and it makes a nice, well-ordered picture. Some day the picture may be spoiled by future discoveries, but until that day comes it is convenient to have this very neat and logical pattern of ceratopsian distribution as a basis for our concept as to where these reptiles lived during the final phases of Cretaceous history.

And in these limited areas, in western North America and eastern Asia, they lived most abundantly, as has been said. They were very successful dinosaurs. But like all of the other dinosaurs, they were unable to survive the transition from Mesozoic to Cenozoic times, and so they became extinct, about 70 million years ago.

Figure 37.   The skeleton of *Monoclonius,* a horned dinosaur. About one thirty-fifth natural size

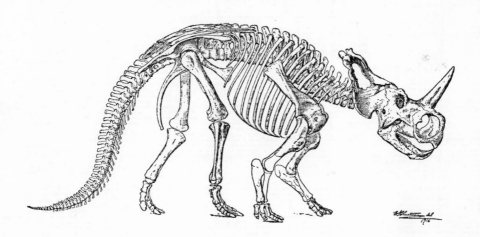

THE MAKING OF TRACKS

So far in this book our attention has been largely devoted to the fossilized remains of the dinosaurs; to their petrified bones, and to what the study and interpretation of these ancient relics tell us about the ruling reptiles of the Mesozoic era. Let us now give some thought to the fossilized footprints of the dinosaurs, the visible evidence of ancient wanderings across ancient lands. There is much that is baffling about these particular fossils, and much to be learned from them.

It should be remembered at this place that fossils, according to the modern definition of these objects, are the *remains* or *indications* of life that is now extinct. The bones of the dinosaurs are their fossil *remains;* footprints or tracks in the rocks are *indications* of these ancient reptiles, and are perfectly valid fossils, as are the bones. Yet footprints must always be regarded as supplementary evidence, giving us additional information that in conjunction with what we know from the bones helps us better to understand the dinosaurs and how they lived.

Dinosaur footprints or trackways (these being extended trails composed of many tracks) are not rare, nor, except in certain particular localities, are they abundant. One might ask why they are not more abundant, because there were undoubtedly a great many dinosaurs living on the Mesozoic continents during a span of perhaps a hundred million years, and these were all fairly active animals that moved about quite a lot. Think of the number of steps that were taken collectively by all of the dinosaurs of Mesozoic times; it staggers the imagination! And to show how it does stagger the imagination, let's play quite briefly with a few figures.

It has been calculated from observations that a work horse, not a free, untrammeled horse of the broad plains, but a plodding old dobbin, will take about 6,000 steps during the course of the day. A step means a stride with one foot, and since it is obvious that the horse plants all four feet on the ground during the day to a total of 6,000 times four, our horse, were he making prints each time he put a foot down, would make 24,000 footprints from sun to sun, and that would be a lot of tracks. Now, suppose the horse lives to an age of 20 years, which is not unusual for a horse, or a total of 7,300 days. By simple arithmetic it can be calculated that the horse would take about 44,000,000 steps during the course of his life, making a total of about 175,000,000 contacts of all four feet to the ground. There are a lot of potential footprints in a figure such as that.

Let us assume that the average dinosaur was not so active as a work horse, and may have taken only 3,000 steps a day, but let us also assume that the dinosaurs, being large reptiles, were comparatively long-lived, as are the large reptiles, such as crocodiles and turtles of our modern world. Thus it is not unreasonable to suppose that the total number of steps taken by the average dinosaur (if there was any such thing as an average dinosaur) might very easily have added up to as large a figure as that for the 20-year-old horse. Now think of the hordes of dinosaurs that inhabited the world for a stretch of time extending over about 100,000,000 years; multiply a figure of say 150,-000,000 (a conservative estimate of foot-to-ground contacts for a single animal) by the untold millions of dinosaurs of Triassic, Jurassic, and Cretaceous times. The result must be somewhere in the billions of billions.

This little excursion into numbers has been hedged about by various suppositions and assumptions, yet no matter how wide of the mark it may be it none the less does indicate that a lot of steps were taken by the dinosaurs during the time they lived on the earth. Then why are not dinosaur tracks quite numerous in the rocks of Mesozoic age?

To answer this question let's think again of our hypothetical friend the work horse. How many of the millions of steps taken by this horse during its life are to be preserved for future generations? Very few— if any. For one thing, much of the horse's walking is done on hard ground, where no footprints are made. Where the horse does make footprints, out in the fields or upon muddy roads, the statistical chances for any such tracks being preserved are infinitesimally small. To be preserved, a track has to be made in stiff mud or soil, where it will harden and be fairly durable. Then before it can be destroyed by the elements it has to be covered by sediments that drift in on top of it by some natural means, thereby keeping it inviolate for posterity. Thus the conditions for the preservation of footprints must be "just right," and such conditions don't occur very often. Nevertheless, over a sufficiently long period of geologic time they do add up, and that is how we have a record of dinosaur tracks. Out of countless billions of tracks that must have been made by dinosaurs thousands have been discovered in the record of the rocks, and more are being discovered with each passing year.

It would seem that the "just right" conditions allowing the preservation of footprints as fossils were usually not just right for the preservation of bones, because dinosaur footprints and dinosaur bones are rarely found together, why we do not know. Most dinosaur footprints would seem to have been made on mud flats, along the shores of lakes or streams. The tracks are commonly associated with ripple marks and raindrop impressions, all preserved in stony immobility, yet in such vivid records of waves and storms of the distant past there are seldom bony remains to be found. And this is inconvenient, because it does not allow for much correlation between skeletons and footprints.

THE NAMING OF TRACKS

Since dinosaur footprints are so seldom found with dinosaur bones, there has grown through the past century a well-established practice of giving to the tracks names all of their own. That is to say, nobody has quite dared to designate the footprints with the same names that have been given to the skeletons, because no scholar has been willing to state categorically that such and such a track was actually made by such and such a dinosaur. This is understandable. Can anybody, no matter how broad his knowledge or deep his insight, be certain as to the relationship between fossil bones and footprints when it is usually quite impossible to make a physical association of the two types of evidence? Therefore, dinosaur tracks must of necessity be considered and studied in the light of what they show by themselves, with of course some reasonable guesses as to how they might be correlated with the dinosaur skeletons known to us.

The labeling of tracks with names of their own may be logically justified, but it has led to a good deal of confusion and even misinformation through the years. A great many more names have been given than have been warranted, thereby creating an impression that the footprints represent a much grander array of dinosaurs than probably is the case. For example, the Triassic footprints of the Connecticut Valley, referred to in Chapter Two, have been classified by a truly impressive list of generic and specific names, and should the unwary reader scan this list he might get the idea that dinosaurs roamed eastern North America in great profusion and astonishing variety during late Triassic times. That these dinosaurs existed in abundance can hardly be doubted; that they formed such a broad range of varied types as is implied by the list can be quite seriously doubted, and with good cause.

For one thing, it is very doubtful that the tracks can be separated from each other in such detail as has been done. Tracks that look different from each other have all too frequently been given different names, without any thought of modifying circumstances. Of these circumstances one is the matter of individual age. How can one be sure that small tracks and large tracks that are generally similar in appearance represent separate species? The chances are quite good that in many cases these are indications of young and adult animals belonging to a single species, especially when they are found close together. Again, how can one be sure that tracks that look different from each other in certain respects actually represent different species or genera of dinosaurs? There have been made in recent years some very searching studies of the tracks of living amphibians and reptiles, and much has been learned from these investigations. It has been found, for instance, that a single animal may make tracks and trackways that have remarkably different appearances according to whether the tracks are made in loose sand, soft mud or stiff mud, whether they are made by the animal going across a level surface or up a slope or down a slope, whether they are made by the animal when resting, or traveling at a leisurely walk or at a fast run, and so on. It is evident that there are certain pitfalls that face the student of fossil footprints, and it does seem obvious that no one should attempt such studies unless he first familiarizes himself with the manner in which footprints are made by modern animals.

But if careful attention is given to such considerations, and if the study of tracks is approached especially as a study of the habits and behavior of animals long since vanished from the face of the earth, rather than as an exercise in the creation of new names, some very interesting and illuminating facts can be brought to light.

THE CONNECTICUT VALLEY TRACKS

Let us look once again at the footprints from the Upper Triassic sediments of the Connecticut Valley. Now, as a result of descriptions by various authors during the past hundred years or more there have been named at least thirteen supposed genera and forty-one supposed species of dinosaurs upon the basis of these tracks. If the tracks are carefully and objectively analyzed, the plethora of names that has been applied to them can be greatly diminished, and a few distinct, principal types can be recognized. These might be:

Grallator—a small, slender three-toed footprint that might very well have been made by the graceful coelurosaurian *Coelophysis*, described in Chapter Four. Bones that may be attributed to this dinosaur have recently been described from the Connecticut Valley. It is also possible that the small coelurosaurian *Podokesaurus*, closely related to *Coelophysis* and known from a partial skeleton found in the Connecticut Valley, may have been responsible for some of the tracks that are called *Grallator*.

Eubrontes—a large three-toed dinosaur, possibly one of the large carnivores, like *Teratosaurus*, for example. Bones of this particular dinosaur are not known from North America, but there is no reason why it or a relative might not be represented among these Connecticut Valley footprints.

Anchisauripus—a large, heavy three-toed track, with indications of a small toe turned to the rear. Here is a track that coincides with the hind feet in *Anchisaurus*, the rather large prosauropod known from bones found in the Connecticut Valley.

Otozoum—a large bipedal dinosaur with four toes and the trace of a fifth, all pointed forwardly.

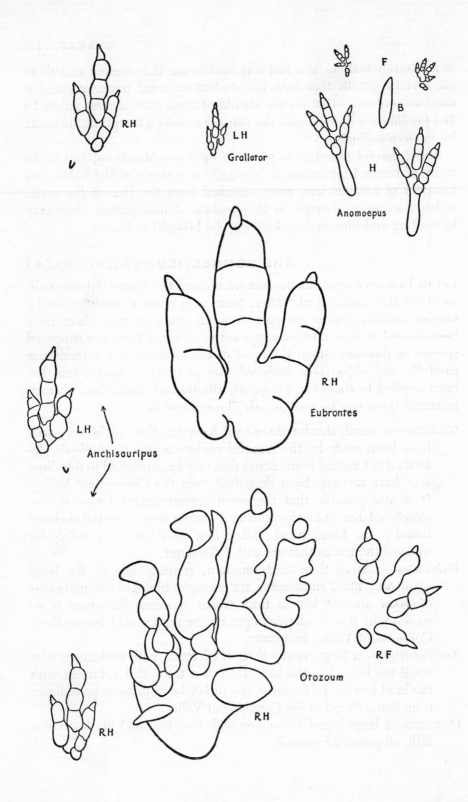

RH

LH
Grallator

F

B

H
Anomoepus

RH
Eubrontes

LH
Anchisauripus

RF

Otozoum

RH

RH

Anomoepus—known from both fore and hind footprints, an indication that this dinosaur assumed a quadrupedal pose at times. The hind foot is slender, with three functional toes; the hand is small with five fingers indicated, these *not* furnished with heavy claws as might be expected in a carnivorous type.

The thousands of footprints that have been found in the Connecticut Valley give us a picture of the several early dinosaurs just categorized, large and small, wandering back and forth across muddy flats near rivers or lakes in search of food, or in search of security from their enemies. Most of the tracks and trackways show us dinosaurs on the move, either walking or running. Some of them show that their makers came to sudden stops; some of them show how they slipped in the mud. At least one set of tracks, of *Anomoepus,* show the dinosaur resting with all four feet and the belly on the ground. Many of the footprints are superimposed upon ripple marks, showing that the dinosaurs wandered across the mud flats following the retreat of shallow waters; perhaps tidal waters or perhaps high waters caused by heavy rainstorms. Many of the tracks are interspersed with the crater-like impressions made by large raindrops, the fossil evidence of storms that swept across the land two hundred million years ago. Many of the tracks were made across surfaces broken into polygonal shapes, the indications of mud cracks formed by the hot sun. Here are stories in stone, and here is the great value of footprint evidence, the evidence of what some dinosaurs were doing on certain, particular days, in a past that seems incredibly distant to twentieth century man.

THE GLEN ROSE TRACKS

For another example of what dinosaur tracks can tell us, let us give some attention to the great, spectacular footprints of giant dinosaurs

---

Figure 38. Footprints of dinosaurs from the Upper Triassic rocks of the Connecticut Valley. Note the long stride in the trackway of *Anchisauripus.* R—right; L—left; F—fore-foot; H—hind-foot; B—imprint of breast. All are about one-sixth natural size

of Lower Cretaceous age, excavated from the Glen Rose formation of the Trinity Marls, near Glen Rose and Bandera, Texas, southwest of Dallas (Plate 90). Some of these tracks and trackways were discussed in Chapter Six.

As may be remembered, the tracks discovered near Glen Rose, along the course of the Paluxy River, indicate a large brontosaur, not necessarily any of the other known genera of North American sauropods, but certainly a dinosaur very close to the familiar giants of the Morrison beds. The tracks, which have *not* been formally named, are huge, those of the hind feet being in each case three feet or so in length and correspondingly broad, those of the front feet being considerably smaller. The tracks of the hind feet show on each one three distinct claw marks, but the front foot tracks give no indications of claws. Evidently the big sauropod dinosaur that made these tracks had a round, rather elephant-like forefoot without claws, a contrast to *Brontosaurus* and other sauropods of the somewhat earlier Morrison beds in which there is a single large claw on the thumb.

As was pointed out earlier, these great tracks must have been made in shallow water, for there are no traces of tail marks, which means that the tail was floating instead of dragging on the ground. Yet the water was not deep enough to have reached the bellies of the animals that made them, for it is quite obvious that in each instance the full weight of the dinosaur was borne by the great padded feet. The tracks are very deep, and around the back of each print the mud was pushed out into a raised rim by the immense pressure of the foot.

The dinosaurs that made these tracks were walking through the shallow waters near a shore, either of a lake or more probably of the sea, where the sediments consisted of very fine limy materials. (Such sediments are often found today in shallow waters along the coast of Florida.) The footprints made in these limy marls, now turned to a chalky limestone, were continuously covered by shallow water, to be preserved intact for a considerable period of time—perhaps for a matter of several weeks or so. In the meantime there were storms and freshets, and mud was washed in to cover the footprints and the limy bottom that enclosed them. So it is that today along the Paluxy River these great trackways are found in limestone, covered by a layer of shale.

The trackway from Glen Rose that is on display at the American Museum of Natural History tells a most dramatic story of the past. Here are seen the tracks made by a huge sauropod dinosaur as it splashed along through the shallow water, and alongside the sauropod trackway, and in some cases superimposed on top of it, are the footprints of a large carnivorous dinosaur, a dinosaur that must have been very much like *Allosaurus*. The disposition of the tracks, looking almost as fresh in the rock as if they were still in mud and still only a day old, shows without doubt that the great meat-eating dinosaur was trailing the giant sauropod, and where the giant herbivore veered to the left, so did the carnivore. Here on a grand scale is the visible record

---

Figure 39. Footprints of a giant sauropod dinosaur from the Lower Cretaceous rocks of Texas. The smaller prints are of the front feet, the larger ones of the hind feet. A three-foot scale is shown

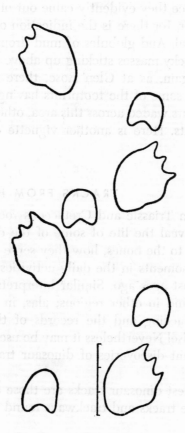

of hunter and hunted, a testament in the rock of an incident that took place a hundred million years ago or more, when Texas was a tropical or subtropical jungle and all the world was very different from what it is today. In looking at these tracks one gets a feeling of the immediacy of life, an impression of movement and action that cannot be realized in quite the same way by contemplation of the bones!

At Bandera, not very far away from Glen Rose, are found trackways that tell a different story. Over a large area of rock forming a sort of floor are trackways that can be attributed to a group of twenty-three sauropods. Some of the dinosaurs were evidently fully grown adults, others were half-grown juveniles. Here again, as at Glen Rose, the dinosaurs were splashing through fairly shallow water, but it was nevertheless deep enough so that the smaller individuals were partially buoyed up, thereby making footprints that are comparatively shallow. Some of the dinosaurs seem to have floated along in the water, walking on the bottom with their front feet, and barely touching it with their hind feet. At one place they evidently came out of the water, or were in very shallow water, for there is the indication of a dragging tail of at least one individual. And globules of mud dropped from their feet to be preserved as rocky masses sticking up above the general level of the rock surface. Again, as at Glen Rose, there are tracks of large predatory dinosaurs, some of the footprints having been made before the herd of brontosaurs waded across this area, others after the passage of the troop of giants. Here is another vignette of things that happened long ago.

TRACKS FROM HERE AND THERE

These examples from Triassic and Cretaceous rocks show how fossil footprints help to reveal the life of some of the dinosaurs, how they give added meaning to the bones, how they serve as the imperishable records of fleeting moments in the daily activities of reptiles that inhabited the earth vast ages ago. Similar interpretations might be extended to tracks found in other regions; alas, in all too many cases interpretations are lacking and the records of the tracks are mere records—and little else! Nevertheless it may be useful to indicate some of the more important discoveries of dinosaur tracks throughout the world.

Of course, the oldest dinosaur tracks are those of late Triassic age, and among these the tracks and trackways found in the valley of the

Connecticut River are of prime importance. As indicated in previous discussions, these tracks have been uncovered by the thousands, and there are many more still to be found. Indeed, these tracks occur in such abundance that at one locality in Massachusetts they are commercially quarried, to be sold to many people as aesthetic objects, or, if you will, as "conversation pieces." Believe me, a flagstone terrace takes on much added interest when it contains a block or two containing some unmistakable dinosaur tracks!

In western North America, where the bones of Triassic dinosaurs are much more numerous than they are in the Connecticut Valley or in other eastern Triassic localities, tracks are correspondingly rare. But at some places in Utah and Arizona tracks may be seen, and these are essentially similar to the ones found in the eastern states.

Tracks of Triassic dinosaurs have been found in South America, particularly in Argentina. In the Old World such tracks are known in Europe, especially in England, and in South Africa, where in Basutoland they occur in some abundance. These tracks in Africa have been attributed to a prosauropod such as *Euskelosaurus,* a dinosaur related to the well-known *Plateosaurus* of central Germany and to *Anchisaurus* of Connecticut.

Lower Jurassic dinosaur tracks occur in Morocco, the footprints of large carnivorous dinosaurs, preserved in a surface that shows a pattern of polygonal mud cracks. Here again we see the record of dinosaurs that were walking across a drying mud flat, which is the type of environment where so very many dinosaur tracks were made and preserved. Other Jurassic tracks of later age are known in Portugal and in Australia.

As for Cretaceous tracks and trackways, there should be mentioned, in addition to the marvelous discoveries made in Texas, the footprints of some truly huge carnivorous dinosaurs that have been removed from the roof of a coal mine in Colorado. These gigantic three-toed tracks indicate a great carnosaur with a long stride—perhaps a dinosaur very much like *Tyrannosaurus.*

In Canada a large series of footprints is exposed in sediments of Lower Cretaceous age along the bed of the Peace River in British Columbia. Many of these are three-toed tracks, indicating the presence of a good-sized carnivorous dinosaur, but there are also tracks that may have been made by a small ornithopod herbivore, possibly a dinosaur like *Camptosaurus.* As is so often the case, not a bone has been found to help in the interpretation of these tracks. But elsewhere in Canada, along the Red Deer River in Alberta, a few tracks have been found that may be correlated with at least one of the dinosaurs of which so many fine skeletons are known from this region. The tracks have been called *Ornithomimipus,* and from their slender, elongated form it is quite possible that they were made by a coelurosaurian closely related to, if not identical with, *Ornithomimus,* the well-known

Figure 40. Correlation of the bones of the hind foot of a hadrosaurian dinosaur, with a footprint found in the same sediments in which the bones were preserved. About one-sixth natural size

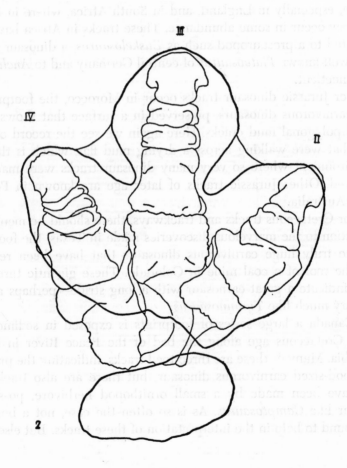

"ostrich dinosaur" from the Upper Cretaceous sediments of western North America.

In the Lower Cretaceous sediments known as the Wealden of Europe, dinosaur tracks have been found at various localities: in England, in central Europe, and on some islands in the Adriatic Sea. The discovery of Cretaceous tracks on these islands, as well as on the Isle of Wight, off the southern coast of England, is some slight indication of the well-known geological fact that the limits of continents in past ages were not the same as they are today. Some of these Wealden tracks are significant because it would seem that they actually can be correlated with *Iguanodon,* of which there are numerous skeletons available. It has been shown that the bones of the hind foot of *Iguanodon* from Belgium (and it may be recalled that a large series of skeletons of this dinosaur were excavated from a Belgian coal mine) can be exactly superimposed upon a Wealden footprint from Hanover, Germany. Consequently, in this case at least it seems reasonably safe to regard the footprint as a track of *Iguanodon,* with no circumlocutions in the form of a separate name for it.

Footprints that show all the appearance of having been made by *Iguanodon* are also found in the Lower Cretaceous beds of Shansi, China. And in Manchuria are footprints that record the passage of a herd of small three-toed dinosaurs. Twelve hundred of these tracks occur at one locality!

The occurrence of large theropod and of sauropod or brontosaur tracks, these last evidently made in shallow water, all of Lower Cretaceous age, has been reported from Russian Georgia, an obvious and most interesting parallel to the trackways of central Texas. These records of the simultaneous (geologically speaking) comings and goings of great dinosaurs in Texas and in Russia, paralleling the wide-flung footprint records of *Iguanodon,* illustrate very nicely the world-wide distribution of the various dinosaurs.

Much more might be written about dinosaur tracks and trackways, but what has been here put down gives a reasonably sufficient idea of what the tracks are like, how they might have been made, and what they may mean. And what they may mean differs according to the predispositions of the people who see them. To some paleontologists they are interesting but not particularly important; to others they are so supremely important that much more is read into them than is warranted; to still others they are interpreted with as much care and insight as possible, and in this way they add significantly to our knowledge of the dinosaur. To those who are not paleontologists the ancient footprints seem to have an almost universal appeal. They stimulate the imagination, frequently in an exciting manner, and he who has a lively mind will be led into many byways of speculation and philosophy when viewing one of these records of reptiles long extinct that wandered to and fro across an ancient land.

CHAPTER THIRTEEN

BRAINS, BRAWN, AND TEMPERATURES

BRAINS AND ENDOCRANIAL CASTS

The tracks and trackways that have through the millennia preserved for us a durable record of the comings and goings of the dinosaurs help us to see in our imagination some of those distant scenes in which the dinosaurs were the principal actors. The footprints give us some clues as to certain events in the lives of the dinosaurs, but they can hardly tell us how these things came about. What motivated the dinosaurs? How did they function as living organisms?

What the backboned animals do is determined to a large degree by the brain and the nervous system, acting in response to stimuli from the outside world. Animals see things or hear noises; they smell or feel or taste things. Impressions go to the brain and then there are reactions, and the reactions depend on what kind of vertebrate is doing the seeing or hearing or smelling, and what kind of brain it has.

What kinds of brains did the dinosaurs have? Do the fossils show us anything about this? The answer is that they do. Of course, the actual brain is never preserved in the dinosaurs, but in many specimens the brain case, the complex, interlocking group of bones that surround the brain within the skull, is intact, and frequently undistorted. So here we have something to go on. It is possible to clean out the brain case in such a fossil, to remove all bits of rock matrix, and then to make an accurate cast in plaster or in modern plastics of the internal cavity in which the brain was enclosed. This is delicate work that takes a skilled hand, but as so frequently is the case in scientific research, much can be accomplished with knowledge, skill, and patience. The result of such application is not a cast of the original brain, but an *endocranial* cast, as it is known in anatomical parlance, which is quite a different thing.

We know from the study of modern reptiles that the brain is suspended within the brain case by numerous fibers of conjunctive tissue, so that the brain in a sense "floats" within its encapsulating brain case, and is anchored in place by these fibers. Among reptiles of the present day the brain is commonly much smaller than its enclosing brain case, so that the size of the brain cavity is not necessarily a true indication of the size of the brain. Indeed, the internal volume of the brain case, the endocranial cavity, may be twice as great as the volume of the brain itself, which introduces a proper note of caution into the study of dinosaurian endocranial casts. We must always remember that they are casts of the inside of the brain case and not exact representations of the brain, but if this fact is kept in mind, and if suitable allowances are made for it, we can then proceed with the study of casts made from dinosaurian brain cases and learn some interesting things about the brain in these ancient reptiles.

BRAINS AND BODIES

How can the brain have been so small? That question is almost invariably asked by anyone who for the first time sees an endocranial cast of a dinosaur. The endocranial cast (*not* the brain) of *Stegosaurus* bulks no larger than an apricot or a large plum; the cast from the brain case of *Triceratops* is of similar size, or perhaps a bit larger, while the cast from the skull of *Tyrannosaurus,* one of the largest of dinosaurian endocranial casts, is an elongated object perhaps eight inches in length and no more than two inches in diameter. Let's say it in another way for additional emphasis: The brain of a gigantic dinosaur, a reptile that might have been sixty feet or more in length, with the weight of thirty tons or more, was perhaps no larger than the brain of a cat. What does this mean?

The study of brains is fraught with many difficulties, and what we don't know about brains, even human brains that have been most intensively investigated, is very impressive indeed. But there are two very general principles that are useful when we get involved in the problem of dinosaur brains. The first is that, generally speaking, the larger the brain, the greater the intelligence. The second is that large animals have absolutely larger brains than small animals, but relatively smaller brains than small animals. Maybe the use of some familiar examples will help to make this clear.

A dog has a larger brain than does a mouse, a gorilla has a larger brain than does a dog, and a man has a larger brain than does a gorilla, and it is evident that the dog is smarter than the mouse, the gorilla smarter than the dog, and the man smarter than the gorilla. Yet in comparison to body weight the mouse has a brain that is *relatively* greater than the other animals of this sequence. Here we see a correlation between absolute brain size and intelligence. As contrasted with this, an elephant has a brain that is absolutely four times as large as the brain of a man, and even though an elephant is one of the most intelligent of mammals it still is intellectually much inferior to the puny men upon which it can cast such a majestic downward look. As for relative weights, the brain of a man is much larger with relation to total body weight than is the brain of an elephant. Thus we see a rather complex series of interrelationships of brain size and body size in these modern mammals.

The brain in reptiles is remarkably primitive as compared with the mammalian brain, so perhaps absolute size is of even less significance in these vertebrates than it is in the mammals. Certainly the dinosaurs seem to show that as these particular reptiles grew into giants, the rate of increase in the size of the brain was remarkably small. The brain of an elephant is many times greater than the brain of a raccoon, but the brain of the largest dinosaur was enlarged only a few times over the brain of a large lizard or of a crocodile.

The brain of a large duck-billed dinosaur like *Anatosaurus* would have been perhaps about $\frac{1}{20,000}$ the weight of the body; the brain of one of the large sauropod dinosaurs like *Brontosaurus* might have been $\frac{1}{100,000}$ of the body weight. In a large crocodile the brain may be $\frac{1}{5,000}$ of the body weight; in an elephant $\frac{1}{1,000}$ of the body weight; in man, $\frac{1}{60}$ of the body weight. From such figures it is evident that the amount of "thinking" that went on in the dinosaurian brain was infinitesimal, that the brain was in these reptiles largely a sense receptor and motor organ, indicative of a life controlled predominantly by reflexes. All of this points up something quite elementary that we should never forget when we think about dinosaurs and about the way they lived, and this something is the fact that dinosaurs were reptiles and properly must be compared with reptiles as we know them. Perhaps there is a tendency to think of dinosaurs in terms of large mammals, because the only really large land-living animals familiar to us are big mammals like elephants and rhinoceroses and hippopotamuses.

THE LOWLY DINOSAURIAN BRAIN

Certainly the dinosaur brain, so far as can be told from the endocranial casts, was of a lowly and characteristic reptilian form and structure. It was elongated, and as seen from the side was curved along an S-shaped flexure, so that the front of the brain was a bit higher than its back portion. The various endocranial casts show that there was a pair of large olfactory lobes at the front of the brain, an indication that the dinosaurs had a good sense of smell. These large bulbous lobes were connected with the cerebrum, the principal part of the forebrain, by a long, horizontal olfactory stalk. In mammals, and particularly in human beings, the cerebrum, which forms the major portion of the brain, is a greatly expanded and frequently a highly infolded structure, but in reptiles it is comparatively small, and consists of a pair of simple, smooth lobes. The cerebrum in the dinosaurs, as indicated by the endocranial casts, conforms to the reptilian plan. The cerebrum in these reptiles was essentially a center for smell and for the association and co-ordination of impulses from other sense receptors. These great reptiles, as has been said, must have been controlled largely by automatic responses to the stimuli of the world in which they lived.

Because endocranial casts do show large optic nerves and large optic lobes behind the cerebral lobes, the dinosaurs evidently had good eyesight, in addition to a keen sense of smell.

Behind the cerebrum and the optic lobes is a downward flexure in the endocranial casts (the S-shaped flexure mentioned above), and this brings us to the cerebellar portion of the brain, that region concerned, among other things, with balance and motor responses. From the bottom and the back of the cerebellum, the medulla oblongata, the hindmost part of the brain, extended back into the forepart of the spinal nerve. Thus the dinosaur brain was stretched out something like a long, crooked, slender sweet potato, enlarged in some parts, contracted in others. To us it seems singularly unimpressive as a control center for animals that rank among the giants of all time. Yet it sufficed.

One feature of the dinosaurian endocranial casts that deserves particular attention is a sort of pendent extension directed down from the base of the brain, just behind the optic nerves. This was the pituitary body, that plays such an important role in the control and secretion of hormones. Among other things the pituitary produces a hormone that is involved with growth, and it is perhaps no mere coincidence that the pituitary body in the giant dinosaurs was of relatively huge size, attaining in some dinosaurs a volume that was 10 per cent of the brain volume.

There should be mentioned also the fact that some of the endocranial casts from dinosaur skulls are so perfectly preserved as to show casts

---

Figure 41. The restored brain within the endocranical cavity of the skull of the hadrosaur *Anatosaurus*. *Abbreviations:* O.L.—olfactory lobe; Cbr.—cerebrum; Op.—optic lobe; Cbl.—cerebellum; Pit.—pituitary; Med.—medulla

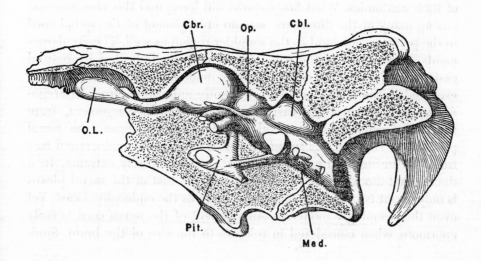

of the semicircular canals, of the inner ear. These are structures of great importance that enable the backboned animals to maintain their balance, to orient themselves with relation to the mass of the earth.

This brief account of the dinosaur brain, as based upon such knowledge as can be obtained from endocranial casts, is generally descriptive for the brains of all of the various types of dinosaurs. In some dinosaurs the brain was larger than in others. *Tyrannosaurus*, for example, had a large dinosaurian brain; *Stegosaurus*, an amazingly small brain. There are certain differences in proportions from one type to another. But these are details with which we need not concern ourselves; what we should keep in mind is that the brain in these reptiles was small and primitive, and yet it was a type of brain eminently sufficient for the rulers of the Mesozoic lands.

BEHIND THE BRAIN

In an oft-quoted poem about dinosaurs a rhymed statement is made to the effect that

> "We clearly see by these remains
> This creature had two sets of brains;
> One in his head (the usual place),
> The other at his spinal base."

Stegosaurus, the subject of the poem, did not have two sets of brains, nor was any other dinosaur so plentifully endowed in this way as to have extra sets of brains in their "spinal bases" or in any other parts of their anatomies. What *Stegosaurus* did have, and this was common among many of the dinosaurs, was an enlargement of the spinal cord in the pelvic region, and in the shoulder region as well. These enlargements or swellings of the spinal nerve cord, as indicated by natural casts from the skeleton or by carefully made and quite accurate casts executed in the laboratory, are frequently amazingly large. In *Stegosaurus*, for instance, the cast of the spinal-cord enlargement, from the neural canal in the several joined sacral vertebrae (the sacral plexus as it is called), is *twenty* times as large as the endocranial cast from the inside of the brain case. This is admittedly extreme. In a duck-billed dinosaur, by way of contrast, the cast of the sacral plexus is only about two and a half times as large as the endocranial cast. Yet even this seemingly moderate enlargement of the nerve cord is truly enormous when considered in relation to the size of the brain. Similarly, the enlargements of the spinal nerve in the shoulder region, the brachial plexus, were also of considerable size, but never so large in the dinosaurs as the sacral plexus.

What is the meaning of this development in the dinosaurian nervous system? Why should there be plexi or enlargements in the shoulder and hip region of such size, and why particularly should the one in the pelvis be so very large, frequently exceeding the size of the brain many times over? Various suggestions have been made, even to the

Figure 42. An endocranial cast from the skull (below) and a cast from the enlargement for the spinal nerve in the sacrum (above) of *Stegosaurus*. About one-third natural size

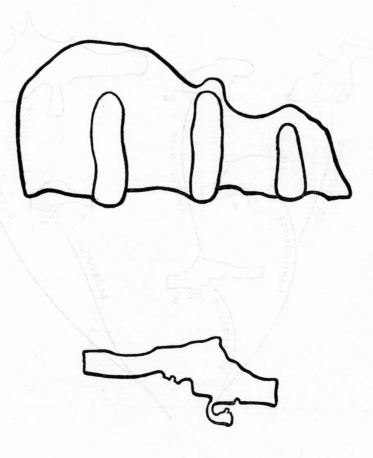

point of considering that such great swellings in the spinal nerve might have had some mysterious functions related to feeding or to digestion or to reproduction. Yet there need be no special mystery about the brachial and sacral plexi in the dinosaurs, for it seems quite reasonable to suppose that they were related to the great development of the legs and the tail in these reptiles. These were obviously nerve centers of great importance for the proper control and functioning of the very

Figure 43. A comparison of endocranial casts of representative dinosaurs, arranged according to their evolutionary relationships. All are drawn to the same scale, about one-sixth natural size. *Abbreviations:* Ac—*Anchiceratops;* As—*Ankylosaurus;* P—*Pachycephalosaurus;* S—*Stegosaurus;* T—*Tyrannosaurus;* B—*Barosaurus*

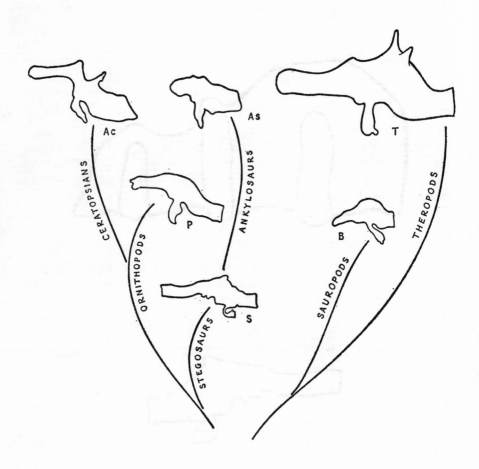

large limbs and the tail. We need look no further than to the modern ostrich for an apt comparison. In this great bird there is an enlargement of the spinal nerve in the region of the pelvis correlated with the great enlargement of the legs for rapid running.

There have been frequent speculations as to the speed of nervous reactions (or rather, the lack of speed) among the large dinosaurs. Certainly the factor of size must be kept in mind when thinking about the motor responses of the dinosaurs to various stimuli. In a mammal the maximum speed of transmission of nervous impulses has been determined as something on the order of sixty meters per second. In a small animal this speed factor is of little consequence; indeed, in very small animals like lizards and small birds and mice reactions appear to be almost instantaneous. Notice how a flock of starlings will veer and wheel in unison, each bird showing a truly split-second reaction to the stimulus that is common for all of them. In larger animals, ourselves, for instance, there is a recognizable reaction time, so that it is a sad and common human experience to carry a painful bump on the head or a bruise on the leg—the result of not moving with quite enough speed to have avoided something hard or sharp. And in some of the largest animals we know, like elephants and rhinoceroses, reactions and movements are ponderous in accordance with the size of these great beasts.

Therefore it is reasonable to think that in the very large dinosaurs there must have been an appreciable time lag between stimulus and reaction; these reptiles very likely were deliberate to a degree that would be very noticeable to us.

THE SLOW DINOSAURS

The big dinosaurs must have been slow animals in ways other than the speed of their nervous systems; they must have had a comparatively slow speed of life, which in scientific terms is called a low rate of basic metabolism. This is true for modern reptiles, to such a degree that a lizard may have a basic metabolic rate that is only a few per cent of that for a mammal of comparable size. This is a fact quite apparent to even the most casual visitor to a zoological park, who sees the foxes and leopards and deer generally moving about in restless patterns, and who sees, in the reptile house, the snakes and crocodiles lying torpid and motionless for minutes, even for hours on end. The mammals have internal mechanisms that maintain their temperatures at approximately constant levels, that keep their body functions going ceaselessly, that give them a reservoir of energy. The reptiles have no such internal controls. Their body temperatures vary as do the environments in which they live, and as their temperatures go up or down their life processes speed up or slow down accordingly.

Thus we can picture the dinosaurs as spending much of their time very quietly, either lying or sitting motionless on the ground, or moving about with slow and deliberate motions. If they lived slowly for the most part, they probably lived long, as do so many modern large reptiles. People often inquire as to how long individual dinosaurs might have lived. It is a question to which there will never be a definite answer, but it seems safe to say that many of the dinosaurs may have enjoyed very long life spans, spans that perhaps bridged a century or two of time.

TEMPERATURES

The problem of temperatures looms very large in the lives of reptiles —much more so than it does in the lives of mammals. As was said, mammals have their own internal temperature controls, so that within certain limits they go on living at a constant rate, whether the days are hot or cold, whereas the reptiles become very sluggish and even inert when the temperature of the environment goes down toward the freezing point, and correspondingly active and alert when the temperature goes up. Even so, the tolerances of reptiles to temperatures are much less than is commonly imagined. People who see lizards or snakes basking in the sun imagine that these animals are lovers of heat—that they soak up hot sunlight almost without limit. Actually, all modern reptiles are very sensitive to high temperatures. A lizard may bask on a log in the sun for a few moments, to bring the body temperature up to a point where the animal becomes active and efficient, but then it scampers off to the shade to hunt insects. If the internal body temperature goes much over a hundred degrees Fahrenheit, the reptile perishes—quickly and with painful contortions and writhings. It is literally cooked to death, for just as it has no internal mechanism for holding the temperature up to a constant level, it has no mechanism for bringing the temperature down from a lethal point. There is every reason to think that the dinosaurs were controlled by the ups and downs of environmental temperatures, as are all modern reptiles.

But many of the dinosaurs had the advantage of being big, and this in certain ways is a real asset to an animal without internal temperature controls. For example, a small lizard heats up rapidly in the sun and cools off rapidly in the shade; hence its body temperature fluctuates up and down all of the time, and this affects its general efficiency. A large alligator, by way of contrast, heats up slowly in the sun because the mass of its body requires a much longer exposure to the sun's rays in order to have the general body temperature raised by one degree than is the case for the small lizard; similarly, the alligator cools off much more slowly in the shade than does the lizard. The result is that the temperature of the alligator fluctuates much more slowly than does the temperature of the lizard, and this leads to a more uniform rate of metabolism for the big reptile than for the small one.

Consider now what must have been the reaction of the giant dinosaurs to fluctuating environmental temperatures. Unfortunately, we have no living dinosaurs to study, but it is probably correct to extrapolate temperature curves upon the basis of what we know about modern reptiles. We know, for example, that a baby alligator, ten inches in length and weighing less than a pound, will experience a rise in body temperature of one degree in slightly more than a minute if it stays out in the midday sun on a summer day in Florida. Furthermore, we know that a moderately large alligator, an animal seven feet in length, weighing fifty pounds or so, will under similar circumstances require about seven minutes for a rise of one degree in body temperature. If the big alligator, 280 times as great in body mass as the baby alligator, heats up five or six times as slowly, perhaps a giant dinosaur like a thirty-ton *Brontosaurus*, 1,000 times as great in body mass as the fifty-pound alligator, would require as much as two or three hours to experience a one-degree rise in body temperature. Therefore it would appear that body temperatures in the great dinosaurs may have remained at fairly constant levels, thus giving these huge reptiles some of the physiological advantages now held by the mammals and birds.

Of course, there are some suppositions here, but they do seem well founded. There may have been other factors of which we have no knowledge that affected dinosaurian body temperatures. Nevertheless, these suppositions are the best we can do upon the basis of what we know, and as is generally the case in paleontological practice we must proceed from the known to the unknown if we are to interpret the past in terms of the present.

When modern reptiles, even large alligators or crocodiles, get too hot in the sun, they get away from the sun. They go into the shade or they go into the water or they burrow underground. The giant dinosaurs were too large to control their temperatures easily in this way. They could go into the shade, if there were large trees in the vicinity, and they could go into water, if there was water nearby, but they could not burrow underground. But with trees and water generally at hand, as would seem to have been usual, and with such slow increments of body temperatures as would seem to have been likely for them, it is probable that their body temperatures were generally reasonably well under control.

One more facet of this temperature tolerance problem in the dinosaurs might be mentioned. Modern lizards frequently keep their temperature down by facing the sun and rearing up high on their front legs, especially in the early morning and in the late afternoon, when the rays of the sun strike the earth at low angles. This means that the sun's rays run more or less parallel to the axis of the body, rather than striking the body laterally and in full force. Perhaps the big dinosaurs did this, too. Such a method of temperature control would have been particularly effective for the bipedal meat-eating dinosaurs, for the duck-billed dinosaurs, and for any other dinosaurs that habitually walked about on their hind legs.

It may be that the dinosaurs were so successful for so many million years because so many of them were giants, and because as giants they had the advantages of fairly constant body temperatures, and correlatively of fairly constant rates of body metabolism. This is something to think about.

Figure 44. Temperatures in the modern alligator. In the upper chart is shown the rate of temperature increase in two alligators exposed to the Florida sun, one in a quadrupedal pose, one in a dinosaur-like bipedal pose. Note that the temperature went up more rapidly in the animal having the body in a horizontal position than in the semi-upright animal. In this latter alligator the rays of the sun struck the body more obliquely than in the other alligator. In the lower chart is shown the rate of temperature increase in a very small alligator (A) as compared with that in a fairly good-sized alligator (B) when both animals were exposed to the Florida sun. Note that the rate of temperature increase was much slower in the large alligator than in the small one. The lengths of the two animals are indicated by the appropriately labeled horizontal lines

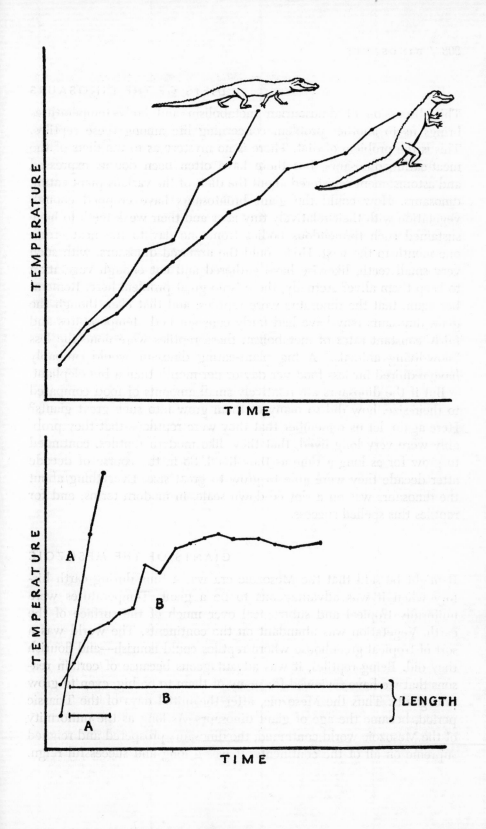

DIETS OF THE DINOSAURS

This discussion of dinosaurian metabolism and body temperatures brings us to another problem concerning life among these reptiles. This is the problem of diet. There is no mystery as to the diets of the meat-eating dinosaurs, but there have often been doubts expressed and astonishment registered about the diets of the various plant-eating dinosaurs. How could the giant brontosaurs have cropped enough vegetation with their relatively tiny jaws and their weak teeth to have sustained such tremendous bodies from one day to the next—from one month to the next. How could the armored dinosaurs, with such very small teeth, likewise have gathered and cut enough vegetation to keep them alive? Actually, there is no great problem here. Remember again that the dinosaurs were reptiles, and that even though the giant dinosaurs may have had fairly constant body temperatures and fairly constant rates of metabolism these reptiles were none the less "slow-living animals." A big plant-eating dinosaur would probably have required far less food per day or per month than a big elephant.

But if the dinosaurs ate relatively small amounts of food compared to their size, how did so many of them grow into such great giants? Here again, let us remember that they were reptiles—that they probably were very long lived, that they, like modern reptiles, continued to grow for as long a time as they lived. So in the course of decade after decade they were able to grow to great size. Everything about the dinosaurs was on a slowed-down scale, in modern terms; and for reptiles this spelled success.

GIANTS OF THE MESOZOIC

It might be said that the Mesozoic era was a time during earth history when it was advantageous to be a giant. Temperatures were uniformly tropical and subtropical over much of the surface of the earth. Vegetation was abundant on the continents. The world was a sort of tropical greenhouse where reptiles could flourish—and flourish they did. Being reptiles, it was advantageous because of certain reasons that we have reviewed for many of them to be big, even to grow into giants. Thus the Mesozoic, after the initial days of the Triassic period, became the age of giant dinosaurs. As long as the uniformity of the Mesozoic world continued, the dinosaurs prospered and reigned supreme on all of the continents. It was a long and successful reign.

Plate 91. The egg of the horned dinosaur *Protoceratops* is quite elongated, like the egg of a lizard, with a surface pattern of wrinkles and ridges

Plate 92. The egg of the Cretaceous sauropod *Hypselosaurus* is, when uncrushed, of round-oval shape, with a surface pattern of small bumps. The other is, of course, a hen's egg

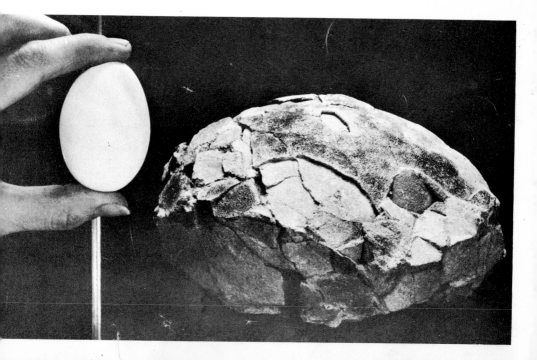

Plate 93. A nest of *Protoceratops* eggs, showing how they were deposited in concentric circles in the sand

Plate 94. Baby dinosaurs enter the world. The hatching of *Protoceratops*—a model by E. Rungius Fulda

Plate 95. A young sauropod dinosaur, *Camarasaurus*. The skeleton when extended would be about sixteen feet from nose to tip of tail; adults are sixty feet long. Note the comparatively large skull and short neck—juvenile characters

Plate 96.   A Triassic scene among primitive trees in a rugged tropical [illegible]d. Two large prosauropods, *Plateosaurus*, in center, with the small theropod *Podokesaurus* at their feet. In the foreground are a mammal-like reptile, *Cynognathus*, left, and the thecodont *Ornithosuchus*, right. By Rudolph F. Zallinger

Plate 97. A Jurassic scene. *Brontosaurus,* left, and *Stegosaurus* inhabited low-
lands and swamps where ancient tropical vegetation flourished. In the air were
flying reptiles (*Rhamphorhynchus*) and the first birds (*Archaeopteryx*). By
Rudolph F. Zallinger

Plate 98. A Cretaceous scene, a subtropical landscape with bright flowering magnolias, willows, and palm trees. The ancestral Rocky Mountains were being born. Two horned dinosaurs, *Triceratops*, are shown at left, and beyond them is *Ornithomimus*. In the center stalks the giant carnivore *Tyrannosaurus*, in front of which, on the right, are the armored dinosaur *Ankylosaurus*, in foreground, and the duck-billed dinosaur *Anatosaurus*, in the distance. In the air is the large flying reptile *Pteranodon*. By Rudolph F. Zallinger

Plate 99. The hunter and the hunted. Swamps and lakes offered havens to the brontosaurs from their aggressive enemies, the meat-eating dinosaurs. By Alexander Seidel

Plate 100.　　There have always been hazards in growing up. The gigantic Cretaceous crocodile *Phobosuchus,* more than fifty feet long, probably preyed upon young dinosaurs such as this *Chasmosaurus.* By Walter Ferguson

CHAPTER FOURTEEN

EGGS, EMBRYOS, AND JUVENILES

DISCOVERIES OF DINOSAUR EGGS

The principle of biological uniformitarianism, which assumes that life processes in the past were similar to what they are today, would lead us to think that reproduction in the dinosaurs was generally similar to reproduction in modern reptiles: turtles, lizards, snakes, crocodilians, and the tuatara. Since it is quite usual for these modern reptiles to lay eggs, from which the young hatch in due course of time as well-formed miniatures of their parents, we might therefore suppose that dinosaurs also laid eggs, a supposition that is well borne out by discoveries of dinosaur eggs, already briefly mentioned. But some lizards and snakes are viviparous: they give birth to living young. Consequently it is necessary to consider the possibility that some dinosaurs likewise may have been viviparous.

What does the fossil evidence show us about dinosaurian reproduction? Unfortunately it does not show us nearly as much as we should like to know. In view of the abundance of dinosaur bones in some regions, one might expect to find a similarly abundant record of eggs, yet dinosaur eggs are, generally speaking, exceedingly rare. And as for the fossil evidence for or against live birth in any of the dinosaurs, the record is at the present time frustratingly indefinite, a point that has been mentioned in our discussion of the dinosaur *Coelophysis,* and that will be considered again in some of the later paragraphs of this chapter.

The paucity of dinosaur eggs in the fossil record is nicely illustrated by the fact that these objects were not recognized for what they are until the third decade of the present century, a full century after the first discoveries and descriptions of dinosaur bones. With recognition there came acclaim and excitement, and dinosaur eggs became objects not only of scientific study but also of public curiosity. For a time in the twenties the eggs of dinosaurs were very much in the news. It makes an interesting story.

The story begins in 1922, when, as described in Chapter Eleven, an expedition from the American Museum of Natural History to Mongolia, discovered at a locality known as Shabarakh Usu, along the ancient caravan trail from Kalgan on the eastern border of Mongolia to Kobdo far to the west, a large and rich deposit of small dinosaur skeletons, together with numerous elongated fossil eggs. Each egg was about eight inches in length, with a shell the surface of which is roughened by many wrinkled ridges (Plate 91). There were also countless thousands of eggshell fragments. The skeletons were those of the ancestral horned dinosaur *Protoceratops,* and it was the definite *association* of these skeletons with the fossil eggs that clinched the matter. There could be no doubting the fact that these were the eggs of dinosaurs.

During all of the excitement that arose out of the discovery and description of the eggs of *Protoceratops,* little attention was given to the fact that fragments of probable dinosaur eggs had been found a half-century earlier in southern France. In 1869 Ph. Matheron described some Cretaceous dinosaur bones from near the mouth of the Rhone River, these representing a rather large sauropod which he named *Hypselosaurus priscus.* In the sediments containing the bones were found many fragments of fossilized eggshells, which Matheron cautiously attributed either to *Hypselosaurus* or perhaps to a large bird. In the years that followed, various students examined the fragments of eggshells, but since there was no definite association of these fragments with the bones no one could be certain that the fossils represented portions of dinosaur eggs.

Then when the eggs of *Protoceratops* were discovered in Mongolia, various paleontologists were inspired to take a new look at the fossils from southern France. By 1928 Dr. Victor van Straelen, the director of the Brussels Museum and the authority who had described the *Protoceratops* eggs, became fairly well convinced that the eggshell fragments from the lower Rhone River should be attributed to *Hypselosaurus.*

Shortly thereafter, in 1930, a French farmer unearthed a complete fossil egg while he was plowing in his vineyard in the vicinity of Aix-en-Provence, and this egg was presented to the museum in Marseille. Subsequently several other eggs came to light. Within the past two or three years there has been a veritable bonanza of *Hypselosaurus* eggs in southern France. This began when M. Raymond Dughi, the director of the museum in Aix-en-Provence, was looking at a scientific periodical in his office. M. Dughi, who is a botanist, was reading an article on lichens, and in the midst of his reading he was called to the telephone. When he got back to his desk he found that the pages of the journal had flipped over so that the article by Matheron, written so many years ago, was in view. The locality mentioned by Matheron was almost literally at M. Dughi's back door, so Dughi decided to go out to see what he could find. What he found has been very exciting indeed—whole batteries of eggs, complete and fragmentary, and thousands of fragments.

As a result of these activities there are now at hand perhaps a hundred eggs, some of them showing their original form, many of them crushed, some of them complete, some incomplete, from the late Cretaceous sediments of southern France (Plate 92). Not all of the eggs are alike, and it seems quite possible that they may represent several kinds of reptiles. But the largest ones, roughly twice the size of ostrich eggs, are much too large to have been laid by any crocodiles or turtles that occur as fossils in the sediments, and there were probably no birds at that distant date, early in the history of bird evolution, that might have produced such enormous eggs. *Ergo*, these are almost certainly the eggs of *Hypselosaurus.*

In recent years new searches have been made in various parts of the world with the certain knowledge that eggs or eggshell fragments found in dinosaur-bearing sediments may very well belong to dinosaurs. The result has been that dinosaur eggs have been found in several localities during the past two or three decades. Most of these eggs have not been found with dinosaurs, it is true, but since the all-important association between bones and eggs was established in Mongolia there has been an appreciation of what to look for.

There is an interesting parallel here to the initial discoveries of dinosaur bones. In the early years of the nineteenth century dinosaurs were unknown, but once the first few specimens had been discovered and described the remains of dinosaurs began to turn up with ever-increasing frequency. The bones had been there all the time, but it was necessary for a *concept* of dinosaurs to be established before discoveries could be made in abundance. The eggs were in the sediments waiting to be discovered, but because of their relative rarity and because of the possibility of confusion between these eggs and the eggs of birds, or of other reptiles, dinosaur eggs did not become ob-

Figure 45. World map showing the locations where dinosaur eggs and footprints have been found

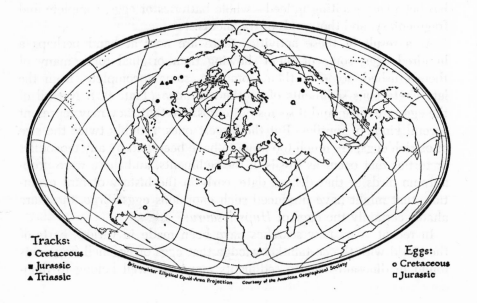

Tracks:
● Cretaceous
■ Jurassic
▲ Triassic

Briesemeister Elliptical Equal-Area Projection   Courtesy of the American Geographical Society

Eggs:
o Cretaceous
□ Jurassic

jects of undoubted identity until the first *association* of the eggs with the animals that laid them was established.

Not many years after the discovery of the eggs of *Protoceratops*, Professor Glenn Jepsen of Princeton University found fragments of fossil eggshells in Cretaceous rocks in Montana. The fragments are small, and before the discovery of *Protoceratops* they probably would have been given scant attention, but the resemblance of their surfaces to the *Protoceratops* egg surfaces leaves little question as to their true nature.

More recently, in 1951, Mr. L. I. Price, a Brazilian paleontologist, announced the discovery of an egg from the Cretaceous beds of that country, rather similar in shape and size to the eggs of *Hypselosaurus* from France. That is all. There is no association of egg with bones to tell us exactly what kind of animal laid the egg so many millions of years ago, but from what we now know of dinosaur eggs there can be little doubt but that the Brazilian egg is a dinosaur egg.

All of these dinosaur eggs, from Mongolia, from France, from Montana, and from Brazil, are of Cretaceous age, laid by dinosaurs that lived near the end of dinosaurian dominance, but there are two other occurrences of dinosaur eggs of an earlier date. In Portugal, a few years ago, there was found an egg of Jurassic age, along with the bones of the stegosaurian *Dacentrurus* or *Omosaurus*. This egg is oval, with a long diameter of about eight inches and a short diameter of five inches or so, which makes it somewhat bulkier than the eggs of *Protoceratops* but not so large as the eggs of *Hypselosaurus*. In 1951, the same year in which the fossil egg was found in Brazil, two eggs that had been discovered in the late Jurassic beds of East Africa were sent to the British Museum. These eggs are incomplete, but it is apparent that if whole they would be about the size of ostrich eggs. They were found in the Tendaguru beds, which have yielded many fine skeletons of dinosaurs. Which of the Tendaguru dinosaurs do they represent?

Such is the record of known dinosaur eggs, and a scanty record it is. Most of the eggs are from Cretaceous rocks, and only three are of Jurassic age. No eggs have as yet been found in Triassic sediments. Of the Cretaceous localities only two, in Mongolia and in southern France, have yielded eggs in abundance. In paleontological research we often have to do the best we can with what we have, and this principle certainly applies to the study of dinosaur eggs. What we have isn't much, but it does teach us some things.

THE VARIETY AND STRUCTURE OF THE EGGS

The various types of dinosaur eggs known to us differ from each other not only in size but also in shape. The eggs of *Protoceratops* are, as we have seen, quite elongated, being shaped something like the eggs of some modern lizards. The egg attributed to *Omosaurus* is of rather similar dimensions, but is somewhat more oval and less slenderly elongated than the *Protoceratops* eggs. The eggs of *Hypselosaurus* are more nearly round in shape; one might describe them as being of round-oval form, with a long diameter of ten inches or so. Other eggs, like those from East Africa and Brazil, that cannot be identified as belonging to any particular dinosaurian genus, are generally similar to the eggs of *Hypselosaurus* in shape. Does this indicate that the eggs in the saurischian dinosaurs were rounder than those in the ornithischians? Unfortunately the evidence is still much too insufficient to enable us to draw any conclusions, but the possibility of differences in egg shapes according to the larger relationships of the dinosaurs must be kept in mind. As against this there is the opposite possibility that perhaps there are no general rules of relationships governing the shapes of dinosaur eggs, that the shapes of the eggs may vary from one genus to the next, that they may be governed more by habits of nest building than by relationships. We are going to have to find many more eggs in association with skeletons than we now have to settle this point, as well as various other facts about dinosaur eggs.

The eggs of *Protoceratops* show a pattern of wrinkled ridges over the surface, except at the large end of each egg, where the surface is rather smooth. These fossil eggs are of a brownish red color, but this is certainly a secondary coloring by iron minerals that occurred during the process of fossilization. The original eggs were probably white in color, as are the eggs of modern reptiles.

When examined under a microscope the rugose shell is seen to consist of two zones, one outer, one inner, the outer surface of the outer (or prismatic) zone being rather rough because of the pattern of wrinkles with which it is covered, the inner surface of the inner (or mammillary) zone being comparatively smooth. Numerous canals or tubes pierce the two zones of the eggshell, and this of course permitted the entrance of air into the interior of the egg, thus providing the developing embryo with the oxygen so necessary for its life and growth. It is an egg very similar to the eggs of modern reptiles, so we can picture life for the dinosaur 80 or 90 million years ago as having begun in the dark recess of the egg very much as life begins for an embryonic alligator today. But after the hatching dinosaur had broken out of the enclosing shell, it faced a world in many ways very different from the world of the present time.

Figure 46. Cross-sections showing the structure of egg shells in two dinosaurs, *Protoceratops* (above) and *Hypselosaurus* (below). Both twenty-four times natural size

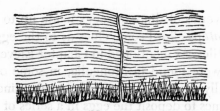

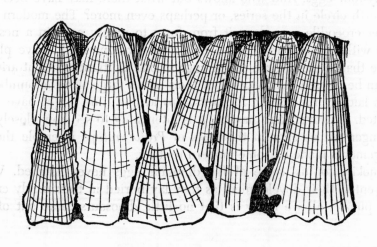

The eggs of *Hypselosaurus,* like those of *Protoceratops,* are typified by a rough outer surface, but in this case the surface is covered with small bumps rather than wrinkles or ridges. The shells are of a gray color, again indicative of the minerals that colored the shells during the process of fossilization. The shell in these eggs also show two layers under the microscope, but it is rather thicker than the *Protoceratops* eggshell, as might be expected in such large eggs. The shell is pierced by canals or tubes, but in the *Hypselosaurus* egg these tubes, instead of being simple as they are in *Protoceratops,* are complicated by branching so that they form networks passing from the outer to the inner surface of the shell.

NESTS

Among the discoveries of dinosaur eggs made up to the present time, those of *Protoceratops* afford some clues as to the egg-laying habits of these ancient reptiles. As mentioned in Chapter Eleven, several clusters of nests of eggs were found in Mongolia, in some of which the eggs were concentrically arranged, as if the female dinosaur had turned around several times to deposit the eggs in a series of expanding circles within the large depression that she had dug in the sand (Plate 93). It is doubtful whether any of the clusters so far unearthed is complete. The largest one contains eighteen eggs, with the large ends up, arranged in three circles; an inner one containing five eggs, a circle exterior to this with eleven eggs and an outer circle represented by two eggs. If the outer circle had been complete, and the nest had consisted of only these three circles of eggs, it would have contained about thirty-four eggs. And who knows but what there may have been still a fourth circle in the series, or perhaps even more? The modern saltwater crocodile may deposit from forty to ninety eggs in a nest, so it is within reason to suppose that *Protoceratops* might have placed more than a mere three-dozen eggs in one of its nests. Contrariwise, it can be argued that because of their rather large size the number of eggs laid by the female *Protoceratops* at one time might have been limited. However that may be, it is interesting to see how closely the arrangement of eggs in the nests of *Protoceratops* resemble the arrangements made by some modern reptiles.

Luckily for us, some of the dinosaur eggs never hatched. What prevented their development as they lay buried in their sandy crypts is a puzzle; all we know is that no little dinosaurs came out of the eggs. Time passed. The shells of the eggs cracked, and sand filtered in to fill the cavities that once had been occupied by the original organic contents of the eggs. The shells themselves were eventually mineralized, and thus the eggs were preserved as fossils, retaining in the shells all of the form and the microscopic structure of the originals. In a few of the Mongolian eggs, as has been said, are traces of fossilized embryonic bone, an indication that development had at least gone on for some time before the hatching of the eggs was interrupted.

In southern France, the only other place outside Mongolia where dinosaur eggs have been found in abundance, some of the large eggs attributable to *Hypselosaurus* were found in groups commonly containing five eggs. Perhaps these represent nests or the remnants of nests made by the big sauropod.

EMBRYOS—OR VICTIMS OF CANNIBALISM?

In the discussion of the primitive Triassic dinosaur *Coelophysis*, in Chapter Four, there was a description of the partial skeletons of small dinosaurs of this species enclosed within the body cavities of two of the adults. And the question was raised as to whether these specimens indicate live birth or cannibalism in this particular dinosaur. As has been pointed out, some modern reptiles are cannibalistic, the adults preying upon newly hatched young of their species, and as already mentioned, various lizards and snakes give birth to their young alive. Perhaps it is significant in this connection that the crocodilians, close cousins of the dinosaurs, all lay eggs, and that the eating of newly hatched babies is a very characteristic crocodilian trait. All in all, therefore, the evidence would seem to favor the view that *Coelophysis* was a cannibalistic dinosaur.

One other dinosaur is known in which bits of a skeleton are contained within the body of an adult, namely, the fine specimen of *Compsognathus*, mentioned in Chapter Four, a very small theropod found many years ago in the Jurassic sediments of Germany. Various students have speculated upon the possibility that this discovery is the record of viviparity in the dinosaurs, but there have been strong arguments advanced to support the idea that here, too, is evidence of cannibalism. Within recent years some authorities have even cast doubt on the identification of the bones contained within the body cavity of *Compsognathus* as being those of a young animal belonging to the same species as the adult. It has been suggested that these might very well have belonged to some other type of reptile that was eaten by *Compsognathus*. Whatever may be the identification of bones within the body cavity of *Compsognathus*, it does seem likely that they are the remains of a meal rather than an embryo.

EGGS AND GROWTH

Even though many of the dinosaurs were giants in the animal world, it does not necessarily follow that they produced gigantic eggs. It is true that some of the largest known dinosaur eggs are of considerable size—say roughly twice the size of an ostrich egg—but the disparity in size between the eggs of dinosaur and of ostrich is nothing like the disparity in size between the animals that produced them. There is nothing astonishing about this, because there is bound to be an upper limit to egg size, based upon certain physical facts.

The shell of an egg is a hard case that protects the developing embryo inside from the harshness of the world outside, yet the shell is porous to allow for the passage of air from the outer world to the dark, quiet environment within which the embryo is growing. Therefore an eggshell cannot be inordinately thick or else it will prevent the exchange of gases between the atmosphere and the little balanced environment inside the shell. Moreover, an eggshell cannot be very thick or else it would not be possible for the embryo to break out of its limy cage, once the hatching stage has been reached. Since there is a very definite limit to the thickness of eggshells, there is a geometric limit to the size of eggs, and this limit is approached when eggs reach such volume as to exceed the strength of the shell to contain them.

So it is possible that the eggs of *Hypselosaurus*, the largest dinosaur eggs known to us, are at about the maximum size to which eggs can grow. It is interesting in this connection to note that the largest known birds' eggs, those of the extinct elephant bird, *Aepyornis*, of Madagascar, are comparable to the eggs of *Hypselosaurus* in bulk. It seems likely that most of the dinosaurs, even the largest of them, started life as very small hatchlings, which is quite in line with what we see in the largest of modern reptiles, such as the giant salt-water crocodile, a reptile that may be twenty feet or more in length, or the great ocean-dwelling leathery turtle *Dermochelys*, which may attain a weight of 1,500 pounds.

The salt-water crocodile begins life as a miniature crocodile about eight inches in length, and since it may get to be twenty feet long, the large adult is therefore some thirty times as long as it was when newly hatched. From the size of the eggs, we can assume that the newly hatched *Protoceratops* may have been ten or twelve inches in length, and from such a baby this dinosaur grew to be six or eight feet in length, a linear increase of only seven or eight times. As for *Hypselosaurus* the increase may have been from a newly hatched dinosaur of about fifteen inches in length to an adult about forty feet long, an increase in length of about thirty times, which is not so different from the salt-water crocodile. Of course, for the greatest dinosaurs the disparity in size between hatching and adult would probably have been somewhat greater. The eggs of *Brontosaurus* or *Brachiosaurus*, the giants among the sauropods, probably were very little if any larger than the eggs of *Hypselosaurus*, yet these dinosaurs were roughly twice the length of *Hypselosaurus*, which means that the growth in length from baby to adult may have been about sixty-fold.

These figures are, as a matter of fact, deceptively simple. More proper comparisons of the growth of dinosaurs from the hatchling to the adult should involve body masses, which increase at much greater ratios than do lengths. For instance, a two-year-old child is approximately half the height of the adult; but, as we all know, the two-year-old generally weighs only a fifth or perhaps even no more than an eighth as much as he will when he is fully grown. As for modern reptiles, the salt-water crocodile shows a truly impressive increase in body mass during its growth from an eight-inch hatchling to a twenty-foot adult. The baby crocodile might weigh about ten ounces, the twenty-foot adult well over a thousand pounds, so that the increase in weight during the growth of the individual crocodile may be on the order of two thousand times, and even more. Perhaps this dramatic example of reptilian growth will help us to appreciate how great was the growth in many dinosaurs during the progression from egg to adult.

Certainly the growth in *Protoceratops* during the individual life span may easily be understood in the light of what we know about modern crocodiles. Indeed, the growth in *Protoceratops* was almost certainly of a lesser magnitude than what has been described for the salt-water crocodile, because the dinosaur began life in a larger egg than does the modern crocodile (which indicates a larger hatchling) and it ended its life as a reptile considerably smaller than the adult crocodile. Perhaps the increase in body mass in *Protoceratops* was on the order of two hundred times.

When we come to *Hypselosaurus,* we find a degree of growth from egg to adult that is extraordinarily impressive. From the size of the eggs found in southern France we may assume that the newly hatched *Hypselosaurus* may have weighed a pound and a half—possibly two pounds. From the size of the skeleton we may assume that the adult weighed perhaps ten tons. Consequently there must have been an increase from hatchling to adult dinosaur on the order of at least ten thousand times, and very likely more.

Then when we think of the large sauropods we encounter figures that might be called astronomical. It has been said that the eggs of *Hypselosaurus* may be at about the maximum size possible for a hard-shelled egg. If this be so, a large brontosaur, or the giant *Brachiosaurus,*

Figure 47. Comparative size of the eggs and adults of *Protoceratops* and *Hypselosaurus.* The large outlines show the shapes of the eggs in these two dinosaurs

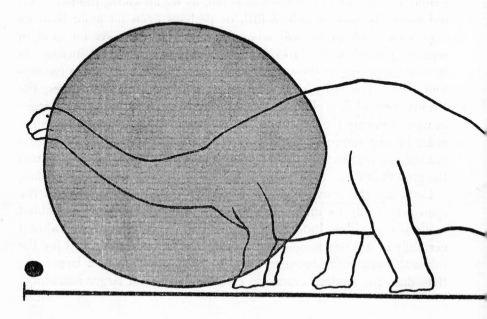

probably began life as little reptiles about two pounds in weight. Since the adult *Brachiosaurus* probably weighed as much as fifty tons, it is apparent that in this dinosaur there may have been an increase in weight during the life span of *fifty thousand times*.

JUVENILE DINOSAURS

What already has been said about the paucity of dinosaur eggs in the fossil record might be applied with almost equal emphasis to the presence, or more properly the lack of presence, in the rocks of the remains of young dinosaurs. Our knowledge of the dinosaurs is based overwhelmingly upon the bones of adult animals. From the fossils dug out of the ground we seem to see the Mesozoic continents as having been populated by hordes of fully grown dinosaurs, wandering far and wide across the lands. This is a one-sided picture; we know that there were young dinosaurs of all ages living along with the adults, and that the young probably far outnumbered their elder relatives, because reproduction in the reptiles is characterized by the prodigiously high rate of infant and juvenile mortality. Therefore one must assume that

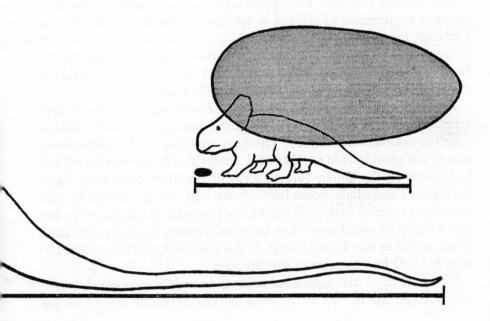

among the dinosaurs, as among other reptiles, the ratio of young animals to adults was very high. Why aren't there more remains of young dinosaurs in the fossil record?

Like so many questions that have to do with past life on the earth, this one is not easy to answer. The skeletons of young dinosaurs, being more fragile than those of the adults, would necessarily have been less frequently preserved as fossils, yet as against this there is the fact that far greater numbers of such skeletons were available for fossilization, And although the skeletons of very young animals might have been rather fragile, those of half-grown animals would be very well formed and supposedly should be common in the rocks. Such skeletons are rarely found.

It may be that young dinosaurs inhabited environments somewhat different from the habitats in which the adults lived, and that the environments sheltering the young were such that fossilization rarely took place. This consideration might be given some weight except that in the few instances where young dinosaurs have been found, they occur along with the skeletons of the adults. A satisfactory answer to the riddle of the absent young dinosaurs is still to be developed; in the meantime there are certain discoveries of young dinosaurs that, together with the evidence of the eggs, help to throw light on the whole wonderful process of birth and growth in these reptiles.

The Triassic theropod *Coelophysis,* frequently mentioned in these pages, is represented by a large series of skeletons of almost all ages. Likewise, *Protoceratops* from Mongolia is represented by a remarkable series of fossils showing a relatively complete sequence of age stages, from the newly hatched baby to the adult. Indeed, this is probably the finest known example of growth in a dinosaur.

Psittacosaurus, the primitive cousin of *Protoceratops,* is also represented by several obvious growth stages among the fossils. Otherwise the evidence is scattered. There are partially grown iguanodonts among the considerable number of skeletons that have been unearthed in Europe. In the Upper Jurassic beds of North America there have been found some half-grown brontosaurs, and among the spectacular record of sauropod footprints from Glen Rose and Bandera, Texas, are prints made by small as well as large individuals. Similarly, the footprints found in the Triassic rocks of the Connecticut Valley were obviously made by dinosaurs of varying ages.

The growth of the individual among animals commonly involves not only increase in size, as has been outlined above, but also changes in proportion. For example, a young backboned animal commonly has a *relatively* larger head than does the adult, so that in the process of growing the body increases at a more rapid rate than does the head, finally "catching up" to the head to establish the proportions typical of the adult animal. Or again, the eye in the baby is often larger in proportion to the size of the head than it is in the adult. Growing up almost always involves *differential* growth in various parts of the body.

Glimpses of such differential growth are seen in the relatively few skulls and skeletons of young dinosaurs that are known to us. The series of *Protoceratops* shows a graded sequence of skulls in which the smallest individuals have a frill that is proportionately somewhat smaller than the frill in the adults. The several young skulls of *Psittacosaurus* show that the very young animal had a much larger opening for the accommodation of the eye than did the fully adult individual. A half-grown sauropod skeleton seems to have a skull that is proportionately larger than is the case in the fully grown skeleton. These examples illustrate the trends to be expected when viewing the growth that took place during life in individual dinosaurs.

But, as said above, these are only glimpses, and tantalizing glimpses, at that. From such scanty evidence, and by analogy with modern reptiles, we have some idea as to what to expect in the growth of the various dinosaurs from egg to adult. But until many more eggs and many more bones of young and juvenile dinosaurs are known than are presently known, the interesting process of reproduction and of growing up in these ancient reptiles must remain largely a matter for educated speculation.

QUESTIONS FOR THE FUTURE

There is much, therefore, to look forward to in this aspect of field work and research on the dinosaurs. There are many things still to be learned about the life histories of these reptiles, and some things that probably will never be known. What were the rates of growth in the various dinosaurs, from baby to adult? How long did it take these reptiles to grow up? How long did they live? Did the young dinosaurs have diets different from those of the adults? These and many more related questions can be asked, and we can only answer that we don't know. Perhaps we shall never know. Perhaps we shall always have to rely upon analogies with living reptiles. Thus, crocodiles grow rapidly to sexual maturity, and this probably was true of the dinosaurs;

crocodiles and other large modern reptiles live rather long lives, and this also probably was true of the dinosaurs; many young modern reptiles have diets different from the diets of the adults, and again this probably was true of some dinosaurs.

For the answers to other questions, we can hope that future discoveries will give us clues. We continue to search along an ever-present frontier of knowledge. This is one of the joys of paleontology; it is a subject that is never closed.

CHAPTER FIFTEEN

AGES AND ENVIRONMENTS OF THE DINOSAURS

WHAT IS ENVIRONMENT?

What is environment? It is many things—the totality of conditions into which an animal is born and within which it must grow, survive and reproduce its own species. "Existence depends upon eating and not being eaten, upon heat and light, upon all the relations of the animal to the world in which it participates." *

The environment is in part the physical and chemical world in which an animal lives, and perhaps this is what we often think of when we use the word "environment." But it is also the biological world surrounding an animal, the world of living things to which it must be harmoniously adjusted. Adjustment of the animal (or of the organism, to be completely inclusive) to its environment spells success, and the lack of such adjustment may very well doom the individual, or even the species to which it belongs.

The relationships of animals and plants to their environments, to

* James R. Beerbower, *Search for the Past* (New York: Prentice-Hall, 1960), p. 72.

the world around them, is known as *ecology*, or, as it is often called, the "balance of nature." Within the past half-century or so we have come to appreciate more and more the importance of the balance of nature to all life, even to what might be considered the highly artificial life of modern civilizations.

The ecological relationships of the dinosaurs, and of a good many fossils for that matter, are not very well known, and for the good reason that the distance in time by which we are separated from the living dinosaurs (and from other organisms preserved as fossils) makes the study of their ecology largely a matter of speculation, based upon analogies with what we know of modern life. But there are some clues that help us to visualize the dinosaurs in their environments, and more clues are coming to light, especially because of the development of new techniques for the study of sediments in which the dinosaurs are buried. It is being learned that sediments frequently tell us much about the physical and even the biological world of ancient times. Thus our concept of the world of dinosaurs is being broadened.

FACTORS OF DINOSAURIAN ENVIRONMENTS

Many things made up the physical-chemical environment of the dinosaurs. One was solar radiation, the energy from the sun that is primarily the basis for all life on the earth. We do not know how the radiant energy from the sun in Mesozoic times compared with that received by the earth today, but the evidence of the fossils indicating that a large part of the earth was then tropical and subtropical, and that the continents were clothed over much of their extent with heavy jungles, would seem to show that the sun was a very strong source of energy in those days. Nevertheless it can be assumed that solar radiation was not of unduly high intensity, otherwise it would have been very damaging to life on the earth.

Related to solar radiation, of course, is heat. Even though tropical and subtropical conditions prevailed over a great portion of the earth's surface, it is probable that temperatures were not extremely high. The highest temperatures today are encountered not in the equatorial belt, but in the temperate zones during the summer seasons. It seems reasonable to suppose, from what we know about temperature tolerances in reptiles, that the giant dinosaurs would have been greatly distressed if subjected to daytime summer temperatures such as one encounters today on the plains of Kansas or in the Arizona desert, yet they might have done very well indeed in the temperatures that today characterize the tropical jungle of the Amazon basin. And related to solar radiation and air temperatures were the patterns of air currents during Mesozoic times. These would certainly have determined climates across the continents of those days, which, needless to say, would have influenced the distribution patterns of the dinosaurs.

Two other factors of the physical environment that would have affected the distribution of the dinosaurs were the nature of the land, that is, its topography, the character of the soil, and so on, and the distribution of continental streams, rivers, and lakes. Mountain systems often serve as barriers to the spread of animal populations, as is shown today by the great differences between the animal life in India, on the south side of the Himalayan Range, and in northern Asia, on the north side. The fact that closely related dinosaurs were so widely distributed throughout the world during Mesozoic times is some indication (among others) that high mountain ranges did not cross the continents in those distant days. The nature of the soil influences the plant life that grows upon it, and of course this bears directly upon the distribution of plant-eating animals. As for patterns of rivers and lakes and swamps, these would have affected very markedly the attributes of dinosaurian populations in local regions. Thus the huge sauropods and the varied duck-billed dinosaurs would have congregated in swampy regions and in regions of numerous watercourses, while the armored dinosaurs and the horned dinosaurs might have been particularly dominant on the dry uplands away from the water. It must be remembered in this connection, however, that large vertebrates like the dinosaurs are and always have been very mobile organisms; they are inclined to wander back and forth, to and from water, to and from feeding grounds. Consequently the populations of dinosaurs probably were constantly fluctuating as groups of animals wandered across the landscape to fulfill the needs of their bodies. One sees the same thing today on the plains of Africa, where the immense herds of hoofed mammals drift across the veldt to feed and to drink, with always a following fringe of predators—lions, hyenas, and jackals.

Gravity was a most important factor in the physical environment of the dinosaurs. We have seen in another chapter how the largest dinosaurs, giants among land-living animals, were subjected to limitations in size by the finite limits in the strength of bone, muscle, and ligament. For them gravity was, in some respects, a trammeling force.

The endless varying combinations of these and undoubtedly of other factors in the physical and chemical environment of the dinosaurs loomed large in determining their evolutionary development, their distribution throughout the world, the sizes of their many populations—in short, their success during a very long span of earth history. Then there was the biological environment, too.

One of the most important factors in the biological environment is food, for all life depends upon food. The herbivorous dinosaurs that lived in such great numbers and variety during much of the Mesozoic era obtained their energy from plants that in turn derived their energy directly from the sun through the process of photosynthesis. The theropod dinosaurs obtained their energy in a secondary fashion; they ate the dinosaurs that ate the plants. There was a dinosaurian *food chain* on a truly magnificent scale.

Predation—the preying of the hunter upon the hunted—was also important in the ecology of the dinosaurs, as it is in all animal life. Many of the plant-eating dinosaurs were eaten, but there was always a surplus of animals that escaped destruction so that these dinosaurs continued through the ages, to make an unending food supply for the predatory theropods. The varying supplies of plant food available to the herbivores and the effects of predation upon populations of plant-eating dinosaurs must have had a great deal to do with the nature of dinosaur populations through Mesozoic times. These relationships are extremely complex, as has been learned from the study of modern herbivores and carnivores, and they are always changing. For example, it is now known from the records of the Hudson's Bay Company, extending over two centuries, that the population of snowshoe hares in Canada may correlate with the eleven-year sunspot cycle, waxing and waning according to the periodicity of the sunspots. Furthermore, the population of the Canada lynx that preys largely upon the snowshoe hare likewise fluctuates with the abundance or the paucity of the food supply. It is certainly conceivable that relationships as subtle as these may have effected dinosaur populations.

Other factors in the biological environment, of great importance to modern animals, are parasitism and symbiosis, the former being the complete dependence of one species upon another, the latter being the interaction of two, or even more than two, species with each other, without injury to the involved animals and with benefit to at least one of the partners. It is axiomatic that wild animals today are infested with parasites, not only on the body surface but also commonly in the digestive tract and other parts of the internal anatomy.

Undoubtedly the dinosaurs, too, had their parasites, but of these there are no clues in the fossil record. As for symbiosis, we can only speculate. The jackal today follows the lion, to pick up such bits of the lion's prey that the lordly cat disdains to eat. Perhaps some of the small carnivorous dinosaurs made a living off of the table scraps left by the great predatory theropods. Who knows?

These are some examples of how dinosaurs may have been related to the environments in which they lived. It is important to have as much of an understanding of these relationships as possible, if we are to know the dinosaurs.

DINOSAURS AND CLIMATES

Some idea of the general nature of the physical environment in which the dinosaurs lived is to be had from the study of dinosaurian distributions through Mesozoic times. If it is granted that by virtue of their limited temperature tolerances the dinosaurs, like modern crocodilians, could have lived only in tropical and subtropical climates, their ranges should then give some evidence as to the extent of tropics and subtropics during late Triassic, Jurassic, and Cretaceous history. The assumption seems reasonable, and the results based upon this assumption certainly seem valid. What is the picture that emerges?

Late Triassic dinosaurs are found in northern Europe, at latitudes somewhat more than 50 degrees north, and in South Africa, at 30 degrees south, as well as at a similar southern latitude in the Triassic of Brazil. At that stage of earth history, therefore, the dinosaurs ranged over a broad belt around the middle of the earth, comprising some 80 degrees or more of latitude. Jurassic dinosaurs are also found in northern Europe, as well as in the southern portion of Africa (at the Tendaguru locality) and in Australia, again occurring within a broad belt comparable in extent to that through which the Triassic dinosaurs ranged. In Cretaceous rocks we find dinosaurs again in northern Europe and as far north as central Alberta in North America, which places them well above 50 degrees north, while to the south they extend far down into Africa, into Australia and in Patagonia, at a southern latitude of between 40 and 50 degrees. This makes their known latitudinal range even greater in the last phase of Mesozoic history than it was during previous periods of this era.

Compare these limits of dinosaurian distribution with those of the modern crocodilians, confined to a tropical and subtropical zone around the earth seldom extending more than 30 degrees on either side of the equator.

From all of this we may assume that much of the Mesozoic world was uniformly rather warm, which is without much doubt one reason why the dinosaurs were so very dominant. Physical environments and temperatures were conducive to abundant and widely spread tropical vegetation, and the combination of such vegetation with favorably warm and uniform climates stimulated (along with other causes) the evolutionary development of giant reptiles. It was an age of brawn.

DINOSAURS IN THE TRIASSIC WORLD

The geologic evidence shows that the Triassic period was a time of emergent continents when land surfaces were extensive. Consequently there were varieties of physical environments in which the early dinosaurs lived, ranging from lush jungles in which there were numerous streams, swamps, and lakes, to areas in which the climate may have been rather arid. The fossils seem to indicate, however, that even in what may have been the arid regions, which were probably located largely in the interiors of the Triassic continents, there were stream courses bordered by fringes of vegetation, along which large amphibians and reptiles, including the early primitive dinosaurs, made their habitations. A modern parallel to such conditions might be the Nile Valley, traversing the deserts of northern Africa.

In this physical setting the first dinosaurs roamed widely. Their fossils are particularly well known in North America from the Triassic Newark sediments along the Atlantic coast, the very extensive Chinle formation as it is exposed in New Mexico, Arizona, and Utah, and from the Dockum beds of western Texas. In northern Europe the early dinosaurs have been found in the classic Keuper beds of southern Germany and contiguous areas. That land connections were extensive in those days, allowing the free interchange of dinosaurs from one continental area to another, is shown by the fact that some of the Keuper types, so characteristic of central Europe, are also found in the Upper Triassic Lufeng beds of western China and in the Stormberg beds of South Africa. The bones of early dinosaurs also are found in the Triassic sediments of South America, specifically in the Santa Maria formation of southern Brazil.

These far-flung dinosaurian pioneers were all theropods. There were no sauropods, and, as outlined in Chapter Seven, except for some very problematical fossils the evidence would seem to show that this was before the advent of ornithischian dinosaurs upon the earth. So it can be said that although dinosaurs were present in the faunas of the time, they were not overwhelmingly dominant.

The Triassic dinosaurs, being so limited in variety, necessarily shared their environments with other reptiles. Perhaps the dominant predators of those days were not dinosaurs at all, but the large phytosaurs, which were thecodont reptiles very much like the crocodiles of today. Some of the phytosaurs were massive giants twenty or thirty feet in length, and many of them were ten or fifteen feet long. Certainly the modestly proportioned theropods of the Triassic period were among the lesser beasts of prey in the forests and glades of that age.

Related to the phytosaurs were the pseudosuchian reptiles, many of which were carnivorous and therefore also competitors with the early theropod dinosaurs for the available food supply. Some of the meat-eating pseudosuchians were small, delicate reptiles, and would therefore have been in direct competition with only the smallest of the theropods, of which none the less there were many during late Triassic times, but some of the carnivorous pseudosuchians were of considerable size, and therefore may have contended with even the largest of the Triassic theropods for victims.

In Eurasia and Africa and in South America there were numerous carnivorous mammal-like reptiles living through the Triassic period. These reptiles were quite advanced in their physiological development, so that some of them approached very closely the status of warm-blooded mammals. (Indeed, good arguments can be put forward to the effect that the more advanced of the mammal-like reptiles were warm blooded and had insulating coats of hair.) The predatory mammal-like reptiles that lived on to the end of Triassic probably competed with the early dinosaurs for food, perhaps to such good effect that the dinosaurs often came out second best. To explain the matter briefly, the mammal-like reptiles by reason of their physiology were equipped to do things that even the most active and agile theropods could not do, and thus placed the dinosaurs at a disadvantage in the pursuit of prey.

The phytosaurs, some pseudosuchians, and certain mammal-like reptiles were perhaps direct competitors with the late Triassic theropod dinosaurs for food, but there were other reptiles that competed less openly with the early dinosaurs, and probably affected their daily activities. It must be remembered that the Triassic world was full of reptiles, most of which were not dinosaurs, and these nondinosaurian reptiles occupied space and frequently ate food that might otherwise have been available to the early theropods. These would have been primarily ancient turtles, the various armored pseudosuchian reptiles, various lizard-like reptiles known as protorosaurs, and the ubiquitous rhynchosaurs and mammal-like dicynodonts, these latter being robust plant-eating reptiles, widely spread through the world in late Triassic times.

Perhaps these remarks will afford a brief and imperfect picture of

---

Figure 48. World map showing the localities at which Triassic dinosaurs have been found. *Abbreviations:* North America: N—Newark, D—Dockum, C—Chinle, K—Kayenta; South America: SM—Santa Maria; Eurasia: Ke—Keuper, R—Rhaetic, L—Lufeng; Africa: S—Stormberg, M—Manda. (In this map, as in the following two maps, the locations of letters that indicate areas of exposures are very general, and because of lack of space some letters are necessarily displaced. The names used are of formations, where such names exist; of stages in Europe, and of localities in regions where formation and stage names are not available.)

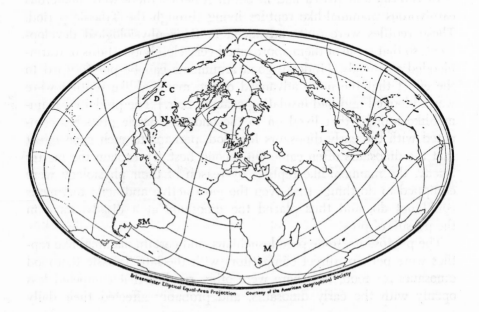

Triassic dinosaurs in their environments—environments in which they were prominent but not dominant members. Dinosaurian dominance was to come in the following geologic period.

DINOSAURS IN THE JURASSIC WORLD

The transition from Triassic to Jurassic times was marked by a certain amount of movement in the rocks of the earth's crust, resulting in some minor mountain-making processes, and seemingly by a brief drop in temperatures from those that had prevailed during the latter part of Triassic history, this indicated by a dwarfing of Lower Jurassic insects and a restriction of coral reefs. But at an early stage in the development of Jurassic events the world settled down into a long period of crustal quiescence, during which lands were low and monotonous, and environmental conditions were uniform to a degree seldom attained during geologic history. The Jurassic period was a time when seas spread widely over the face of the earth, so that many of the continental areas which today are regions of high plains and great mountains, seemingly immutable in their massive solidity, were then actually covered with warm, shallow tropical seas. A great sea covered western North America during much of Jurassic times, while northern Europe, now a land of snow-tipped mountains, sunny fields, and pine forests, was then an islanded ocean, where low tropical shores were fringed with colorful coral reefs. It is no wonder, then, that the fossil record of Jurassic land-living animals, including dinosaurs, is rather restricted.

But the world is a big place and time is long, and in spite of the prevalence of marine conditions during a great part of Jurassic history there are none the less a few very good continental deposits of this age, particularly at the very beginning and at the end of the period, in some of which there are excellent fossils of dinosaurs and of the animals and plants that surrounded them.

The most important discoveries of Lower Jurassic dinosaurs have been made in Europe, where a few bones and skeletons have come to light in the lowermost Jurassic sediments of the English Channel coast. These rocks are predominantly marine, and as such contain fine skeletons of marine reptiles—ichthyosaurs, plesiosaurs, and the like, of sea shells and other marine organisms. But the discovery of the skeleton of *Scelidosaurus*, for example, on the Dorset coast would seem to show that in early Jurassic times northern Europe was a region of low lands across which the dinosaurs wandered, never very far from the shores of the tropical seas. There probably were many dinosaurs living at that time; unfortunately they seldom appear in the fossil record.

The southwestern part of North America was evidently a desert at the beginning of Jurassic times—an interesting exception to the widely extended tropical seas and the low jungle-covered lands of that time. This is shown by the Navajo sandstone, a spectacular formation made up of long slopes of dune sands. It may be that dinosaurs lived among the Jurassic dunes of North America; the discovery of one partial skeleton in this formation would point to this, but dune sands seldom contain fossils, so again our record is lacking.

Thus we get mere glimpses of the dinosaurs and the environments in which they lived at the beginning of Jurassic times. Then the curtain of obscurity is drawn as a result of the spreading of the seas.

That the dinosaurs were evolving abundantly during Middle Jurassic times on lands forever lost is indicated by the record of the Upper Jurassic dinosaurs, a record that bursts upon us with a spectacular display of small, medium-sized, and giant dinosaurs of considerable variety, preserving one of the high points in the evolutionary history of these ancient reptiles. The record is available in three areas: throughout the widely spread exposures of the Morrison formation in western North America, ranging from New Mexico through Utah and Montana; in the Upper Jurassic of northern and western Europe, particularly in Portugal, and in southern England, where the Oxford, Kimmeridge, and Purbeck beds have yielded various reptiles characteristic of this phase of earth history; and in East Africa, where dinosaurs remarkably close to the Morrison dinosaurs of North America have been found in the Tendaguru beds. In these widely separated parts of the world we see for the first time many dinosaurs as absolute and veritable giants, constituting the dominant animals in late Jurassic environments.

The general similarity of these late Jurassic dinosaurs to one another is strong evidence for the availability of migration routes from one part of the world to another, and also, as has been pointed out, for the uniformity of climates and environments throughout a large part of the Jurassic world. Yet in spite of such indications of climatic uniformity, the three areas in which late Jurassic dinosaurs are well known, the Morrison exposures at about 35 to 45 degrees north latitude and 110 degrees west longitude, the Purbeck beds at something more than 50 degrees north latitude and at about the zero meridian, and the Tendaguru beds at 10 degrees south latitude and at a longitude of 30 degrees east, show interesting differences of the local environments.

The Morrison sediments are varied river, pond, and swamp deposits, evidently laid down in a vast tropical basin that must have covered much of western North America. Picture, if you will, an environment not unlike the Amazon River basin today, a low land of dense jungles and glades, crossed by muddy rivers and streams, these interspersed with ponds and lakes and extensive swamps. Picture this rather lush scene in the humid heat of a tropical noon, a landscape in which many small reptiles lurked beneath the protection of the foliage and in which the giant dinosaurs crashed and blundered through the forests. It was a land far removed in time and character from the North America we know.

In southern England and in Portugal the dinosaurs contemporaneous with the Morrison dinosaurs of America were living in a rather different setting. It would seem that there were no vast river basins such as the one just pictured, but rather low islands and peninsulas in a tropical sea. The dinosaurs lived on these comparatively restricted land surfaces, perhaps in more scattered and isolated population groups than did the inland dinosaurs of western North America. Here they must have frequented the shores of the sea, where they could often see the great marine reptiles of that distant age swimming in the shallows.

In Africa, the Tendaguru sediments show that the dinosaurs of that region were living where a great river flowed out to the ocean, its mouth protected by a long bar. Here they lived and died, and not infrequently their carcasses were deposited near the edge of the land, to be mixed with the remains of marine animals washed in from the ocean. This is fortunate for the student of ancient life, because the alternation of marine fossils with the bones of reptiles is very helpful in establishing the geologic age of the Tendaguru dinosaurs, and by extension the age of the Jurassic dinosaurs of southern Europe and of western North America. To be a little more specific, the sediments containing the Tendaguru dinosaurs have rocks below and above them that contain fossil sea shells of Upper Jurassic affinities.

The dominance of the dinosaurs in the late Jurassic environments was in part a result of their abundance, in part of their variety, and in part in the prevalence of giants among these reptiles. Life on the late Jurassic continents has a counterpart in the life of the African veldt today, with of course the difference that everything in the Jurassic scene was on a grand scale. Instead of two-ton hippopotamuses there were gigantic thirty- and forty-ton brontosaurs and other sauropods, frequenting rivers and swamps and often coming out on dry land to feed, or to go from one aquatic habitat to another. Instead of antelopes there were camptosaurs that wandered across the dry ground, to browse upon the numerous plants that grew in this situation. Instead of rhinoceroses there were the plated stegosaurs, also dwellers of the uplands, that fed upon the leaves of trees and bushes and probably blundered their way through life in a vague rhinoceros-like fashion. Instead of lions and leopards there were the predaceous theropods, *Allosaurus* and *Ceratosaurus,* that preyed upon such large

Figure 49. World map showing the localities at which Jurassic dinosaurs have been found. *Abbreviations:* North America: M—Morrison, N—Navajo; South America: Pt—Patagonia; Eurasia: L—Lias, O—Oxford, K—Kimmeridge, P—Purbeck, Ky—Kuangyuan, S—Shansi, C—Chinchou; Africa: T—Tendaguru, N—Nyassaland, Md—Madagascar; Australia: W—Walloon, Yp—York Peninusla

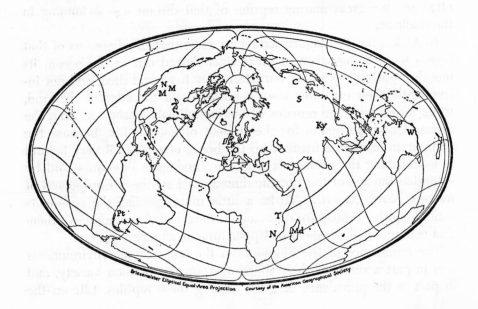

Briesemeister Elliptical Equal-Area Projection   Courtesy of the American Geographical Society

dinosaurs as they could pull down, and probably were not above feasting upon carrion as well. Instead of jackals there was *Ornitholestes*, moving lightly through the vegetation in search of lizards and other small prey.

But we must not allow the spectacular dinosaur giants and their smaller relatives to divert our attention completely from other inhabitants of the late Jurassic continents. There were various reptiles that would seem quite familiar to a modern man—turtles of many kinds, lizards and possibly snakes, and many crocodilians, large and small.

In contrast to these reptiles so like their modern cousins there were strange backboned animals flying through the air, the pterosaurs or flying reptiles, and the earliest birds, represented in the Upper Jurassic deposits of Germany by the famous ancestral type *Archaeopteryx*. Of course, the flying reptiles and birds probably made little difference in the day-to-day life of the various dinosaurs, but they certainly added new elements to Jurassic faunas. Here were vertebrates exploiting the air for the first time; here we see the beginnings of great new opportunities in the evolution of backboned animals.

Of especial importance in the late Jurassic environments were the small, seemingly obscure, warm-blooded mammals. Their fossils are not numerous, but this does not mean that they were then rare. Such tiny animals would seldom be preserved as fossils, and then under only the most favorable conditions. It is consequently valid to suppose that the undergrowth of the Jurassic jungles were teeming with a wealth of minute, furry mammals, most of them no larger than mice and rats. They were of primitive types, and their lineages were for the most part doomed to extinction. But some of them were the ancestors of mammals (including ourselves) that were to become so important in later geologic ages. The Jurassic period was certainly the Age of Reptiles, as was the following Cretaceous period, because as long as the great dinosaurs remained dominant the mammals would seem to have been doomed to relative obscurity. None the less the active, comparatively intelligent mammals were on the scene, and in them were harbored great potentialities for the future.

DINOSAURS IN THE CRETACEOUS WORLD

One way in which the long continuum of earth history is divided into eras, periods, and lesser units is by the geological record of large changes that occurred at various intervals, in each instance to bring to an end one segment of the earth story and to usher in the next. These changes usually involved the lifting or the depression of great continental areas, the building of mountain chains, or the wide spread of shallow seas. They were sometimes of vast dimensions and import, at other times of lesser consequence.

The changes that marked the end of Jurassic history and the beginning of Cretaceous times seem to have been of limited extent, even though there was a certain amount of mountain building known in geological parlance as the Nevadian Disturbance. The advent of the Cretaceous period was in general marked by depression of the continents, so that in various regions great shallow mediterranean seas spread across the faces of the lands. Such seas occupied much of western North America during a considerable part of Cretaceous history, spreading through the Rocky Mountain region and over large areas of the Gulf Coast and Mexico. They were predominant in other continents too, as shown by the remnants of their limy floors, for instance by the dazzling white chalk cliffs of the English Channel coast (from which the name *Cretaceous* is derived) and the chalks and white limestones that are exposed through various parts of northern and central Europe.

Generally speaking, Cretaceous events made up a much more varied segment of earth history than did those of the Jurassic period. Following the first submergence there was a considerable span of time during which seas were widely spread, after which there began a marked and perhaps a rather dramatic emergence of land areas that took place during the latter portion of Cretaceous history. Here was the beginning of what geologists call the Laramide Revolution, the series of earth movements that marked the birth of modern mountain systems—the Himalayas, the Andes, the Alps, and the Rockies. Land surfaces toward the end of the Cretaceous period became high and varied, offering vast theaters for the development of dinosaurs and other land-living animals.

With all of these things taking place during Cretaceous times, one might expect that climates were more varied than they had been during the preceding Jurassic period, and so they were. There may have been a slight drop in world temperatures at the beginning of the Cretaceous period when the seas began to spread, and there is evidence to show that in the Cretaceous highlands of Australia there were even glaciers that flowed westwardly into the ocean. But cool conditions did not last for long, geologically speaking, and with the extensive spread of the shallow Cretaceous seas there was a correlative spread of warm climates so that the world probably became as widely tropical and subtropical as it had been in Jurassic times. Certainly the presence in Greenland of Cretaceous fossil figs, breadfruits, cinnamons, and treeferns, which gives to latitude 70 degrees north some of the aspects of the South Sea spice islands, and the discovery in Alaska of Cretaceous figs, cycads, and palms, point quite clearly to the fact that warm and mild climates enveloped most of the earth's surface during that distant age.

Yet the forests that clothed the Cretaceous lands, especially those of later Cretaceous times, were not entirely the dense, dark jungles that had characterized so many Jurassic landscapes, for during Cretaceous days there was a great revolution in the plant world. It was at this time that the angiosperms, or flowering plants, arose. The vegetation of the world, which hitherto had displayed monotones of green, became quite varied, and the colors of flowers were part of the Cretaceous scene. Deciduous trees, rhododendrons, willows, poplars, sassafras, birch, oaks, maples, walnuts, and many others, had appeared by the middle of Cretaceous times, and during the latter part of the period forests of these trees, with the more primitive evergreens interspersed among them, were common in Cretaceous landscapes. The last of the dinosaurs lived in woodlands that would seem very familiar to us.

It is probably no mere happenstance that the great proliferation of the plant-eating ornithischian dinosaurs took place *after* this evolutionary burst of the flowering plants. The development of a new and varied food supply certainly made possible the wide and varied growth of the herbivorous dinosaurs, and established the distinctive characters of Cretaceous faunas. The several groups of theropods, the giant sauropods, and some of the camptosaurs continued their late Jurassic success into and through the Cretaceous period. Other Jurassic dinosaurs, notably the stegosaurs, held over into Cretaceous times, to become extinct soon after the advent of this latest Mesozoic period. But the great preponderance of ornithischian herbivores, the iguanodonts and pachycephalosaurs, the varied duck-billed dinosaurs, the ponderous armored dinosaurs, and the numerous horned dinosaurs, arose and evolved during an age of flowering plants. This was the true zenith of dinosaurian evolution.

Cretaceous dinosaurs are found at many localities throughout the

world. Good Lower Cretaceous dinosaur-bearing horizons are known
on each of the continents, but by far the majority of geologic levels
yielding dinosaurs are of late Cretaceous age. These dinosaur-bearing
sediments and localities are too numerous to mention in detail; the
reader is referred to the chart on page 247 for a listing of the formations in each of the continents and their probable relationships to each
other. For our present purposes certain very characteristic horizons
and their contained faunas will be discussed, with passing reference
to some of the others.

Among the better known Lower Cretaceous dinosaurs, both ana-
tomically and historically, are those found in the Wealden beds of
southern England and the northern part of the European continent.
This is the horizon that has produced such abundant and superb remains of *Iguanodon,* the dinosaur described early in the nineteenth
century by Gideon Mantell, and subsequently known from the un-
excelled series of skeletons found in a Belgian coal mine. Through
the years since the original discoveries of *Iguanodon* were made, a
large and interesting fauna of land-living vertebrates, in which the
dinosaurs are the most prominent and numerous representatives, has
been excavated from the Wealden beds. This assemblage of reptiles,
and the sediments in which they occur, give us a rather clear picture
of life on the land during early Cretaceous times.

Imagine Europe as a landscape of low lands and islands, bordered
by a tropical sea, a scene somewhat similar to the one of late Jurassic
age that we have already examined. Perhaps the vista was rather more
colorful than that of Jurassic times, with the land covered by a considerable variety of trees and some flowering plants. In this environment the dinosaurs lived. There were remnants of the past among the
animals that frequented the Wealden landscape: large water-loving
sauropod dinosaurs, the ever-present predators, such as *Megalosaurus,*
that lurked in the shadows or pushed through the foliage in search
of victims; and small camptosaurs that fed upon leaves and other
vegetation. But the fauna had a new look none the less, by reason
of the interesting dinosaurs that had arisen since Jurassic times: giant
iguanodonts browsing among the vegetation, their diminutive relatives, the hypsilophodonts, that scurried through the undergrowth and
perhaps even climbed up the branches of trees; and on the higher and
firmer ground between rivers and swamps the armored dinosaurs,
such as *Polacanthus.* In addition to the dinosaurs there were croco-

diles, turtles, lizards, and perhaps snakes, flying reptiles, and birds. This is a partial sample of early Cretaceous animals.

Glimpses of reptilian life similar to that of the Wealden are to be had in the fossils found in the Cloverly formation of western North America, the Nequen beds of Argentina, the Uitenhage sediments of Africa, and the Lower Cretaceous beds of Shantung, China. The dinosaurs of this age from various parts of the world clearly show the evolutionary advances that had taken place during the geologic interval since Morrison-Tendaguru-Purbeck times.

The marked increase of ornithischian dinosaurs during early Cretaceous times, great in significance and most striking in its effect on the composition of reptilian assemblages of that day, is small when contrasted with the development of the ornithischians in late Cretaceous times. During the final phases of Cretaceous history the ornithischians went through a veritable evolutionary "explosion," in the course of which many new and distinctive genera, and even families and suborders arose, evolved, and increased, and finally became extinct, all within the span of a few million years.

There is no better place in the world in which to excavate the fossils of Upper Cretaceous dinosaurs than western North America, where one encounters a sequence of successive horizons containing vast quantities of dinosaur bones. In general terms the sequence of sediments from bottom to top, and as exposed in Montana and Alberta, may be listed as the Belly River, Edmonton, and Lance or Hell Creek, and it represents a succession of deposits ranging through the last few million years of Cretaceous history, with the top of the Lance formation showing us the very close of Mesozoic events. In this sequence of beds one can follow the development of various lines of dinosaurs, these frequently showing in a most graphic way the perfection of anatomical specializations and the increase in variety of types from the earlier to the later horizons. For example, the giant carnivore *Tyrannosaurus* of the Hell Creek beds of Montana is an enlarged and more extreme predatory type than its earlier relative *Gorgosaurus* of the Belly River. Many other examples might be cited.

Essentially this same sequence of deposits is represented in the southern part of North America, where dinosaurs from the Aguja formation of Texas and the Difunta formation of Mexico may be compared with the Belly River dinosaurs, while those of the Ojo Alamo beds of New Mexico may be compared with the dinosaurs of the

Lance. Furthermore, rather fragmentary but important glimpses of these late Cretaceous dinosaur assemblages are to be had in some of the deposits of the Atlantic coastal plain, especially in New Jersey. In other continents similar developments are evident: in a large series of formations in Mongolia and contiguous parts of Asia, where within recent years spectacular discoveries of dinosaurs have been made; in Morocco and adjacent parts of North Africa; in certain sections of Europe; and in Patagonia. But let us turn our attention to an examination of the Belly River and the Lance-Hell-Creek faunas, to get some idea of what the dinosaurs and other reptiles of late Cretaceous times were like, and what may have been the environments in which they lived.

It would appear that what is now the Rocky Mountain region of North America was in Belly River times a rather low land of rivers and lakes, in part covered with forests and in part a region of open glades. The forests, as we have seen, were quite varied, and were made up of broad-leaved deciduous trees and green, fragrant conifers. There were flowering bushes, too, while a tropical touch was added to the scene by the presence of palm trees, cycads, and the like. Ferns and other low plants flourished beneath the trees, but it is probable that few if any grasses carpeted the ground in the open glades, because the development of grasses did not take place until later geologic times. This land, a region of warm and moderate temperatures far up into what is now Alberta, probably extended continuously from north to south, quite in contrast to the islands or peninsulas of northern Europe. Thus dinosaurs could wander freely through wide ranges of latitude, and perhaps of longitude as well.

In this land of Belly River times the dinosaurs occupied a large range of *ecologic* environments—undergrowth, forests, open land, swamps, rivers, lakes, and even the shores of the sea. They filled the land and dominated it as never before in Mesozoic times. The world was theirs.

In the cover of the forest floor were lightly built coelurosaurian dinosaurs, not so greatly different from the ancestral theropods of late Triassic times. They were the small predators that lived upon lizards and other small game that they could catch. They may be compared with the foxes in a modern forest. There were other coelurosaurians in this land, too, the medium-sized ornithomimids that have been described in Chapter Five, the so-called "ostrich dinosaurs" that very likely occupied the "niche" in late Cretaceous times occupied by ostriches today. These long-legged, lightly constructed dinosaurs, obviously fast runners, probably kept away from the dense forests of that time, to make their living in the open spaces where they could escape from enemies by great leaping strides. The giant carnivores, such as *Gorgosaurus*, ranged back and forth in search of their prey, through forest and glade. Theirs was probably not a stealthy hunt; they were too big and ponderous to slink through the woodlands. Indeed, they did not have to rely on such stratagems, because their victims, other large dinosaurs, were generally slow, clumsy reptiles that could be overcome by force, if the force were sufficiently great and sufficiently violent. These large theropods were very probably stopped at the rivers and lakes and swamps where they might easily have become mired, and where some of their victims, particularly the duck-billed dinosaurs, fled when they were being pursued or attacked. Yet the waters of late Cretaceous lands were not entirely safe for those dinosaurs that went into the water, especially for the smaller ones or for the half-grown individuals of large species, because the streams and lakes and swamps were infested with crocodiles of all kinds, some of which were giants, far greater in size than the largest crocodiles of our day. *Phobosuchus*, the bones of which have been found in Montana and in Texas, was a tremendous reptile, a terrifying monster fifty feet or more in length, with six-foot jaws. Certainly this crocodile must have been a predator of dinosaurs; otherwise why would it have been so overwhelmingly gigantic? It hunted in the water where the giant theropods could not go.

Among the host of plant-eating dinosaurs there were still huge sauropods inhabiting the rivers and swamps. Such habitats were far less extensive in late Cretaceous times than they had been at the close of the Jurassic period, so the giant swamp-dwelling dinosaurs would seem to have been somewhat reduced in numbers. Nevertheless they were there, as proved by their huge bones, found in some deposits of Belly River age.

But the majority of the plant eaters were the ornithischians, some small, many large. There were hadrosaurs with different kinds of large crests on their heads, frequenting the waters, and ceratopsians with variously developed horns, living on the hard ground. These dinosaurs were well equipped to cope with the predatory theropods —the duck-bills by splashing into deep water, as has been described, and the horned dinosaurs by challenging and fighting off their adversaries.

On the high, firm ground between rivers and lakes were, in addition to the ceratopsians, the strange armored dinosaurs, the ankylosaurs, protected by their heavy armor plates and their wicked clubbed tails. Other upland dinosaurs that look queer to us were the so-called bone-headed dinosaurs, the pachycephalosaurs, described in Chapter Seven. Just where these particular dinosaurs fit into the ecologic picture is a little difficult for us to see; we can only guess that they frequented forests and glades, where they browsed upon the leaves of bushes and trees.

There were lizards and snakes and turtles living along with this great array of dinosaurs, and in the air the flying reptiles and the birds, which latter by now had become highly specialized and varied, and not so very different from the birds of modern times.

Again, as in Jurassic times, but to a much greater degree, small mammals frequented the undergrowth beneath the feet of the gigantic dinosaurs and climbed high among the branches of the trees. These mammals of late Cretaceous times were probably more numerous than those of the Jurassic period, and some of them were far more advanced in structure than their Jurassic relatives. Indeed, in the late Cretaceous environments were some mammals directly ancestral to modern mammals; these were marsupials and primitive placentals. The marsupials of the Cretaceous were generalized types, some of them very close to the common opossum that today inhabits much of eastern North America. The placental mammals of the Cretaceous period were insectivores, related to modern shrews and European hedgehogs, and in truth not very different from these particular insectivores of the modern world. From some such obscure little mammals all of the dominant mammals of today evolved, to take over the world once the dinosaurs had become extinct. We owe them much.

The great dinosaurian menagerie of Belly River times continued through the remainder of Cretaceous history, with advances taking place among some groups, with little change among others. Of course, many of the typical Belly River types died out before Lance times, but they were for the most part replaced by related descendants. Certain smaller theropods, such as the small coelurosaurians and the ornithomimids, continued from Belly River into Lance times with virtually no changes. The giant theropods got ever bigger, so that *Gorgosaurus* was replaced by its gigantic descendant *Tyrannosaurus*. A parallel growth in size is to be seen in the dome-headed dinosaurs. Among the duck-billed dinosaurs and the horned dinosaurs, by way of contrast, there were only moderate-size increases of Lance over Belly River types, but there were changes in design so to speak. The crested duck-bills, so numerous and prominent in the Belly River scene, were replaced by large flat-headed hadrosaurs. The horned dinosaurs of Belly River times were replaced by somewhat larger and rather different Lance ceratopsians. The armored dinosaurs continued with only minor changes. Thus the dinosaurs that lived at the very end of the Cretaceous period were very much like their predecessors that had inhabited the land several million years before them; the changes were largely of degree rather than of kind. The history of the

---

Figure 50. World map showing the localities at which Cretaceous dinosaurs have been found. *Abbreviations:* North America: M—Monmouth (and associated formations), D—Difunta, A—Aguja, K—Kirtland, OA—Ojo Alamo, BR—Belly River, E—Edmonton, L—Lance; South America: N—Nequen, P—Patagonia, B—Bauru; Eurasia: W—Wealden, S—Senonian, M—Maestrichtian, Da—Danian, Lm—Lameta, SK (lower)—Sinkiang, Kn—Kansu, O—Oshih, ID—Iren Dabasu, D—Djadochta, SH—Shantung, AR—Amur River, SK (upper)—Sakhalin; Africa: M—Morocco, Sa—Sahara, B—Baharija, Bl—Bushmans R., U—Uitenhage, Md—Madagascar; Australia: Op—Opal beds

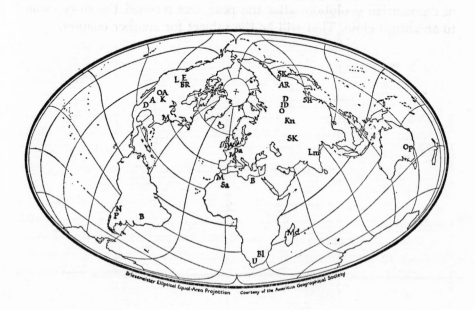

Briesemeister Elliptical Equal-Area Projection   Courtesy of the American Geographical Society

dinosaurs during this culminating phase of their long existence was a story of continuous development, a saga of progressive and successful evolution up to the very end, when within a geological instant, almost, they disappeared from the face of the earth.

Our account of the last of the dinosaurs has been centered upon the late Cretaceous faunas of North America. Similar developments were taking place on the other continents, as well, but for the most part the record is not nearly so complete as is that of the North American dinosaurs. It should be emphasized, once again, that recent work in central Asia is uncovering a story of the late Cretaceous dinosaurs comparable in scope and in many details to what we know from North America. Evidently there was a free passageway between the two continental areas, with consequent interchanges of many dinosaurs. The late Cretaceous dinosaurian faunas of other continental regions—of South America, Africa, and Europe—are perhaps less closely related to those of North America than are the Asiatic assemblages, yet so far as known they also are of the same general complexion. At the end of Mesozoic times the dinosaurs inhabited the continents in great numbers.

It is a fact that the dinosaurs were quite successful up to the very end of their long reign on the earth. At no time during their existence was their success so complete or their dominance so firmly established as in the final phase of Cretaceous history. Here was the peak of dinosaurian evolution; after the peak was reached the story came to an abrupt close. That will be the subject for another chapter.

AGE CORRELATIONS OF
IMPORTANT DINOSAUR-BEARING SEDIMENTS

	SOUTH AMERICA	NORTH AMERICA		ASIA	EUROPE	AFRICA
CRETACEOUS UPPER		Lance	Ojo Alamo	Trichinopoly	Danian	Baharija
	Patagonia	Hell Creek	Kirtland	Lameta	Maestrichtian	
				Kansu		Morocco
		Edmonton	Selma	Amur		Sahara
			Aguja	Sakhalin		Madagascar
		Belly River	Difunta	Shantung	Senonian	
	Bauru			Sinkiang		
				Djadochta		
				Iren Dabasu		
				Oshih		
CRETACEOUS LOWER	Nequen	Cloverly	Arundel		Wealden	Uitenhage
JURASSIC UPPER		Morrison		Kuangyuan	Purbeck	Tendaguru
JURASSIC MIDDLE				Shansi	Kimmeridge	Nyassaland
				Chinchou	Oxford	Madagascar
JURASSIC LOWER		Navajo				
					Lias	
TRIASSIC UPPER		Kayenta			Rhaetic	
		Chinle	Newark	Lufeng	Keuper	Stormberg
		Dockum				
		Popo Agie				Manda
	Santa Maria					

CHAPTER SIXTEEN

THE EXTINCTION OF THE DINOSAURS

THE PROBLEM OF EXTINCTION

There can be no doubt about it. All of the dinosaurs, along with various other Cretaceous reptiles, became extinct at the end of that period of geologic history. Not one of them survived into a later geologic age, as is amply proved by the fact that during almost a century and a half of paleontological exploration, the wide world over, no trace of a dinosaur bone or tooth has ever been found in any post-Cretaceous rocks, not even in the earliest of them. The proof of the geologic record on this score is irrefutable.

Such evidence is not completely satisfactory to some people, and thus for many decades various romantically minded persons have been suggesting that even though the fossil record may indicate dinosaurs to have become extinct with the close of Cretaceous times, there are none the less some of these reptiles still living in the hidden remoteness of a tropical jungle, perhaps in South America. Although this idea may have had some of its stimulus in the past from Sir Arthur Conan

Doyle's fascinating and fanciful book *The Lost World*, it is the kind of idea that will flourish without any particular prompting from literary or other sources. It is a thought that naturally comes to mind. In recent years the few misguided souls who support this theory have pointed excitedly to the discovery in 1938 of *Latimeria*, a coelacanth fish, a representative of a line that, like the dinosaurs, was supposed to have become extinct at the close of Cretaceous times. "Look," they say, "if coelacanth fishes could be completely absent as fossils in post-Cretaceous rocks, and then turn up as living animals, might not the same be true for dinosaurs?"

It is an argument, but not a valid one. It is something like saying that since gazelles abound in the deserts of Mongolia, we ought to find them also in the deserts of North America. We don't find them in North America because of various circumstances, past and present. Likewise, we haven't found living dinosaurs in remote tropical jungles, nor shall we, because of various circumstances, quite different from the circumstances that led to the survival and the eventual discovery of the coelacanth fish *Latimeria*. In the first place the post-Cretaceous coelacanths quite obviously lived in a very limited and specialized environment that, it so happens, was never preserved in the Cenozoic (or post-Cretaceous) fossil record. The land-living dinosaurs, had they been living at any stage since the end of the Cretaceous period, would because of their habits almost certainly have shown up by now in some of the abundant Cenozoic land deposits that contain the bones, often very small and fragile, of so many varied mammals. Second, the modern coelacanth was living in a sea-bottom environment that had not until recent years been explored by white men, although there is now good circumstantial evidence showing that the natives of the Comoro Islands, between Africa and Madagascar, very probably have been acquainted with this fish for generations. But the jungles of the world, even the most remote jungles, have now been sufficiently explored by scientific men so as to establish the fact that no dinosaurs inhabit the green depths of these regions. This statement might not have been made with confidence a century ago, but today the world is a much smaller and a much less mysterious globe than it used to be.

Therefore let us say quite categorically that the dinosaurs disappeared completely and absolutely about 70 million years ago. What were the reasons for this very spectacular disappearance of the dinosaurs and of other reptiles with which they were contemporaneous? This is one of the big questions of paleontology for which as yet no satisfactory answer has been set forward. It is a question that has intrigued many people, scientific and nonscientific, perhaps in part for the very reason that it is such an unanswerable one. We are all prone to find fascination in the riddles of the world and the universe, such as the problem of life on Mars or the ever-recurrent question of where the Vikings landed in North America. Consequently the problem of extinction is one to which we return, time and again, even though very little is known about it. The most hardheaded and blasé geologist is more often than not apt to get excited when he becomes involved in a discussion of the extinction of the dinosaurs.

Extinction is one of the great evolutionary processes, yet it has received far less attention than has the problem of origins, again probably because it is such a difficult and baffling phenomenon to analyze and understand. Certainly more work needs to be done on the problem of extinction if we are to understand the complexities of evolution on the earth, for although evolution depends in part upon the origin of new species, it is equally dependent upon the extinction of old species. If this were not so, the earth would long ago have become completely clogged with fixed and static life; there would have been no room for progress, for the replacement of animals and plants that had become "out of tune" with the world around them by new and progressive types, adapted to a changing environment.

In very general terms it can be said that extinction is the result of animals or plants being unable to adapt themselves to changing conditions. But what does this mean? Is it possible to cite examples of this generalization, to make it more understandable? As a matter of fact, such examples are known, namely, the disappearance of certain species of animals and plants in modern times, but whether they add to our understanding of the process of extinction is a moot point. One example would be the disappearance of the passenger pigeon of North America, a bird that once inhabited this continent in countless millions, a bird so numerous that flocks of pigeons literally blotted out the sun during their seasonal migrations. The accounts of the passenger-pigeon flocks, as they darkened the sky in the early days of the nineteenth century, have an almost legendary quality to them, and yet we know them to be true. Then, by the closing years of that century the pigeon was almost extinct, partly the result of uncontrolled hunting, partly the result of the destruction of virgin beech forests in which the pigeons nested and fed. Their world had changed about them, and the pigeons for some reason were unable to adapt themselves to the change. One would think that small flocks of pigeons might have survived, particularly under the protection of man, but once the pigeon population had fallen below some critical number it was impossible to save the species, in spite of all the belated, valiant efforts that were made to do so.

This is, of course, an example of extinction brought about by what we might consider rather artificial or at least unusual causes. Nevertheless it helps us in a vague way to get some insight into the problem of extinction in general. The words "in general" must be emphasized, because when we try to apply what little we know from specific modern cases like this to the problem of dinosaurian extinction we find that very few correlations can be made. Consequently we are forced to fall back largely upon speculation. As for speculation, there have been many varying ideas brought forward to account for the extinction of the dinosaurs—some of them plausible, some of them plainly ridiculous. Let us look at a few of the more plausible ones.

SOME THEORIES CONCERNING THE EXTINCTION OF DINOSAURS

Since we define extinction as the inability of life to adapt itself to changing conditions, it seems logical to look for some great change that took place at the end of Cretaceous times, thereby bringing to an end the multitudes of dinosaurs and other reptiles that then populated the earth. This is not to imply that there was of necessity a great world-wide catastrophe, which by the violence of its expression suddenly wiped out the dinosaurs. Catastrophes are the mainstays of people who have very little knowledge of the natural world; for them the invocation of a catastrophe is an easy way to explain great events. But the modern student of nature is quite aware that the evolution of the earth and the evolution of life upon the earth have not proceeded by catastrophic events, even though local catastrophes—the eruption of a volcano or the sweep of an epidemic—may temporarily affect the progress of nature in some specific area. The history of the earth and of its life have advanced through the ages by a grand succession of events, by the action of forces of immense scope and significance.

There was an event of late Cretaceous development that it is natural to associate with the disappearance of the dinosaurs—the Laramide Revolution, mentioned in a previous chapter, the sequence of earth forces that gave rise to our modern great systems of mountains. Is it not possible that massive mountain uplifts so affected climates and plants that various animals, including the dinosaurs, were unable to change with the changing environment, and thereby became extinct?

As we have seen, there was a profound change in plant life that took place during Cretaceous times, which may have been in part a result of the Laramide uplift. The dinosaurs that lived at the advent of Cretaceous history inhabited a world of primitive plants; the dinosaurs of late Cretaceous times were the denizens of "modern" forests composed of familiar broad-leafed trees, and conifers and palms, with an intermingling of primitive plants that survived from earlier ages. But the significant point here is that hordes of late Cretaceous dinosaurs *did* live in a changed world for many millions of years. The early post-Cretaceous world does not seem to our eyes so very different from the late Cretaceous world. Why did not at least some of the dinosaurs live on?

These considerations point up a fact that must be kept in mind when we think of or discuss the Laramide Revolution, namely, that this mountain-making process lasted for a long time, for it began in the early stages of Cretaceous history, or possibly even before, and continued through a large segment of post-Cretaceous or Cenozoic history. There may have been a sort of climax, so to speak, at the end of Cretaceous times, but certainly continental uplifts and mountain making went on before and after this date, and at a very slow rate indeed in terms of living things. For example, we think of the world as a very stable place, the abode of the "everlasting hills," yet we are living in a most active period of geologic history, a time of mountain making that is probably the equal of any that occurred during past geologic ages. Therefore it is difficult to think of the Laramide Revolution in itself as being the single factor that might have brought about the extinction of the dinosaurs.

But what about climatic changes that may have been instituted by the Laramide Revolution, changes that could have resulted in the permanent lowering or raising of average temperatures around the world? It has long been the considered opinion of many geologists that the Laramide Revolution inaugurated a world-wide lowering of average temperatures, and this phenomenon may have been instrumental in bringing to an end the long reign of the dinosaurs. The evidence shows that any such changes certainly took place slowly. There was a gradual replacement of world-wide tropical and subtropical environments by zoned temperature belts such as typify our world today, but it took many millions of years to effectuate. It appears to us as if some of the dinosaurs at least might have lived just as successfully and happily in the epochs following the close of the Cretaceous period as they did in those days of dinosaurian abundance.

In contrast to the theory of lowered temperatures as being instrumental in bringing an end to dinosaurian dominance is the theory, formulated by Professor R. B. Cowles, that perhaps there was a raising of average world temperatures at the end of Cretaceous times. The large dinosaurs, because of their inability to lose heat quickly, might have been adversely affected, either because of increments in body temperatures that would have brought about the death of adult, reproducing dinosaurs, or because of damage to the heat-sensitive germ cells. It is an ingenious idea, but there is no geological evidence to support the concept of temperature increases at the close of the Cretaceous period. Moreover, even if conditions were such as to affect the large dinosaurs, why did not some of the smaller dinosaurs continue past the end of Cretaceous history? Numerous crocodiles did just this, and these were reptiles closely related to the dinosaurs.

It has been suggested that the changes brought about by the Laramide Revolution resulted in changes of food supply. The herbivorous dinosaurs as a result died out, and with their passing the carnivores also disappeared. As was mentioned above, however, the dinosaurs of late Cretaceous times did live in modern forests of a modern aspect, so if there was a change in food supply that affected the plant-eating dinosaurs it was too subtle to be registered in the geologic record. Moreover, not all of the carnivorous dinosaurs fed upon dinosaurs; the smaller ones certainly must have preyed upon various small reptiles—lizards and the like. Why did not these smaller meat-eating dinosaurs continue their life beyond the limits of the Cretaceous period, pursuing and eating lizards in early Cenozoic times?

Another suggestion has been made to the effect that "competition" between the late Cretaceous mammals and the dinosaurs brought about the demise of the latter. It is not at all easy to fit this theory with the fossil record. As long as the dinosaurs were on the earth, the mammals remained very small and unobtrusive; it was not until *after* the dinosaurs had become extinct that the mammals developed along many lines of evolution, to become the lords of the land. This is nicely illustrated by the occurrences of fossils in the rocks in some sections of western North America. Here there is a continuous sequence of rocks with no physical indications whatsoever of any kind of break or interruption in the processes of sedimentary accumulation. Through the lower parts of these sediments are the remains of dinosaurs and other Cretaceous reptiles. Then there is a barren zone of about twenty feet, above which there is a numerous and varied assemblage of early Cenozoic mammals. We see in this example what must have been the transition from Cretaceous to Cenozoic times in a geologically short period of time, yet before the transition the dinosaurs are supreme, and after, the mammals. There are few mammals mixed in with the dinosaurs and their reptilian relatives, and certainly no dinosaurs mixed in with the mammals above the zone of transition. The idea of dinosaurs being crowded off the face of the earth by early mammals does not withstand a close analysis.

If the mammals did not actually compete with the dinosaurs, is it not possible that they brought about the end of the great reptiles by robbing dinosaur nests and eating dinosaur eggs? This theory has often been mentioned. It is quite probable that many early mammals ate dinosaur eggs, as did other dinosaurs and other reptiles, but it seems unlikely that such forays against the hatching eggs of dinosaurs could have wiped out the dinosaurs. The nests and eggs of various modern reptiles, such as the large sea turtles, are subjected to intensive onslaughts by all sorts of animals, not the least important of which is man, but the reptiles continue. And if any of them do disappear as a result of such attacks, it will be through the agency of man's greed and not through any "natural" enemies. Egg stealing may have been a slight factor in controlling the size of dinosaur populations, but it probably had little effect on the final disappearance of these reptiles.

Were the dinosaurs exterminated by great epidemics that swept the Cretaceous world? This is hard to believe, because most epidemics are very specific or relatively limited in their effects. We know from modern experience that an epidemic may wipe out a species just as a blight killed all of the American chestnuts a half-century ago, but its effects generally are not felt by other species, even closely related ones. One can suppose that all tyrannosaurs or all hadrosaurs might have been eliminated by some epidemic sweeping through the populations of these particular dinosaurs at the end of Cretaceous times, but it is stretching credulity far beyond the bounds of reason to suppose that a series of epidemics could have brought about the disappearance of all dinosaurs.

There is an old theory called "racial senescence" that envisages a "life" for species or for other categories of animals and plants, just as there is an individual life. According to this theory any particular group of dinosaurs, for example, would go through its youth, its maturity, and its old age, so that its final disappearance would be a sort of natural process needing no particular explanation. It has been argued that the development of numerous spines on animals, or the growth of individuals along proportions that seem strange or "bizarre" to us, are indications of racial old age—of senescence. True enough, such developments are not uncommonly seen in evolutionary lines shortly before their extinction, but one need not suppose that these indicate any mysterious type of racial old age. Rather they probably indicate specific specializations to some narrowed environment, soon to disappear, taking with it the animals so particularly suited to its limits.

A suggestion that may be bracketed with the theory of senescence is one to the effect that the eggs of late Cretaceous dinosaurs had lost their viability, thus bringing about the extinction of these dinosaurs through the failure of the eggs to hatch. This theory is based particularly upon the discovery of large numbers of eggs and egg fragments in the Upper Cretaceous deposits of southern France, described in Chapter Fourteen. Do not the large numbers of unhatched eggs in these deposits indicate, it is argued, that something was interfering with reproduction in the last of the dinosaurs, which may explain why they *were* the last of the dinosaurs? In this respect, we must not be unduly impressed by the numbers of dinosaur eggs discovered in southern France. A hundred or so eggs, and fragments indicative of several thousand more, may seem like a lot, but these should be viewed as a small fraction of the hundreds of thousands or perhaps millions of eggs laid during the time the Cretaceous sediments of that region were being deposited. Furthermore it must be realized that the dinosaur eggs from southern France are found through a certain thickness of Upper Cretaceous rocks. If the eggs had been so sterile as to bring about the extinction of the dinosaurs in this region, one would expect them to be limited to a very narrow zone of sediments. It would have been a biological phenomenon of short duration in time. Consequently this explanation, like other single-factor explanations of dinosaurian extinction, does not seem very probable when carefully analyzed.

There have been other suggestions made to account for the extinction of the dinosaurs, such as the idea that there may have been a change in oxygen concentration in the atmosphere that affected them (although it must have affected other air-breathing animals as well). Perhaps the various theories already set down here are sufficient to give some idea as to the hypothetical depths that have been probed in an attempt to solve the riddle of dinosaurian extinction.

It seems likely that the extinction of the dinosaurs was a very complex phenomenon; that it cannot be explained on the basis of a single cause and effect. Perhaps a combination of factors brought about the disappearance of these reptiles at the end of Cretaceous times, among which may be some of the suggested causes discussed above. Other factors of extinction may have been of such subtle nature that we are quite unaware as to what they were.

THE FINAL YEARS

This extinction has the appearance of having taken place very abruptly, and so it did, geologically speaking. There were numerous dinosaurs inhabiting the continents up to the very end of the Cretaceous period, according to the record of the rocks. We must remember, however, that the extinction of the dinosaurs actually must have been spread out over a very considerable span of years, a span that might seem long indeed in terms of human experience. It seems quite probable that species of dinosaurs disappeared from the Cretaceous world one by one or in small groups, that their exits, though inevitable, may have been drawn out through the years, just as today what appears to be the extinctions of the five species of rhinoceroses are being prolonged through a good many human lifetimes.

To elaborate this example, the Sondaican rhinoceros of the East Indies may already be extinct, although there are probably men living today who have seen this animal alive. If it is not extinct, it surely will be within the very near future. The Sumatran rhinoceros, also an East Indian form, has a slightly longer existence ahead of it, but not much longer. Likewise the great Indian rhinoceros, which can still be seen in various zoological parks, probably cannot continue as a natural species for more than a few centuries, perhaps for even a shorter time span. The wild population of this magnificent animal is down to a few hundred individuals, and when a population becomes so small its continuation is very perilous indeed. The next on the list is probably the white rhinoceros of Africa, also represented by a restricted population. Finally the African black rhinoceros may continue for some time into the future, especially if it is rigidly protected, but even this interesting mammal must be regarded as a species probably in the final stages of its career.

Here is a small object lesson as to how extinctions may have taken place among the dinosaurs. They did drag through the years. But for events that took place 70 million years ago the course of a few thousand years or even a few hundred thousand years will not be detectable in the geologic record. Consequently the extinction of the dinosaurs appears to us to have been abrupt.

Let us come back to one other question: Why did *all* the dinosaurs become extinct? Likewise, why did various other Cretaceous reptiles, especially the marine ichthyosaurs, plesiosaurs, and mosasaurs, also become extinct? One might suppose that these oceanic reptiles of Cretaceous days, living in an environment that was more uniform and more stable than that inhabited by the land dwellers, would have continued beyond the limits of Cretaceous history, in seas that during early post-Cretaceous days would appear to have been hardly less warm and mild than were the seas of Mesozoic times. Yet they, like the dinosaurs, failed to survive the transition from uppermost Meso-

Figure 51. The abundance of late Cretaceous dinosaurs of pre-Lance and Lance age, as based upon the records of described species. Note that in the geologic record there is a sharp decline in the abundance of dinosaur species somewhat before the end of Cretaceous times. Perhaps this is the record of a process of extinction that extended over a considerable lapse of geologic time

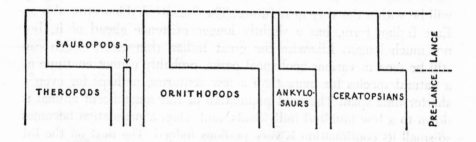

zoic to Cenozoic times. Why was dinosaurian extinction so complete zoologically? This is just another of the many questions that arise in connection with the riddle of dinosaurian extinction.

FINAL THOUGHTS

And so we have completed the circle of speculation and contemplation; we have discussed the problem of the extinction of the dinosaurs, and are back about where we started. We know that they became extinct because they could not adapt themselves to changing conditions, and that is about all we do know. Having said this, we display the extent of our ignorance upon a subject that is at once baffling and intriguing, a subject that it is hard to pass by without the hazard of a few guesses or a few theories. Such will be the problem of dinosaurian extinction for years to come; many people will speculate on it, but no one will have any definite answers, at least not until much more is known about the problem of extinction in general and the specific problem of dionsaurian extinction than is now known. There is much hard and detailed work to be done in the future on this problem.

At the present time we can therefore only look upon the problem of extinction of the dinosaurs as a hard fact, as the closing of a most spectacular chapter in the history of life on the earth. We can close this chapter with an epitaph for the dinosaurs written in 1933 by Professor Richard Swann Lull, a great scholar and a keen student who devoted many years of a long and productive life to the study of these ancient reptiles. Said Lull, "They [the dinosaurs] do not represent a futile attempt on the part of nature to people the world with creatures of insignificant moment, but are comparable in majestic rise, slow culmination, and dramatic fall to the greatest nations of antiquity."

CHAPTER SEVENTEEN

A CLASSIFICATION

SOME GENERAL REMARKS

Classification may seem like dull business, but if we are to have a true understanding of animals and plants it is essential that we have some knowledge of their relationships to one another. Moreover, the classification of organisms need not be in the least a dull subject, for it deals with something that is basic to our knowledge of life.

This knowledge was very inadequate and in many respects quite erroneous until the modern system of zoological and botanical classification was established in the middle of the eighteenth century by a great Swedish naturalist, Carl von Linné, generally known by his latinized last name, Linnaeus. His *Systema Naturae*, the tenth edition of which was published in 1758, marks the beginning of the scientific classification of animals and plants, and correlatively the beginning of a true understanding of the world of nature. Before Linnaeus there were many strange and curious ideas in general circulation about plant and animal relationships, even though there also were frequent flashes of insight. Men of the Middle Ages, and even those of Renaissance times, might sincerely believe that the giraffe or "camelopard" was an animal that had arisen from the crossing of a camel (with a long neck) and a leopard or "pard" (with spots), to mention but one of the mistaken ideas that was held before the days of Linnaeus. Such notions did not quickly disappear, even after Linnaeus had founded the classification upon which modern scientific natural history is based, because old folk beliefs will persist from one generation to the next. But with the "systemization" of Nature it soon became apparent that many of the established tales concerning animals and plants were erroneous, and often ludicrous. Linnaeus tried to make as close and objective comparisons as possible between animals and between plants, and upon the basis of anatomical characters to arrange all forms of life in a system of categories.

Linnaeus established the *species* as the basic unit of classification in nature. The species is a single kind of animal or plant, in modern terms a population of freely interbreeding individuals. Linnaeus realized that the designation of separate species by single names would be inadequate if a system of classification was to be at all useful; therefore he united closely related species into a higher category, the *genus*. Horses, zebras, and asses are contained within several species, all of which may be included within a single genus, the name of which is *Equus*. The domestic horse is *Equus caballus*, one of the zebras is *Equus chapmani*, one of the asses is *Equus asinus*. Here we see illustrated the *binomial* system of naming animals that has continued in use quite successfully from the days of Linnaeus to modern times.

Why, you may ask, bother with what seems a cumbersome manner of naming common animals? Why not call a horse a horse? But a horse is not a horse to a Frenchman; it is *un cheval*. To a German it is *ein Pferd*. And so on through hundreds of modern languages and dialects. Yet *Equus caballus* is a horse the world around, and is so understood by people with a zoological training, whether they be Americans, Norwegians, Brazilians, or Chinese.

THE HIERARCHY

What we have just been considering is *nomenclature*, the naming of animals and plants. Nomenclature is, however, a part of *classification*, which latter includes not only species and genera (the plural of genus) but higher categories as well. Consequently several genera may be included within a *family*, several families within an *order*, several orders within a *class*, classes within a *phylum*, and phyla (the plural for phylum) within a *kingdom*. Thus is established the hierarchy, by means of which every animal and every plant on the face of the earth can be placed where it belongs, in a manner that expresses its relationship to the whole.

In a descending order of categories we have, for example:

Kingdom—Animal
  Phylum—Chordata or chordates (animals with backbones)
    Class—Mammalia or mammals (warm-blooded animals with hair)
      Order—Perissodactyla or perissodactyls (odd-toed hoofed animals)
        Family—Equidae or equids (horses, zebras, and asses)
          Genus—*Equus* (in this case, also horses, zebras, and asses)
            Species—*caballus* (the horse)

Actually, there are often many more grades used in the hierarchy than are indicated by this example. The additional categories are obtained, however, not by adding anything on to either end of the sequence as it has here been presented, but rather by sandwiching grades in between the basic units that have been listed above. Thus there may be a *subclass* below the class, a *suborder* below the order, or even an *infraorder* below the suborder. There may be a *superfamily*, a *subfamily*, and so on. These are details with which we need not concern ourselves at the present time.

To get back to the species, this is the unit with which most zoologists (or botanists) work at the present time. The modern species is generally a clear-cut thing; as already mentioned, a population of interbreeding individuals. A student of modern animals may be concerned with the red foxes of North America or the alligator of southeastern United States or the wood thrush of New England, and he knows pretty well what the limits of these species may be. More often than not each modern species may be subdivided into a number of geographical subspecies, but this does not affect the validity of the species as a basic unit of classification.

THE NAMING OF FOSSILS

Paleontologists, however, have much more trouble with species than do their brethren who work with living animals and plants, for the good reason that they, the students of ancient life, are not dealing with interbreeding animals in recognizable populations. They are working with fossil remains, and the recognition of species is consequently much less objective for them than it is for the students of living animals and plants. Much close work can and has been done on fossil species, but for general discussions, such as the ones in which we have been indulging, the *genus* is the most satisfactory unit to use.

Perhaps the procession of generic names—*Coelophysis, Tyrannosaurus, Corythosaurus, Monoclonius,* and the like—has been at times confusing. What new and strange names are not confusing? People who are first introduced to the dinosaurs often complain about the supposedly jaw-breaking names by which these ancient reptiles are designated. (Interestingly enough, such complaints almost always come from the adults; the children accept the names and master them without much trouble.) Many of the names admittedly take a little study when they are first encountered, but if they are approached without fear and trembling and are calmly analyzed it will be found that they are not so very difficult to handle.

Would it not be practical to have simpler names? it is often asked. But how? These are the scientific names of animals that never have had any common names in any language. We might call *Triceratops* "three-horn-face" or "horned dinosaur number 27" or something like that, but such circumlocutions would in the end prove to be more difficult and more cumbersome than the single generic name. Moreover, this name has the advantage of being available to all people, no matter what languages they may speak or read. So we have to learn and recognize and use the names of the genera of dinosaurs, just as the readers of a novel must become acquainted with the names of the characters in the story.

Most names of animals and plants are based upon Greek and Latin roots, but they may incorporate or consist entirely of elements from other languages. They are coined as *names* for the animals or plants to which they refer, and this must be kept in mind. They are *not* intended as descriptions of the organisms, although many scientific names attempt to indicate something of the character of a designated animal or plant. *Triceratops* means "three horns on the face," which is a pretty good description, but *Titanosaurus*, which means "titanic reptile," is not particularly descriptive of this rather small sauropod dinosaur.

A few more points. The generic names of many dinosaurs contain the suffix *saurus*, which is a transliteration of the ancient Greek word meaning "lizard." *Dinosaur* is a combination of two Greek words meaning "terrible lizard" ("terrible reptile" would be a more satisfactory though less accurate rendition), and for this reason many people insist on thinking of the dinosaurs as being overgrown lizards. They are not, as we know. Rather, as has been so frequently said in this book, they are close relatives of the modern crocodiles. Here is another instance of the pitfalls encountered if one is going to accept the scientific name in a literal sense. Again let it be emphasized that the name is a name and should be looked at in that way. One does not expect all people named Smith to work at forges, or people named Miller to grind wheat.

CLASSIFICATION OF THE DINOSAURS

For our purposes it will suffice to use a comparatively simple classification of the dinosaurs, one that has already been set forward informally in the various chapters of this book. As we have seen, there are two orders of these reptiles, one of which, the Saurischia, may be divided into two suborders, the theropods and the sauropods; the other, the Ornithischia, being divisible into four suborders, the ornithopods, stegosaurs, ankylosaurs, and ceratopsians. Three of the suborders, the sauropods, stegosaurs, and ankylosaurs, are used here without further subdivision, all genera in each one being lumped together. This is done because of the uniformity of the genera contained within these three suborders. The other three suborders contain more varied assortments of genera. Thus the theropods can be subdivided into three categories, the coelurosaurs, carnosaurs, and prosauropods, these having ranks of infraorders. Each of these infraorders is divisible in turn into families, but for the sake of simplicity the families of theropods are here being by-passed. The genera of ornithopods and ceratopsians are simply grouped within families. This is not entirely consistent with what has been done for the theropods, but logically it is proper, because the differences between the various groups of ornithopods and ceratopsians probably do not deserve more than family rank. In the classification of larger categories that follows, those chosen for use in this book are indicated by asterisks:

THE LARGER UNITS

Order Saurischia *—saurischians
>> Pubis directed forwardly; large openings in skull; teeth around margins or in front of jaws.

> Suborder Theropoda *—theropods (mostly meat-eating dinosaurs)
>> Bipedal: strong hind legs; grasping hands; mostly carnivorous. Triassic-Cretaceous.

>> Infraorder Coelurosauria *—coelurosaurs (small carnivores)
>>> Small to medium size; hollow bones; small skull; long neck; bird-like hind feet. Triassic-Cretaceous.

>>> Families Ammosauridae
>>>> Hallopodidae
>>>> Podokesauridae
>>>> Segisauridae
>>>> Coeluridae
>>>> Ornithomimidae

>> Infraorder Carnosauria *—carnosaurs (large carnivores)
>>> Large to gigantic; heavy bones; large skull; short neck; forelimbs very small; bird-like hind feet. Triassic-Cretaceous.

>>> Families Palaeosauridae
>>>> Teratosauridae
>>>> Megalosauridae
>>>> Tyrannosauridae

>> Infraorder Prosauropoda *—prosauropods (sauropod ancestors)
>>> Small to large; heavy bones; small skull; leaf-shaped teeth; probably omnivorous; enlarged forelimbs; heavy hind feet. Triassic.

>>> Families Thecodontosauridae
>>>> Plateosauridae
>>>> Melanorosauridae

> Suborder Sauropoda *—sauropods (giants—the brontosaurs)
>> Quadrupedal; gigantic; bones very heavy; relatively.small skull; teeth in front of jaws; long neck and tail; feet broad; herbivorous. Jurassic-Cretaceous.

>> Families Brachiosauridae
>>> Titanosauridae

Order Ornithischia *—ornithischians
>> Pubis parallel to ischium; openings in skull reduced; teeth along sides of jaws; front of jaws beak-like; all herbivorous.

Suborder Ornithopoda *—ornithopods (diverse, bipedal plant eaters)
  Bipedal or semiquadrupedal; diverse. Jurassic-Cretaceous.
  Families Hypsilophodontidae*—hypsilophodonts (primitive types)
    Small; small skull; clawed feet. Jurassic-Cretaceous.
  Iguanodontidae*—iguanodonts and camptosaurs (mostly
    rather generalized)
    Small to large; generalized skull; heavy limbs. Jurassic-
    Cretaceous.
  Hadrosauridae*—(duck-billed dinosaurs)
    Large to gigantic; front of jaws flat and broad; skull fre-
    quently crested; complex tooth batteries; forelimbs often
    somewhat elongated. Cretaceous.
  Pachycephalosauridae*—pachycephalosaurs (dome-headed
    dinosaurs)
    Small to large; domed skull. Cretaceous.
Suborder Stegosauria*—stegosaurs (plated dinosaurs)
  Quadrupedal; small skull, camptosaur-like; forelimbs short but
    heavy; hips high; feet short and broad; double row of upright
    plates on back, and spikes on tail. Jurassic-Lower Cretaceous.
  Family Stegosauridae
Suborder Ankylosauria*—ankylosaurs (armored dinosaurs)
  Quadrupedal; skull small, or large and broad; teeth very small;
    forelimbs short but heavy; hips high; feet short and broad.
    Skull and body covered by bony armor; frequently large
    spikes around sides and on tail, or massive club-like tail. Creta-
    ceous.
  Families Acantholidae
  Nodosauridae
Suborder Ceratopsia*—ceratopsians (horned dinosaurs)
  Mostly quadrupedal; large or gigantic skull; front of jaws narrow
    and deep, like a beak. Cretaceous.
  Families Psittacosauridae*—psittacosaurs (ceratopsian ancestors)
    Small; bipedal; forelimbs enlarged.
  Protoceratopsidae*—(primitive ceratopsians)
    Small; quadrupedal; skull with or without a frill.
  Ceratopsidae*—ceratopsids (large horned dinosaurs)
    Large; quadrupedal; enormous skull, the back of which is
    produced into a wide, flaring frill; horns variously de-
    veloped on skull; teeth doubly-rooted.
  Pachyrhinosauridae*—pachyrhinosaurs (thick-nosed cera-
    topsians)
    Large: like ceratopsids, but top of nasal region partly cov-
    ered by a large, rough boss.

THE GENERA

It is a common practice in the presentation of a zoological classification to list the genera or the species and their geographic distribution in some determined order, under the larger categories to which they belong. In the case of fossil forms, the geologic age for each genus and species is indicated after the name of the form in question. This is a logical treatment, but it may be confusing in some respects. The reader is apt to lose sight of the larger divisions of the classification, buried as they are in long lists of genera and perhaps species. In the case of fossils he does not readily remember the geologic ages, or even the geographic distributions.

Therefore this present classification is put forward in a different manner. All of the larger categories have been presented together, with indications of some of their outstanding distinguishing characteristics. The genera are now set down in several tables, arranged according to geologic age. These tables show the larger categories to which the genera belong, and they also indicate geographic occurrences.

Perhaps this method of presentation will prove to be no better than the more conventional one, but perhaps it may prove to be effective. Perhaps it will help the reader to remember *what* dinosaurs lived together, *where* they lived together, and *when* they lived together:

GENERA OF UPPER TRIASSIC DINOSAURS

SOUTH AMERICA	NORTH AMERICA	ASIA	EUROPE	AFRICA
		THEROPODS		
		Coelurosaurs		
	Ammosaurus	Lukousaurus	Avipes	
	Coelophysis		Dolichosuchus	
	Podokesaurus		Saltopus	
			Velocipes	
			Halticosaurus	
			Procompsognathus	

SOUTH AMERICA	NORTH AMERICA	ASIA	EUROPE	AFRICA
		THEROPODS		
		Carnosaurs		
	Zatomus	Sinosaurus	Palaeosaurus	Aetonyx
			Cladeiodon	Gryponyx
			Gresslyosaurus	Orosaurus
			Teratosaurus	
		Prosauropods		
Spondylosoma	Thecodontosaurus	Gyposaurus	Thecodontosaurus	Dromicosaurus
	Yaleosaurus	Massospondylus	Plateosaurus	Gyposaurus
		Thecodontosaurus		Massospondylus
		Yunnanosaurus		Thecodontosaurus
		Lufengosaurus		Eucnemesaurus
				Euskelosaurus
				Melanorosaurus
				Plateosauravus

GENERA OF LOWER JURASSIC DINOSAURS

SOUTH AMERICA	NORTH AMERICA	ASIA	EUROPE	AFRICA	AUSTRALIA
		THEROPODS			
		Coelurosaurs			
	Hallopus				
	Segisaurus				
		Carnosaurs			
			Megalosaurus		
			Sarcosaurus		
		SAUROPODS			
Amygdalodon					Rhoetosaurus
		STEGOSAURS			
			Scelidosaurus		
			Lusitanosaurus		

GENERA OF MIDDLE AND UPPER JURASSIC DINOSAURS

NORTH AMERICA	ASIA	EUROPE	AFRICA	AUSTRALIA
		THEROPODS		
		Coelurosaurs		
Ornitholestes	Sinocoelurus	Caudocoelus	Elaphrosaurus	Agrosaurus
		Compsognathus		
		Carnosaurs		
Allosaurus	Chienleosaurus	Megalosaurus		
(Antrodemus)	Szechuanosaurus			
Ceratosaurus				
		SAUROPODS		
Dystrophaeus		Cetiosaurus	Bothriospondylus	
Elosaurus		Bothriospondylus	[Madagascar]	
Haplocanthosaurus		Pelorosaurus	Brachiosaurus	
Astrodon			Tornieria	
Brachiosaurus		Brachiosaurus	Barosaurus	
Camarasaurus			Dicraeosaurus	
Apatosaurus		Apatosaurus		
(Brontosaurus)				
Uintasaurus				
Amphicoelias				
Barosaurus				
Diplodocus				
		ORNITHOPODS		
		Hypsilophodonts		
			Dysalatosaurus	
		Camptosaurs		
Camptosaurus	Sanpasaurus	Cryptodraco		
		STEGOSAURS		
Stegosaurus	Chialangosaurus	Dacentrurus	Kentrosaurus	
		(Omosaurus)		
		Saurechinodon		

GENERA OF LOWER CRETACEOUS DINOSAURS

NORTH AMERICA	ASIA	EUROPE	AFRICA	AUSTRALIA
		THEROPODS		
		Coelurosaurs		
		Aristosuchus		Walgettosuchus
		Calamospondylus		
		Thecocoelurus		
		Thecospondylus		
		Carnosaurs		
Acrocanthosaurus	Embasaurus	Megalosaurus		
		Erectopus		
		SAUROPODS		
	Euhelopus	Cetiosaurus	Algoasaurus	
	Tienshanosaurus	Camarasaurus		
		Aepisaurus		
		ORNITHOPODS		
		Hypsilophodonts		
		Hypsilophodon		
		Camptosaurs		
Camptosaurus		Vectisaurus		
		Iguanodon		
		Anoplosaurus		
		STEGOSAURS		
Priconodon		Craterosaurus	Paranthodon	
		ANKYLOSAURS		
Hoplitosaurus	Sauroplites	Acanthopholis		
	Syrmosaurus	Hylaeosaurus		
		Polacanthoides		
		Polacanthus		
		CERATOPSIANS		
		Psittacosaurs		
	Psittacosaurus	Stenopelix		
	Protiguanodon			

GENERA OF UPPER CRETACEOUS DINOSAURS

SOUTH AMERICA	NORTH AMERICA	ASIA	EUROPE	AFRICA
		THEROPODS		
		Coelurosaurs		
	Chirostenotes	Compsosuchus		
	Coelosaurus	Jubbulpuria		
	Dromaeosaurus	Laevisuchus		
	Troödon	Saurornithoides		
	Ornithomimus	Velociraptor		
	Macrophalangia	Ornithomimus	Betasuchus	
		Oviraptor		
		Ornithomimoides		
		Carnosaurs		
Genyodectes	Dryptosaurus	Dryptosauroides		Bahariasaurus
	Gorgosaurus	Orthogoniosaurus		Carcharodontosaurus
	Tyrannosaurus	Alectrosaurus		Spinosaurus
		Prodeinodon		
		SAUROPODS		
Antarctosaurus	Alamosaurus	Antarctosaurus	Hypselosaurus	Aegyptosaurus
Argyrosaurus	Parrosaurus	Laplatasaurus	Macrurosaurus	Laplatasaurus
Laplatasaurus		Titanosaurus	Succinodon	[Madagascar]
Titanosaurus		Chiayüsaurus	Titanosaurus	
		Omeisaurus		
		ORNITHOPODS		
		Hypsilophodonts		
	Parksosaurus			
	Thescelosaurus			
		Camptosaurs		
			Rhabdodon	
			Craspedodon	
		Hadrosaurs		
	Anatosaurus	Bactrosaurus	Orthomerus	
	Cheneosaurus	Jaxartosaurus		
	Claorhynchus	Mandschurosaurus		

SOUTH AMERICA	NORTH AMERICA	ASIA	EUROPE	AFRICA

ORNITHOPODS

	NORTH AMERICA	ASIA		
	Claosaurus	*Nipponosaurus*		
	Corythosaurus	*Saurolophus*		
	Dysganus	*Tanius*		
	Edmontosaurus	*Tsintaosaurus*		
	Hadrosaurus			
	Hypacrosaurus			
	Hypsibema			
	Kritosaurus			
	Lambeosaurus			
	Ornithotarsus			
	Parasaurolophus			
	Procheneosaurus			
	Prosaurolophus			
	Saurolophus			
	Thespesius			
	Trachodon			

Pachycephalosaurs

	Pachycephalosaurus	*Stegoceras*		
	Stegoceras			

ANKYLOSAURS

Anodontosaurus	*Dyoplosaurus*	*Brachypodosaurus*	*Acanthopholis*	
Loricosaurus	*Edmontonia*	*Heishansaurus*	*Onychosaurus*	
	Euoplocephalus	*Lametasaurus*	*Rhodanosaurus*	
	Ankylosaurus	*Peishansaurus*	*Struthiosaurus*	
	Heirosaurus	*Pinacosaurus*		
	Nodosaurus	*Stegosauroides*		
	Palaeoscincus			
	Panoplosaurus			
	Scolosaurus			
	Stegopelta			

CERATOPSIANS

Protoceratopsids

	Leptoceratops	*Protoceratops*		
	Montanoceratops	*Microceratops*		

GENERA OF UPPER CRETACEOUS DINOSAURS (continued)

SOUTH AMERICA	NORTH AMERICA	ASIA	EUROPE	AFRICA
		CERATOPSIANS		
		Ceratopsids		
? Notoceratops	*Agathaumas*			
	Anchiceratops			
	Arrhinoceratops			
	Brachyceratops			
	Ceratops			
	Chasmosaurus			
	Diceratops			
	Eoceratops			
	Manospondylus			
	Monoclonius			
	Pentaceratops	*Pentaceratops*		
	Sterrholophus			
	Styracosaurus			
	Torosaurus			
	Triceratops			
		Pachyrhinosaurids		
	Pachyrhinosaurus			

CHAPTER EIGHTEEN

BONES AND BOOKS

WHERE TO SEE DINOSAURS

No matter how much one may learn from reading about dinosaurs, one must also *see* them, as they are known to us by their fossil skeletons, if a true appreciation of these rulers of Mesozoic times is to be had. Seeing them is not always easy, because, as so often mentioned in this book, there is much involved in the collecting, preparing, and setting up for display of a dinosaur skeleton; consequently not many institutions have attempted programs of work on these fossils. But to him who is interested and determined, it is possible to become acquainted with the dinosaurs at firsthand, or at least with some of them, especially in this day of automobiles and good roads.

On page 48 it was said that the reader would be presented at the back of this book with a list of places in the United States and Canada where dinosaurs may be seen. Here is the list, with some accompanying comments. It is the fond hope of the author that his list is complete; if any institution is left out, the omission is purely accidental.

The most comprehensive exhibit of dinosaurs is at the *American Museum of Natural History,* in New York City, where in two large halls of the museum are displayed more than thirty skeletons of dinosaurs, several partial skeletons, and numerous skulls and other bones. There may also be seen a trackway from Texas of a large sauropod dinosaur, as well as a dinosaur mummy, various examples of fossilized skin, and dinosaur eggs.

At the *United States National Museum,* in Washington, D.C., are several fine skeletons of Upper Jurassic dinosaurs from North America, a skeleton of *Triceratops,* and other late Cretaceous specimens.

Another institution displaying a series of Upper Jurassic dinosaurs is the *Carnegie Museum,* in Pittsburgh. Here are seen skeletons that were excavated from the famous dinosaur quarry that is now contained within the Dinosaur National Monument near Vernal, Utah. Of particular interest is a skeleton of a half-grown sauropod dinosaur. There is also a skeleton of *Tyrannosaurus.*

Mention of *Dinosaur National Monument* leads to mention of the museum that has recently been completed there, a most unusual structure, built with imagination and foresight. In short, a large section of an almost vertical cliff containing Upper Jurassic dinosaur bones has been utilized as one wall of the museum, and around it a light, airy building has been constructed. Here the visitor may see bones exposed in the rock, and for the time being may watch the work of uncovering more bones. The bones are being left in place, and eventually it is hoped that the entire cliff will be a vast display of dinosaur bones in the rock.

Notable Upper Jurassic dinosaurs are to be seen at the *Yale Peabody Museum,* in New Haven, Connecticut, these fossils collected for the most part by Professor Marsh and his assistants at Como Bluff, Wyoming. There are also displayed here various Upper Cretaceous dinosaurs from the western states. In addition there is a notable collection at Yale of dinosaur footprints from the Connecticut Valley.

The *National Museum of Canada,* in Ottawa, has on display an excellent series of dinosaur skeletons from Alberta. These are the varied dinosaurs found in the famous Upper Cretaceous sediments that are exposed along the Red Deer River, below Edmonton.

Another very extensive exhibit of Upper Cretaceous dinosaurs from Alberta is to be seen at the *Royal Ontario Museum,* in Toronto. For many years this institution carried on a vigorous program of work along the Red Deer River, with the result that a particularly fine series of Belly River and related dinosaurs was brought together for display at this museum.

The *Chicago Natural History Museum* displays several dinosaur skeletons, including a large sauropod from the Upper Jurassic beds of western North America, and various Cretaceous dinosaurs. A notable dinosaur at Chicago is the skeleton of *Gorgosaurus,* which occupies a place of honor in the middle of the great entrance hall. This skeleton is so mounted that no supports are visible, giving it a very life-like appearance. It stands triumphant over the recumbent skeleton of a duck-billed dinosaur.

The *Academy of Natural Sciences* in Philadelphia has on display a skeleton of *Corythosaurus.* Also to be seen here are some of the bones of *Hadrosaurus,* the first partial dinosaur skeleton to be discovered and described in North America.

At the *Museum of Comparative Zoology,* Harvard University, Cambridge, Massachusetts, is a skeleton of *Plateosaurus.*

The *Cleveland* (Ohio) *Museum of Natural History* exhibits a skeleton of a large sauropod dinosaur, *Haplocanthosaurus,* from Canyon City, Colorado.

At the *Amherst College Museum,* in Amherst, Massachusetts, is the finest collection of Triassic footprints from the Connecticut Valley. Many of these are the tracks discovered and described by Professor Hitchcock, as has been related in Chapter Two of this book. There is also a skeleton of a duck-billed dinosaur in this museum.

There is a skeleton of a duck-billed dinosaur at the *University of Michigan Museum,* in Ann Arbor.

A skeleton of *Stegosaurus* is to be seen at the *University of Nebraska Museum* in Lincoln.

In the geological museum at the *University of Utah,* in Salt Lake City, is a skeleton of *Allosaurus,* and in addition fossils of other dinosaurs from the Upper Jurassic sediments of that state.

The *Denver Museum of Natural History* has on exhibit a fine skeleton of *Diplodocus* and one of the duck-billed dinosaur *Anatosaurus.* Other fossils of dinosaurs are to be seen at this museum.

At the *Stovall Museum* of the University of Oklahoma, in Norman, are bones of Upper Jurassic dinosaurs collected in the western part of that state. Lack of space prevents the display at the present time of a complete skeleton.

Some of the large sauropod tracks from Glen Rose, Texas, are exhibited at the *Texas Memorial Museum,* at the University in Austin.

The *Centennial Museum* in El Paso has a large collection of dino-saur bones made in the Big Bend region of that state. Some of these are now on display.

At the *Museum of Paleontology* of the University of California, in Berkeley, is an extraordinarily fine skeleton of *Megalosaurus* from the Upper Triassic or Lower Jurassic rocks of northern Arizona.

A skeleton of *Allosaurus* is on display at the *Princeton University Museum.*

SOME BOOKS

The following list of books, with comments, includes authoritative works, mostly in English, on dinosaurs and on subjects closely related to the study of dinosaurs (such as general works on paleontology, fossil reptiles, evolution, stratigraphy, and the like):

Augusta, Joseph. 1956. Prehistoric Animals. Illustrated by Zdenek Burian. Translated by Dr. Greta Horn. London, Spring Books. 47 pp., 60 pls.

> A large picture book with unusually good color illustrations by Burian, done under the supervision of Professor Augusta, who wrote the text.

Beerbower, James R. 1960. Search for the Past. Englewood Cliffs, New Jersey, Prentice-Hall. xiii, 562 pp.

> A new and very original book on general paleontology. Particular attention is given to population problems, speciation, and evo-lution.

Bellairs, Angus d'A. 1957. Reptiles. London, Hutchinson's University Library. 195 pp.

> A most excellent, though small, treatise on reptiles, living and extinct. One chapter is devoted to dinosaurs.

Colbert, Edwin H. 1951. The Dinosaur Book. Second Edition. New York, McGraw-Hill Book Co. 156 pp.

> A book that deals not only with dinosaurs but also with other rep-tiles and with amphibians.

————, 1955. Evolution of the Vertebrates. New York, John Wiley and Sons. xiii, 479 pp.

> Vertebrate evolution for the general reader.

Dunbar, Carl O. 1960. Historical Geology. Second Edition. New York, John Wiley and Sons. xi, 500 pp.
> A standard work, dealing primarily with the history of North America and its life.

Goodrich, E. S. 1958. Studies on the Structure and Development of Vertebrates. New York, Dover Press. lxix, 837 pp.
> Reprint of a classic book on the comparative anatomy and evolution of the vertebrates.

Gregory, William K. 1951. Evolution Emerging: A Survey of Changing Patterns from Primeval Life to Man. New York, The Macmillan Co. Vol. 1, xxvi, 736 pp. (text); Vol. 2, viii, 1,013 pp. (figures and plates).
> A monumental essay on vertebrate evolution by a great scholar.

Hesse, R., W. C. Allee, and K. P. Schmidt. 1951. Ecological Animal Geography. Second Edition. New York, John Wiley and Sons. xiv, 597 pp.
> A standard text on the environmental controls of animal distribution.

Lull, Richard S. 1947. Organic Evolution. Revised Edition. New York, The Macmillan Co. xx, 744 pp.
> A useful textbook, of long standing, on evolution.

Moody, Paul A. 1953. Introduction to Evolution. New York, Harper and Brothers. xii, 475 pp.
> A very good modern text on the subject. Dinosaurs receive due consideration.

Moore, Raymond C. 1958. Introduction to Historical Geology. Second Edition. New York, McGraw-Hill Book Co. ix, 656 pp.
> A standard work, concerned primarily with North America.

Piveteau, Jean (Editor). 1955. Traité de Paléontologie. Vol. 5. Amphibiens, Reptiles, Oiseaux. Paris, Masson. 1,113 pp.
> One volume of a series. This is a particularly fine and comprehensive treatise, of great value to students of ancient life. The section on dinosaurs is by De Lapparent and Lavocat.

Romer, Alfred S. 1945. Vertebrate Paleontology. Second Edition. Chicago, University of Chicago Press. ix, 687 pp.
> Required for all students of vertebrate evolution. A very comprehensive work by one of the world's leading authorities.

Romer, Alfred S., 1949. The Vertebrate Body. Philadelphia, W. B. Saunders Co. viii, 643 pp.

A masterly treatise on comparative anatomy, in which much attention is given to extinct forms. A condensed version is available.

————, 1956. The Osteology of the Reptiles. Chicago, University of Chicago Press. xxi, 772 pp.

An invaluable work on reptilian osteology.

Simpson, George Gaylord. 1949. The Meaning of Evolution. New Haven, Yale University Press. xv, 364 pp. (also available as a paperback book).

A thoughtful discussion by one of the great modern students of vertebrate evolution.

————, 1953. Life of the Past. New Haven, Yale University Press. xii, 198 pp.

A clear and very readable account of the evolution of life.

————, 1953. The Major Features of Evolution. New York, Columbia University Press. xix, 434 pp.

Probes deeply into evolutionary problems.

Swinnerton, H. H. 1947. Outlines of Paleontology. Third Edition. London, Edward Arnold and Co. x, 393 pp.

An excellent brief textbook.

Swinton, William E. 1934. The Dinosaurs. London, Thomas Murby and Co. xii, 233 pp.

A valuable book, unfortunately now out of print.

Zittel, Karl A. von. 1932. Textbook of Palaeontology. (Revised by A. Smith Woodward). London, Macmillan and Co. Vol. 2. xvii, 464 pp.

A useful handbook.

FOR THOSE WHO WOULD DELVE MORE DEEPLY

The scientific literature on the dinosaurs is enormous, as might be expected. Some of the greatest authorities on these Mesozoic reptiles have published exclusively in technical papers and not in books. Listed here are the names of scholars who have made significant contributions to our knowledge of the dinosaurs. The reader who may be interested in looking into the literature on dinosaurs will find contributions by these authorities listed in the catalogues of some of the large libraries, particularly the libraries of large natural-history museums and universities. Of inestimable value are the bibliographies of vertebrate paleontology, published during the past two or three decades. These are appended, following the list of names:

AUTHORS

Ameghino, Florentino
Andrews, C. W.
Broom, Robert
Brown, Barnum
Cabrera, Angel
Camp, Charles
Colbert, Edwin H.
Cope, Edward Drinker
Deperet, Charles
Dollo, Louis
Edinger, Tilly
Edmund, Gordon
Efremov, I. A.
Gilmore, Charles W.
Gregory, Joseph T.
Gregory, William King
Hatcher, John Bell
Haughton, Sidney
Holland, W. J.
Huene, Friedrich von
Janensch, Werner

Lambe, Lawrence
Lapparent, Albert F. de
Lavocat, René
Leidy, Joseph
Lull, Richard Swann
Lydekker, Richard
Mantell, Gideon
Marsh, Othniel Charles
Matthew, William Diller
Mook, Charles C.
Nopcsa, Franz
Orlov, J. A.
Osborn, Henry Fairfield
Owen, Richard
Parks, W. A.
Peterson, Olaf A.

Piveteau, Jean
Price, Llewellyn I.
Romer, Alfred S.
Rozhdestvensky, A. K.
Russell, Loris S.
Simpson, George Gaylord
Sternberg, Charles S.
Stromer, Ernst
Swinton, William E.
Tornier, Gustav von
Welles, Samuel P.
Williston, Samuel Wendell
Wiman, Carl
Woodward, Arthur Smith
Young, Chung Chien
Zittel, Karl von

BIBLIOGRAPHIES OF VERTEBRATE PALEONTOLOGY

Hay, Oliver P. 1902. Bibliography and Catalogue of the Fossil Vertebrata of North America. Bulletin, U.S. Geological Survey, No. 179, 868 pp.

———, 1929. Second Bibliography and Catalogue of the Fossil Vertebrata of North America. Carnegie Inst. of Washington, publ. No. 390, Vol. 1. 916 pp.

———, 1930. *Ibid.* Vol. 2. 1,074 pp.

Camp, Charles L., and V. L. VanderHoof. 1940. Bibliography of Fossil

Vertebrates, 1928–1933. Geological Society of America, Special Paper No. 27, 503 pp.

Camp, Charles L., D. N. Taylor, and S. P. Welles. 1942. Bibliography of Fossil Vertebrates, 1934–1938. Geological Society of America, Special Paper No. 42, 663 pp.

Camp, Charles L., S. P. Welles, and M. Green. 1949. Bibliography of Fossil Vertebrates, 1939–1943. Geological Society of America, Memoir 37, 371 pp.

————, 1953. Bibliography of Fossil Vertebrates, 1944–1948. Geological Society of America, Memoir 57, 465 pp.

Romer, Alfred S., T. Edinger, and N. E. Wright. Bibliography of Vertebrate Paleontology Exclusive of North America to 1927. In press.

CREDITS FOR PLATES

All plates illustrate specimens, original drawings or paintings, field photographs or other photographs on file, in the American Museum of Natural History, except for those listed below.

Plate:

4. From *Notice of the Iguanodon,* etc., by Gideon Mantell. *Philosophical Transactions of the Royal Society of London,* 1825.

5. From *Illustrations of the Geology of Sussex,* etc., by Gideon Mantell. London, 1827.

13. Courtesy of Professor Karl M. Waage, Yale University.

14. From United States Geological Survey, Oil and Gas Investigations, Map OM 145, Sheet 1, by A. A. Wanek and J. G. Stephens, 1953.

26, 40, 45, 51, 53, 64, 76. From *Dinosaurs,* a handbook by W. E. Swinton. Courtesy of the British Museum (Natural History).

50. The Museum für Naturkunde, Berlin.

54. From *Troisième Note sur les Dinosauriens de Bernissart,* by Louis Dollo. Bulletin, Museum Royale Histoire Naturelle, Belge, Volume II, Plate 5.

65, 67–73. From *Osteology of the Armored Dinosauria in the United States National Museum,* etc., by Charles W. Gilmore. United States National Museum, Bulletin 89, plates 2, 32–36.

74, 87. Courtesy of the Chicago Natural History Museum.

96–98. Courtesy of the Peabody Museum, Yale University.

95. Courtesy of the Carnegie Museum, Pittsburgh.

CREDITS FOR FIGURES

The following figures were drawn or compiled especially for this present book by Michael Insinna, adapting material from various sources. Lettering on these figures was done by Margaret M. Colbert:

Figures 1, 2, (most of the restorations used in these figures from *Evolution of the Vertebrates* by Edwin H. Colbert (New York: John Wiley and Sons, Inc., 1958), 7, 11, 15 (adapted in part from R. T. Bird in *Natural History*, 1944), 16, 19, 23, 25, 33, 34 (restorations from Colbert, *op. cit.*), 35, 38, 39, 42, 43, 44, 46 (redrawn figures from van Straelen, 1925 and from de Lapparent, 1947), 47, 51.

The maps (figures 13, 17, 26, 28, 36, 45, 48, 49, 50) were drawn by George M. Colbert, using an adapted Briesemeister Equal-Area Projection, through the courtesy of the American Geographical Society.

Figures 3, 4, 5, 10 are from Colbert, *op. cit.*

Figures 21, 24, 41 from *Cranial Morphology of the North American Hadrosauridae* by John H. Ostrom, *Bulletin of the American Museum of Natural History* (in press), by permission of the author.

Figure 6 from the *Illustrated London News*, by permission of the proprietors and of Mr. Richard Carrington.

Figure 14 from the files of the American Museum of Natural History.

The following figures are from scientific monographs and papers, the authors and dates of which are listed below:

Figure 8. Osborn, Henry Fairfield, and Charles C. Mook. 1921. *Memoirs of the American Museum of Natural History*, N.S., Vol. 3, Pt. 3.

Figure 9. Colbert, Edwin H. 1952. *Bulletin of the American Museum of Natural History*, Vol. 99, Art. 10.

Figures 12, 34 (in part). Colbert, Edwin H. 1949. *The Scientific Monthly*, Vol. 69, No. 2.

Figure 18. Hulke, J. W. 1873. *Quarterly Journal of the Geological Society of London*, Vol. 29, pp. 522–532.

Figures 20, 22: Lull, Richard Swann, and Nelda Wright. 1942. Geological Society of America, *Special Papers*, No. 40.

Figure 27. Von Huene, F. 1956. *Paläontologie und Phylogenie der Niederen Tetrapoden.* Jena, Gustav Fischer Verlag. xii + 716 pp.

Figure 29. Maleev, E. A. 1954. "Armored Dinosaurs of Mongolia." Paleontological Institute, Academy of Sciences, U.S.S.R., *Trudy*, Vol. 48, pp. 142–170.

Figures 30, 31. Brown, Barnum. 1908. *Bulletin of the American Museum of Natural History*, Vol. 24, Art. 12.

Figure 32. Osborn, Henry Fairfield. 1924. *American Museum Novitates*, No. 127.

Figure 37. Brown, Barnum. 1917. *Bulletin of the American Museum of Natural History*, Vol. 37, Art. 10.

Figure 40. Langston, Wann, Jr. 1960. *Natural History Papers*, National Museum of Canada, No. 4.

INDEX